STATISTICAL METHOD

STATISTICAL METHOD

BY

HARRY JEROME

Assistant Professor of Economics
University of Wisconsin

HARPER & BROTHERS PUBLISHERS

NEW YORK AND LONDON

STATISTICAL METHOD

To
S. A. J.

CONTENTS

vii

CONTENTS

CONTENTS

CONTENTS

x

CONTENTS

xi

LIST OF CHARTS AND PLATES

xiii

LIST OF CHARTS AND PLATES

LIST OF TABLES

LIST OF TABLES

APPENDIX TABLES

EDITOR'S INTRODUCTION

The recent development of a strong interest in statistics has been responsible for the publication of a number of general treatises on the subject. Most of these books, however, are too mathematical for the average student to comprehend. The present book was written with this circumstance in mind. Although devoid of complicated mathematical explanations, it treats the subject in such a manner as to furnish a foundation to the student for further study in mathematical statistics. It also has the advantage of an adequate presentation of the newer developments which have taken place in statistical method.

The book has been written chiefly for students in economics and sociology. Most of the illustrations and exercises are drawn from those fields. The book devotes considerable space to methods of statistical investigation, tabulation, and graphs, which are valuable to the student of the social sciences. Several chapters are devoted to time series, including index numbers and cycles, which are at present of paramount importance in economics. The book should prove a useful text for schools and colleges desiring to equip their students with a fundamental knowledge of statistical method. It is expected that the publication of this volume will be followed by another, written by a specialist in mathematical statistics and designed to carry the subject forward for advanced students in economics.

JOHN R. COMMONS.

PREFACE

This volume originated in the desire of the author for a text suited to the needs of his own pupils, whose interest in statistical method lay in its commercial applications and its use in the analysis of economic and social phenomena. The author has tried to present the subject in such a way that those who, like himself, are drawn into the study of statistical method with a training in economics rather than in mathematics may grasp the nature and purpose of the more common statistical processes. The necessary minimum of formulas and mathematical processes has been presented without rigid mathematical demonstration of their validity, but merely with such explanation as it is thought will clarify their meaning. If it appears that there is too scant attention to the underlying assumptions and reasoning upon which the validity of processes rests and too little reiteration of the dangers involved in the blind use of statistical methods, it is not because the writer minimizes the importance of these things but because he believes that the beginner in statistical practice is deterred rather than enlightened by too much emphasis upon limitations. One must understand what a process is before he profits much from consideration of the limitations upon the usefulness of that process.

Attention is directed to the following facts concerning the contents and arrangement of the book:

(1) All charts and tables are listed in the front of the book; all symbols and formulas, with pages where explained, at the end.

(2) Suggestions for equipment and exercises suitable for giving students the practice in statistical methods which is indispensable to successful instruction are in the appendixes, together with various aids to computation and the data tables upon which the exercises are based.

(3) To make more obvious the interrelations of statistical

xxi

processes. the same data have been used in several illustrations (see Tables I, II, III, IV, XXVI, XXIX, XXXI, XXXIII, and XXXVIII). The complete list from which this basic sample is taken is given in Table 101, Appendix B; and Series R, Appendix C, contains suggestions for organizing coördinated practice exercises which, in similar manner, carry one set of data through several processes.

(4) Numerous references to enable the teacher or student to extend his study beyond the elementary presentation in this text are given in footnotes, chapter references, and the classified bibliography in Appendix A. For many of the chapters the *Handbook of Mathematical Statistics,* by E. L. Rietz, et al., will be found helpful. This book was issued after the lists of references had been prepared.

(5) The order of treatment does not follow strictly the usual order in the planning and analysis of a statistical problem, the chapters on the sources and methods of collecting statistical data being deferred to the end of the book, in accordance with the experience of the author that these subjects appear of little interest to the student until he has obtained a reasonable grasp of the methods of analysis. Some teachers may prefer to take up Chapter XVI, and possibly XVII, immediately after Chapter I or Chapter II. Those who wish to reduce to a minimum the attention to the mathematical aspects may find it desirable to omit Chapter X.

This book obviously does not purport to be an original contribution. It represents an effort to incorporate the best of the work of previous writers of text-books in statistical methods and also the newer improvements in method, particularly in charting and in the analysis of chronological data, which have arisen as by-products of the recent increased activity in the application of quantitative methods to economic and social problems. The author is indebted to numerous text-books for suggestions and has quoted freely from several writers, to whom he wishes to extend acknowledgment and thanks. An effort has been made to give full credit in all cases for data, quotations, or ideas.

During the gradual evolution of this text from a set of mimeographed outlines for class use, the writer has received helpful assistance from so many colleagues, students, and other friends that he finds it difficult to recognize adequately their contributions to the final result. He is particularly indebted to Dr. Willford I. King, who has read most of the manuscript in some stage of its evolution and to whose influence as former teacher and as kindly but searching critic such merit as the book may possess is largely due. Also the author owes a special debt of gratitude to those who have been associated with him in the University of Wisconsin and who, by coöperation in the development of instructional procedure, the preparation of exercises, and the criticism of manuscript, have made substantial contributions to the volume. This group includes Messrs. R. E. Baber, F. A. Buechel, J. D. Blanchard, H. F. Clark, C. G. Dittmer, J. B. Dennison, O. M. Elvehjem, M. H. Ingraham, C. L. Jamison, H. L. Jome, V. P. Lee, D. D. Lescohier, A. J. Mertzke, Jacob Perlman and J. P. Troxell, and Miss Margaret Pryor.

Several members of the staff of the National Bureau of Economic Research have assisted by criticism of portions of the manuscript. Professor Wesley C. Mitchell kindly read the draft of the chapter on the "Construction of Index Numbers" and made valuable suggestions for its revision; and Miss E. Gail Benjamin, Mr. Maurice Leven, Mr. Frederick R. Macaulay, Miss Elizabeth W. Putnam, and Mr. Willard Thorp also contributed helpful suggestions.

The author is especially indebted to Mr. Jacob Perlman for assistance in the preparation of practice exercises upon which many of the suggestions in Appendix C have been based, and for reading a large portion of the manuscript; and to Mr. L. S. Baldwin, instructor in Drawing and Descriptive Geometry in the University of Wisconsin, who drafted the lettering guide in Appendix C and prepared practically all of the charts for reproduction. Miss Edith Handler and Miss Laura Weissbuch assisted in checking the arithmetical computations and in proofreading the tables and text.

The author also wishes to express his thanks to the editor,

Professor John R. Commons, for advice and encouragement at various stages in the progress of the work.

Lastly, to an extent which cannot be adequately acknowledged by any formal statement, the author is indebted to his wife for painstaking and discriminating reading of the manuscript and proofs, without which assistance he finds it difficult to see how the book, delayed at best by the pressure of other work, could have been brought to completion.

HARRY JEROME.

August, 1924

STATISTICAL METHOD

Statistical Method

CHAPTER I

THE NATURE AND USES OF STATISTICAL METHOD

STATISTICAL method is the art of extracting the significant truths concealed in masses of numerical facts. We may gain more quickly a clear grasp of the scope of this subject if we first distinguish between statistical facts, statistical method, and statistical theory. The term statistics is used somewhat indiscriminately to refer to any one of these three concepts, but they are not identical. The 1920 population of the United States is stated by the Census Bureau as 105,710,620,[1] and the average income per person in the United States has been estimated as $629 for the year 1919.[2] These are *statistical facts*.

But if we turn our attention to the methods used by the Bureau of the Census in determining the population, or to the devices by which the per-capita income for 1919 is estimated, then we are dealing with *statistical method,* or technique.

If we go still further and inquire into the mathematical or economic principles which underlie and justify many of the practical statistical methods, then we are dealing with *statistical theory,* or science.

Deaths classified into a mortality table are statistical facts; the use of this table as a sample from which to approximate the chances of death among prospective purchasers of insurance is a matter of statistical method; the analysis of the mathematical law of probabilities upon which this sampling process rests, a matter of statistical theory. It is primarily to the second of

[1] Fourteenth Census of the United States, 1920, vol. i, *Population*, p. 13.
[2] National Bureau of Economic Research, *Income in the United States— Its Amount and Distribution, 1909-1919*, vol. i, p. 13.

these phases of statistics, statistical method, that we shall devote our attention.

For our purpose, we may define statistical method as the *principles of the collection and analysis of numerical data and of the accurate and effective presentation of such data and the results of their analysis.*[1]

As implied by this definition, statistical method may be conveniently analyzed into three processes—the collection, the analysis, and the presentation of statistical data.

(1) **The collection of statistics.** The student of the methodology of gathering statistical data seeks answers to questions such as these: What facts are pertinent? In what forms do they exist? Have they been gathered and classified or do they exist only in crude, unassembled form? Who has possession or knowledge of the desired facts? What is the most effective and feasible way of obtaining the data? One must learn to decide between using data already collected and attempting to obtain new material; between the relative advantages of inquiries in person and by mail; in short, to choose wisely from the many methods of procedure which challenge his judgment.

(2) **Analysis of the facts.** The mere gathering of facts is essential, but is useless if no further steps are taken. The data must be sorted, winnowed, classified, and subjected to the methods of analysis best suited to bring out significant aspects. Means must be found to summarize, in concise word pictures, the typical attributes of the data, the degree of variation from type, the relations between groups of facts. It is not enough to require of physicians reports of all deaths of infants and then merely to bury these reports in official archives. We want to examine the causes of death, to arrange and analyze these facts so that we may discover, if possible, underlying causes. We may have an hypothesis that poverty and infant mortality are closely related. What, by a scrutiny of the death records, are the best methods of testing the accuracy of this hypothesis? This is the problem of correlation. (See Chapter XV.)

[1] See the list of definitions by various authors at the close of this chapter.

(3) **Presentation.** Efficient collection and scientific analysis of statistics may bring the statistician to important conclusions, but there still remains the problem of advertising the facts and conclusions. Many a splendid idea has failed of its mission because not effectively presented. The employer, the reader, the audience, cannot readily follow the statistician in the detailed and painstaking processes by which he has reached certain conclusions. How, then, can facts, comparisons, or statistical relations be so presented that they will command the attention of the reader and convey accurate impressions to him? How may "figures be made to talk" in plain, yet emphatic language?

Facts may be presented in descriptive or verbal style, in tabular form, or by varied types of charts and diagrams. The limitations on mere verbal description as a means of effectively marshaling numerical facts are too obvious to require extended discussion. The construction of a statistical table may almost be said to be the fundamental process in statistical practice, in that practically all statistical data appear in the tabular form at some stage of their analysis. The study of how best to prepare a table may seem forbidding and unpromising, but on closer examination it will be seen that it offers an unusual challenge to the ingenuity and judgment of the statistician. The acme of the art of presentation is found in the fascinating and rapidly developing science of visual presentation through graphs, statistical maps, and other diagrams.

THE USES OF STATISTICAL METHOD

Thus far we have assumed that it is worth while to acquire a command of statistical method. A survey of modern tendencies confirms this assumption; even a superficial consideration of the character of present-day economic and social conditions suggests the growing necessity of perfecting devices for interpreting masses of numerical facts. Three pre-eminent *causes* appear *for the modern importance of statistics to the student of economics:*

(1) This is *an age of large numbers*. Numbers and quantities have become so great that they require special methods of statement and interpretation. Population runs into the hundreds of millions; in war we marshal our soldiers by the millions; crops, taxes, moving-picture attendance, marriages, divorces, births, deaths, all occur in such numbers, or are expressed in terms so large, that new devices must be worked out to elucidate and interpret them. Mere personal impressions as a guide to judgment will not suffice.

(2) In the second place, *modern science demands* that its theories be based upon *facts*. This implies no essential criticism of deductive reasoning as such, or of the use of hypotheses as starting points in scientific thought; but an idea once conceived, modern science then proceeds to verify this idea by inductive analysis of the available facts. This is as true of the social sciences as it is of the more exact sciences, but the verification is more difficult. The modern sociologist or economist seeks to substantiate his social or economic theories by reference to the cold logic of facts. He cannot, however, ordinarily use the experimental method so fruitful of results for the chemist or physicist. The experimental method rests on a degree of control not available in the study of social data. One cannot artificially make "other things equal" and isolate the influence of one cause. In essence statistical method comprises the means of handling "complex evidence in the mass." It takes intricate social phenomena as they arise out of the uncontrolled progress of human life, and despite their complexity, attempts to bring out significant comparisons, trends, and causal relations.

(3) Lastly, the fact that *business is becoming more and more a matter of scientific procedure* offers a fruitful field for the application of statistical method. The day of the great business resting on the personal knowledge of one individual is passing, together with the rule-of-thumb methods apt to characterize such an establishment. The modern business institution is subject to influences which are world-wide in their ramifications, and the business executive, in order to keep in touch with

the trends in his own field and with the movements in the business world in general, is forced to call statistical method to his aid.

To repeat, statistical method is not an end in itself, except for the satisfaction in a piece of work well executed. It is a tool, an agency useful in many fields—in biology, in applied psychology, in educational methods, in business, and in the social sciences. Let us turn our attention particularly to the applications which are of special interest to the student of human activities.

Applications of statistical method to social problems.

(1) Statistical method is finding an increasing use in the *scientific analysis of social phenomena*. It affords methods of making summary statements of social facts and means of determining and expressing the direction of movements. As suggested above, it provides a substitute for the unavailable laboratory method in the collection and analysis of social data. It affords the basis for empirical social laws, such as Engel's law [1] of the distribution of expenditure. Deductive analysis has blocked out the main features of social science, but the details remain to be filled in, largely through the scientific application of statistical methods.

(2) *The use of statistics in the economic conflict.* It may be a far cry to the day when the parties to the economic struggle will abandon resort to force as exemplified in the strike, the lockout, or the boycott, but both the labor and the employing elements have recognized the necessity of winning the support of public opinion by the use of arguments fortified by statistics. As an agent of employers, the National Industrial Conference Board [2] conducts investigations of the cost of living, wages, taxation, and other important economic phenomena. Likewise, in 1920, when the railway brotherhoods wished to defend their position on the wage question, they did not rest content with the mere expression

[1] Cf. R. T. Ely, *et al., Outlines of Economics,* 3d ed., pp. 144-147, and F. H. Streightoff, *The Standard of Living Among the Industrial People of America,* pp. 12-23, quoted in Marshall, Wright, and Field, *Materials for the Study of Elementary Economics,* pp. 27-33, for statement of Engel's law and the basis therefor.

[2] The "National Industrial Conference Board" is a co-operative body composed of representatives of national and state industrial associations.

of their desire, backed by the threat of a strike. They employed W. Jett Lauck, a consulting economist, to assemble the facts as to the relative increase in the cost of living and the share of profits from increased prices going to the laborers. Through the analysis of corporation reports, income-tax returns, and other available data, he prepared a brief [1] to the effect that the lion's share of the war-time prosperity had gone to the corporations—to capital rather than to labor. In our great cities, private organizations [2] are developing with the avowed function of affording to labor unions the advantages of trained assistants in the preparation of arguments in labor controversies, and a statistical staff is recognized as an important adjunct of these labor advisory bureaus.

The increasing use of statistics in the settlement of labor disputes is indicated by the fact that in recent years wages have in many instances been adjusted on a sliding scale varying with changes in index numbers of the cost of living.[3]

(3) *The use of statistics in public administration.* Nearly every important administrative department of our federal and state governments has its statistical staff. The need for comprehensive quantitative information in the conduct of the war caused a marked expansion of the statistical departments of the federal government,[4] and the continual expansion of state functions is bringing a similar result in the several states.

The processes and purposes of statistical procedure in public administration are substantially similar to those common to other

---

[1] *The Nation,* June 12, 1920, pp. 796-797; also, *The Relation Between Wages and the Increased Cost of Living: An Analysis of the Effect of Increased Wages and Profits upon Commodity Prices,* presented before the United States Railroad Labor Board by W. Jett Lauck on behalf of seventeen organizations. Washington, 1920.

[2] See the 1921 *Annual Report* of "The Labor Bureau, Inc." In 1921 this organization made seven original investigations to determine the "living-wage level" and also "rendered its clients 46 reports on the cost of living based on published records." It has offices in New York, Chicago, and other cities.

[3] For articles dealing with the use of index numbers in fixing wages, consult the index of the *Monthly Labor Review* for 1921 and 1922; also the *Literary Digest,* September 4, 1920, pp. 83-84.

[4] See articles on statistics of the Federal government in the March, 1919, number of the *Quar. Pub. of the American Statistical Association* and in other issues thereof during the war period.

uses of statistics, but it may be appropriate to note some of the particular applications to which statistical method is put in the government service. Facts are sought by the administrative departments for various purposes:

(a) *To reveal conditions of public interest.* The Department of Agriculture collects estimates of crop conditions as aids to those concerned with agricultural affairs, and Boards of Health gather data to show trends in death rates from various causes. For example, a recent bulletin of the Wisconsin Board of Health directs attention to the increasing death rate from cancer, both in Wisconsin and in the United States as a whole.

(b) Statistics are compiled as a means of *testing compliance with statutes.* Thus Tax Commissions gather comparative facts in regard to assessments and sales to determine to what extent assessors are complying with laws requiring assessment at full value; and Industrial Commissions collect statistics in regard to violations of child-labor laws.

(c) Facts are assembled as *guides to the conduct of departmental duties.* To illustrate, the Departments of Education in certain states must have statistics of school attendance to guide them in the distribution of state school funds.

The commercial uses of statistics. It is scarcely an exaggeration to say that all modern business on an extensive scale is based on statistics. In a large organization it is impossible for the executive to direct the intricate business machine in his care without something more than custom or personal intuition and judgment upon which to base his decisions. He must know the facts, and the desired information is largely statistical, requiring the application of statistical method for its efficient collection and analysis for use in business control. Many of the larger industrial and financial concerns have a special statistical department; and there is developing a literature on the application of statistics to business,[1] which gives a partial though incomplete picture of the many respects in which the efficient business executive is coming to depend upon reliable statistics.

For convenience in discussion, business statistics are desig-

[1] See references at close of chapter and also in Appendix A.

nated as internal and external. *Internal business statistics* apply
to a given business unit such as the United States Steel Corporation, the International Harvester Company, or any similar business enterprise. In a broad sense of the term, accounting is a
phase of internal statistics, but, owing to the relatively high
development of this phase, it has, in common use, attained an
independent status and the term statistical method is usually reserved for processes other than the analysis by the usual accounting methods of receipts and expenditures measured in dollars
and cents. Internal statistics include such data as sales statistics;
purchasing and stores statistics, involving records of quantities
used, quantities on hand, and seasonal variations in prices; and
production statistics, including records of production per man,
machine production, wasted materials, labor turnover, etc. The
statistical problems connected with the last-mentioned phase, labor
turnover, afford a subject of special interest to the student of the
human aspects of industry. How shall we measure the turnover
of labor? Shall it be in terms of new men hired? Or of separations—that is, of men leaving? With what shall these accessions
or separations be compared, with the total number on the payroll
or with the total days worked? What statistical evidence can be
gathered with regard to the causes of rapid turnover or its cost?
These are merely suggestions of the many questions answers to
which are sought by statistical means. There are also sales statistics, which attempt to give the sales manager concise, intelligible
records of what is being accomplished. Or, reaching out into the
field of prophecy, the statistician seeks to aid in the process of
market analysis in an effort to ascertain profitable potential markets or better ways of utilizing present markets.

External statistics may be concerned either with the statistical
aspects of a given industry or with business conditions in general.
Thus the statistical organization of the Northwestern University
Bureau of Business Research has published a survey of the retail
clothing business in the United States.[1] From an examination of

[1] Northwestern University Bureau of Business Research, *Costs, Merchandising Practices, Advertising and Sales in the Retail Distribution of Clothing;*
also, *Selling Expenses and Their Control.*

the results of this "Retail Clothing Survey," the retailer is enabled to judge, for example, whether the standards attained in his particular establishment are equivalent to those which are typical of the industry as a whole, or whether his percentage of delinquent accounts, his expenditures for rent, or his percentage of returned goods, is abnormal.

In the study of general business conditions, the business man finds it of advantage to have the best available statistics, presented in the most effective manner, for the trends in prices, for movements in interest rates, for the indices of business activity, such as pig-iron production and railroad tonnage. He wants to know the amount of unemployment; the amount of new construction; the trends in the great speculative markets; in fact, all those things which are indicators of commercial tendencies, straws showing which way the wind blows. If possible, he wishes the statistician to construct for him a composite index of all these business factors so arranged that its fluctuations will act as a business barometer, as an indication of the most probable movement in future business conditions.[1]

REQUISITES FOR SUCCESS IN STATISTICAL STUDY AND PRACTICE

It may not be amiss to conclude this introductory chapter with an enumeration of the qualities important to those who wish to achieve success in statistical work, to become qualified to act as directing statisticians.

In the first place, the statistician needs a fertile, *constructive imagination*. One may do the drudgery of statistics without imagination, carrying out mechanically the instructions of another, but he will not become a true statistician without the intellectual zeal which stimulates an anticipation of both the problem to be solved and the methods to be used in the solution. Statistics, like all real science, is a search for causes or relations, but causes are seldom discovered by blind effort. One must guess where the truth is hidden before one can hope to find it. It is for this reason that the teacher anticipates good work from the

[1] See chap. xiv, on "Business Cycles and Barometers."

student whose mind is constantly searching beyond the immediate details of his problem.

Intellectual integrity is perhaps the most vital requisite in a dependable statistician. The temptations are great. The tendency to the unquestioned acceptance of facts presented in numerical form is so strong, and the difficulty of ascertaining the exact steps by which a statistician has reached his results is so great, that it is imperative that his work be done with a scrupulous regard for truth. The data must not be "doctored," the processes inaccurate, or the presentation of the facts misleading. Violation of this principle should be considered the gravest of statistical sins; and violation, it should be remembered, is not necessarily a deliberate, intentional falsity, but may arise with equally serious consequences from intellectual sloth, from the unwillingness to make the effort required to ascertain the real truth.

As applied to the business statistician, the importance of this characteristic has been stated by the head of the statistics and accounting department of one of our large flour manufacturers in these words:

> "Our ideal statistician would be honorable. He would be fair and square. He would be able to merit the confidence of his associates in business and of the men he would come in contact with. He would not juggle his figures to fit some superior's whim, but would base his conclusions upon hard, cold facts." [1]

Closely akin to the need of intellectual integrity is the requisite of a *capacity for careful work*. Some one has said that genius is an infinite capacity for taking pains. Certainly it is equally true that success in statistical work depends to an unusual degree upon the commonplace but essential qualities of carefulness and neatness, and upon the possession of the necessary stamina to keep working on a problem until the solution is reached or the possibilities of solution exhausted.

[1] Letter from Harry A. Bullis, Auditor of the Washburn-Crosby Co., Minneapolis, Minn.

The statistician must know his *subject matter*. If one is to do statistical work in the study of labor turnover, he should learn all that it is possible to learn about the conditions of hiring and firing. If he is studying the statistics of population, he should know the principles of population as developed by past studies. It is for this reason that the statistician is seldom only a statistician. He is an economist using statistics as a tool; he is a sociologist seeking to widen his knowledge by use of quantitative studies; or he is a business man applying the best methods available to the analysis of the quantitative aspects of his business.

To summarize, the good statistician will be gifted with a high degree of constructive imagination, with a standard of intellectual integrity which will not permit him to do slipshod or misleading work, with a capacity for persistent, painstaking effort, and will be as thoroughly familiar as possible with the social phenomena in which he is carrying on his statistical investigations. In addition, he will be *trained in proper statistical methods*. He will be able to perceive any statistical principle involved and will know how to apply it to reveal most clearly the significant facts. This is an age of preparation. The doctor, the lawyer, the minister, the teacher, spend years in preparation for their task. Likewise the statistician must become familiar with his tools and their uses before he can hope to make most effective use of them.

DEFINITIONS OF STATISTICS AND STATISTICAL METHOD GIVEN BY VARIOUS WRITERS

BOWLEY, A. L., *Elements of Statistics,* 4th ed.

"Statistics may, for instance, be called the science of counting" (p. 3).

With special reference to the science of demography, he says: "Statistics is the science of the measurement of the social organism, regarded as a whole, in all its manifestations" (p. 7).

Again, "Statistics may rightly be called the science of averages" (p. 7).

DAVIES, G. R., *Introduction to Economic Statistics,* p. 3.

"The term 'statistics' when used to designate a branch of study, implies an exposition of certain methods employed in presenting and interpreting the numerical aspects of a given subject."

King, W. I., *Elements of Statistical Method,* p. 23.

"The science of statistics is the method of judging collective natural or social phenomena from the results obtained by the analysis of an enumeration or collection of estimates."

Secrist, Horace, *An Introduction to Statistical Methods.*

"We shall use the term statistics as meaning aggregates of facts, 'affected to a marked extent by a multiplicity of causes,' numerically stated, enumerated, or estimated according to reasonable standards of accuracy, collected in a systematic manner for a predetermined purpose, and placed in relation to each other" (p. 8).

"The expression statistical methods is used to include all those devices of analysis and synthesis by means of which statistics are scientifically collected and used to explain or describe phenomena either in their individual or related capacities" (p. 9).

Yule, G. U., *An Introduction to the Theory of Statistics,* p. 5.

"By statistics we mean quantitative data affected to a marked extent by a multiplicity of causes. By statistical methods we mean methods specially adapted to the elucidation of quantitative data affected by a multiplicity of causes. By theory of statistics we mean the exposition of statistical methods."

REFERENCES

1. Doten, Carroll W., "Statistics in the Service of Economics," *Jour. Am. Stat. Assoc.,* March, 1922, pp. 1-7 (presidential address).
2. Giddings, F. H., "The Service of Statistics to Sociology," Quar. Pub. of the Amer. Stat. Assoc., vol. xiv, pp. 21-29.
3. Kinley, D., "The Service of Statistics to Economics," *Quar. Pub. of Amer. Stat. Assoc.,* vol. xiv, pp. 11-20.
4. King, W. I., *The Elements of Statistical Method,* chaps. i, ii, iii.
5. Secrist, Horace, *An Introduction to Statistical Method,* chap. i.
6. —— *Readings and Problems in Statistical Method,* Selections Nos. 2, 3, and 5.

CHAPTER II

THE SAMPLING PROCESS

By the sampling process is meant the use of an analysis of a part from which to draw conclusions as to the whole. It is a partial canvass as compared with a complete count. It is in the use of sampling that statistical method and accountancy usually part company. A primary aim of the accountant is to assign properly every dollar of receipts and expenditures, to account for the "last red cent." Statistics endeavors to carry the formation of significant judgments beyond the limit where perfect or complete count is possible. It looks to the formulation of helpful decisions by estimates, based largely upon various applications of the sampling process. If it were practicable, a complete count would, it is true, be preferable, but in a great many cases a full canvass is impossible. In historical sampling, some of the events concerning which a judgment is to be formed may even not yet have happened. An estimate of the probable duration of life of a group of living persons cannot conceivably be based upon a complete count. Again, even in the study of past events or present facts, not all of the items may be ascertainable within the limits of the time, energy, and funds available.

Extensive use of the sampling process. The uses of the sampling process in the field of social phenomena are myriad. In determining racial characteristics, consciously or unconsciously the sampling process is used. No one ever measured the height or noted the color of the hair of all the members of a race. Decisions in regard to racial characteristics must of necessity be based upon the analysis of a sample. Even if we narrow the "universe" [1] to a much smaller group than a race, we usually find

[1] "Universe" and "population" are conventional expressions used in statistical terminology to designate the total or aggregate of items under consideration or from which a sample is taken. Thus, if one were taking a sample

ourselves still forming judgments on the basis of a consideration of only a part or sample taken from the universe. Let us note some of the applications of sampling to economic and social problems.

(1) *Life Insurance.* Insurance rates rest entirely on the sampling process. For life insurance, the sample consists of the mortality records of persons insured in the past; for example, the American Experience Table.

(2) *New types of insurance.* A steadily increasing use of statistical method is found in the rapid expansion of many newer kinds of insurance, such as accident, sickness, unemployment, theft, hail, tornado. For each of these the actuary must work out from the sample furnished by recorded past experience the best estimate he can of the probable losses in similar risks in the future.

(3) *Cost-of-living studies.* It is manifestly impossible to study the cost of living of all families or even all families of a given class. Much of the discussion of the cost of living in this country rests on studies of groups of several hundred families or the study made in 1901 by the Bureau of Labor, covering some 11,156 laboring-class families, and a similar study made in 1918.[1]

(4) *Index numbers.* Two subsequent chapters are devoted to the analysis of index numbers, chiefly price index numbers. These all depend upon the sampling process. Suppose one wishes to measure the change in the general price level. Would it be possible to average the prices of all commodities sold? Obviously not. The task of compilation would be too great; no machinery exists for recording and reporting all prices to a central agency. In fact, some articles are so far from being standardized or the terms of sale are so indefinite, that an average price would have

of Ford cars to determine the proportion of them equipped with speedometers, the universe would be the total number of Ford cars in use. This universe might be widened to include all automobiles or narrowed to include only 1924-model Fords owned by residents of a specified city.

[1] See the *Eighteenth Annual Report* of the U. S. Commissioner of Labor, and also several articles in the 1919 *Monthly Labor Review.*

..ittle significance. Furthermore, it is not possible to determine the price for even a single article of importance without recourse to the sampling process. We speak of the price of wheat on July 1, 1923, but wheat was sold at many different prices on that day in the various markets of the world and even in any one market. The compiler of a price average must choose those prices which appear typical.

(5) *Market analysis.* The business man who wishes to sound out the possibilities of a given market does not necessarily send salesmen to all potential customers in the market. By some means deemed adequate to secure a representative sample, he picks out a portion of the prospective clientele and sends to that portion a salesman or a sales letter, and from the results of this sample he judges of the possibilities of the territory or the effectiveness of the method used.

(6) *The "sales method" of equalization.* An interesting application of the sampling process is found in the use of the "sales method" in equalizing taxes in the state of Wisconsin. It is a well-known fact that the values placed by assessors on property are not always the full market values and that some assessors undervalue to a greater extent than others. Consequently it would not be fair to apportion the state or county property tax on the basis of the valuations made by the respective local assessors. Some means must be found of making an independent estimate of the true value of the property in each district. This is done by comparing the actual contract price of real estate sold within the year with the assessed value of the identical pieces. If it is found that real estate is selling for twice its assessed value, then the total assessed value of the district is doubled to get the estimated true value. (Strictly speaking, an average of five years is taken.) This amounts to taking the assessments on the sold pieces as a sample of the assessments on all parcels of real estate. To the extent that the samples are too small or are non-representative, the resulting equalization is imperfect, but it is believed that this method is as good or better than any other method of equalization yet devised.

LAWS OF SAMPLING

The principle upon which the extensive use of the sampling process rests is known as *the law of statistical regularity.* This law is, "that *a moderately large number of items chosen at random from among a very large group are almost sure, on the average, to have the characteristics of the larger group.*" [1]

This law does not imply that the resemblance between the sample and its universe will be perfect. The range of error due to a failure to use random selection cannot be mathematically determined, but it is possible to determine the range of variation which may occur due to mere chance, even if the sample be selected strictly at random. (See Chapter X, "The Theory of Probability and Error.")

Corollary—the permanence of small numbers. If it is true that a reasonably large sample is representative of the whole, then a second large sample should be similar to the first; and if in one sample there are found a certain few individuals with a given rare characteristic, we should expect to find about the same number with the given characteristic in the second sample. Bowley states this principle of the permanence of small numbers in the following paragraph: [2]

"If among a great number of things there are a few which present some particular feature, it is a matter of common experience that this small number is seldom much exceeded and seldom entirely vanishes; this experience applies to accidents, fires . . . and to the rare events and coincidences with which some newspapers fill their columns. Specialists in all professions, from the doctor who treats only one obscure disease of the ear to the dealer in curiosities, make their livelihood dependent on this permanence of small numbers."

[1] See W. I. King, *The Elements of Statistical Method,* p. 28. Also, F. S. Chapin, in his *Field Work and Social Research,* pp. 116-118, gives a short but illuminating statement of the logical basis for the sampling process.
[2] A. L. Bowley, *Elements of Statistics,* 4th ed., p. 286. The algebraic demonstration of this principle is found in Bowley, 4th ed., pp. 284-285; see limitation thereon, in case of a small sample, *ibid.,* p. 279.

Corollary—the inertia of large numbers.[1] In the absence of
any cause tending to bring a material change from one period to
another, we may consider phenomena of two periods as samples
from the same universe and consequently as subject to the law of
statistical regularity. Thus we should expect to find a considerable degree of constancy in the total amount of inheritance taxes
received year after year if we take a large enough area into consideration and assume that the inheritance-tax law does not
change. The receipts in one county may vary widely from year
to year, but increases in one county are apt to be offset by decreases in some other county, thus tending to stabilize the receipts
over the entire state. This principle of the inertia of large
numbers holds likewise for losses from fire or accident, and the
banker, in determining the amount of cash to keep on hand is
largely guided by it—that is, by the assumption that the proportion of business which must be settled in cash will continue to be
much the same as it has been in the past.

Obviously, however, this principle of the inertia of large
numbers cannot be literally relied upon if there is at work any
influence tending toward a constant increase or decrease. The
increase of average wealth may make for a steady increase in
inheritance-tax receipts; the development of fire protection may
cause a steady decrease in fire losses.

The verification of the law of statistical regularity and its
corollaries rests partly on the theory of probabilities, and partly
on empirical test. Professor Bowley, in his *Elements of Statistics*
(4th ed., pp. 277-284, or 3d ed., pp. 305-315) shows the close
similarity between certain samples and the universes from which
they were taken. The explanation, however, is in terms somewhat
too technical for the beginner in statistics. A simpler statement
is found in his *Elementary Manual of Statistics,* Chapter VII.

[1] W. I. King, *op. cit.,* p. 30, states the principle of inertia of large numbers
thus: "in most classes of phenomena, when one part of a large group is varying in one direction, the probabilities are that another equal part of the same
group is varying in the opposite direction; hence, the total change will be
slight."

The Conditions of Accurate Sampling

"No formal rules," says Professor Bowley,[1] "can replace judgment and experience in the selection and interpretation of samples." The following suggestions, however, may aid in the avoidance of pitfalls:

The necessity of fair sampling. In the use of the sampling process it is obvious that the accuracy of the results will depend upon the degree to which the sample is truly representative of the group from which it is taken. To obtain representative or unbiased sampling it is necessary that every item in the total must have the same chance of inclusion in the sample,[2] and that the choice of one thing does not influence the choice of any other.[3] Representative sampling depends upon random choice or its equivalent in deliberate selection. Let us note the several *methods of striving for fair samples,* which we may designate respectively as strictly random selection, selection at regular intervals from a haphazard or unbiased arrangement of the items, and proportioned selection. Often a combination of these methods will be used.

(1) *Strictly random selection.* A fairly conducted lottery, such as the drawing made in the draft registration during the Great War, affords an illustration of random sampling. If numbers are placed in an urn and so thoroughly mixed that any one number has as good a chance of being drawn as any other, then the drawing is determined by chance or random selection. A short-cut method to the result of the lottery process consists in the random selection of numbers with the aid of tables of logarithms. The reader has doubtless noticed that the last digits in such tables appear to vary in a haphazard manner. Hence, if the universe to be sampled numbers 1,000 items and a sample of 200 is to be taken, random selection can be secured by assigning numbers from 1 to 1,000 to the items in the universe and then taking the last three digits from numbers in seven-place logarithmic

[1] A. L. Bowley, *Elementary Manual of Statistics*, p. 62.
[2] A. L. Bowley, *Elements of Statistics*, 4th ed., p. 279.
[3] *Ibid.*, p. 277.

tables until we have 200 numbers, all between 0 and 1,000. Then the items bearing these 200 numbers may be used for the desired sample.[1] The samples in Table I were selected by the use of tables of logarithms, the steps in the process being as follows:

(a) The 307 relative prices in Table 101, Appendix B, were numbered from 1 to 307.

(A relative price is a percentage obtained by dividing the price of one period by the price of another period taken as a standard or base and multiplying the result by 100.)

(b) The table of logarithms was consulted and, beginning with the logarithm of 94, the last three digits of the logarithm of each successive number were set down, except where those three digits exceeded 307.

(c) Then the relative prices in Table 101 bearing the numbers so selected were taken for the sample. To illustrate, the logarithm of 94 is 1.9731279. The relative price numbered 279 in Table 101 is 215.1, which is the first entry in sample No. 1 of Table 1.

(2) *Selection at regular intervals.*[2] This method of securing an impartial, unbiased selection of a sample is frequently used in statistical studies. First the desired proportion between the universe and the sample is determined. Let us assume that a sample equal to one-tenth of the total will be adequate. Then, if the items are arrayed in order of magnitude, as in Table XXXI, Chapter VII, a fair sample may readily be obtained by taking every tenth item. In fact, provided the basis of arrangement is unbiased with reference to the characteristic for which the sampling is being conducted, the items need not be arrayed in the order of the degree to which they possess that characteristic. For example, selection at equal intervals from an alphabetical list will ordinarily accomplish chance sampling. Or, if there is no relation between alphabetical arrangement and the characteristic involved in the sampling, all items beginning with a given letter of the alphabet may be taken.

[1] Cf. A. L. Bowley, *Elements of Statistics,* 4th ed., pp. 278-279.
[2] A. L. Bowley, *ibid,* p. 278, describes the selection of a sample of houses to be surveyed in Reading by marking one house in twenty.

TABLE I.—RANDOM SAMPLES

Selected from the relative prices in Table 101, Appendix B,
by method explained in accompanying text

Sample No. 1	Sample No. 2	Sample No. 3	Sample No. 4
215.1	153.5	227.9	260.1
233.3	301.0	260.0	187.1
194.3	108.7	169.5	194.3
246.0	236.6	255.4	186.7
253.9	206.6	132.7	146.7
160.4	165.6	360.9	315.6
228.8	296.7	258.1	200.5
194.7	209.4	179.3	188.6
164.5	234.2	142.3	165.6
221.9	223.3	171.6	199.5
188.0	293.8	185.3	269.0
190.1	213.8	169.5	216.7
183.1	199.7	248.4	198.2
194.7	162.7	174.4	225.2
189.0	163.7	191.1	121.1
194.7	290.9	215.9	213.8
190.7	181.2	193.6	215.5
150.9	188.0	246.0	382.8
273.8	257.2	178.1	214.6
260.1	153.5	193.0	194.3
186.7	212.3	211.6	190.7
219.9	256.4	190.7	95.0
131.4	359.6	199.5	288.2
200.5	256.4	262.4	336.0
209.4	217.1	286.1	261.8

Arithmetic average

203.0	221.7	212.1	218.7

Thus, a sample of university students might be obtained by marking each tenth name in the student directory, or by taking all whose names begin with B. The latter method would be biased, however, if the sampling were for nationality. For example, a relatively large proportion of Chinese names begin with C, T, or Y, hence a sample from one letter of the alphabet would not give a true proportion of Chinese.

(3) *Proportioned selection.* When the composition of the total group is known, the chances of selecting a fair sample are

increased by taking sub-samples proportioned in size according
to the significant elements in the total. Thus in a sample of the
student body, the degree of accuracy will be improved by taking
a sample having the same proportions of men and women, of
seniors and juniors, of fraternity and non-fraternity men, etc.,
as are found in the entire student body. Within each sub-group,
however, some method of random selection must still be used.

The size of the sample. A sample may be chosen by random
selection and yet be inadequate for its purpose because too small
to give a truthful picture of the whole from which it is taken.
This is particularly true if there are groups in the total with but a
small representation.[1] Among the several thousand students in a
university, there are probably only a few taking advanced mathematics or a highly specialized course in economics. A sample of
twenty-five or thirty, or even a much larger number, might not
include any students for a given small class. The lower limit of
the proper size of a sample, consequently, is the smallest number
which is at least large enough to include a representation of all
the essential elements if the sample is perfect. The specific size
of the sample necessary will vary according to the circumstances
and the characteristics of the universe to be sampled,[2] and to a
large degree is one of those matters which must be determined
by personal judgment based on a familiarity with the subject
matter and the sampling process. However, it should be noted
that it may be mathematically demonstrated that, under the assumption of random sampling, the precision of a sample increases
with the size of the sample, varying directly with the square root
of the number of items in the sample. Thus to double the precision of a sample it is necessary to quadruple the size of the
sample; to treble the precision, it is necessary to increase the size

[1] Cf. example given by Bowley, p. *279, op. cit.,* 4th ed.
[2] The size of the universe is not so important as the size of the sample.
"The accuracy of the result," says Bowley, "depends on n, the number in the
sample, and not on N, the number in the universe. The size of the universe
only affects the problem in that, when the N things are numerous and scattered, it is difficult to get an accurate enumeration and secure that each has
an equal chance of being chosen, and it becomes possible that parts are
omitted from ignorance of their existence which differ essentially from the
major parts included."—*Elements of Statistics,* 4th ed., p. *279.*

of the sample ninefold. In a later chapter we shall return to a somewhat more technical explanation of the relation between the size of a sample and its probable accuracy. (Chapter X, "The Theory of Probability and Error.")

The stability test. One of the simplest and most practicable tests for the adequacy of sampling is to take several samples, each consisting of about the same number of cases. Then, if the results obtained do not show a reasonably close similarity, increase the size of the samples until the successive samples do evidence substantial similarity.

Bias in estimates.[1] The accuracy of a comparison based upon samples of estimates is not always seriously impaired by an element of bias in the estimates, for there may well be a greater likelihood of similarity between estimates, and hence of successive samples from them, than between the estimates and the actual phenomena. Thus, if in making estimates of crop conditions the reporting agents tend to overestimate the condition of the crop, that bias does not prevent reasonably accurate conclusions being drawn in terms of increase or decrease from past years, as the same element of bias has entered into the estimates for those years as well. Likewise, even if it be true, as is sometimes suggested, that merchants, in reporting the prices charged by them, tend to understate, it is still possible to construct a fairly accurate index of the relative change in prices from one period to the next. If the bias in the estimates is constant, valid comparisons may be made between samples from those estimates. The same principle would hold, of course, if a complete enumeration of estimates, rather than merely a sample, were available.

The results of various methods of sampling applied to the data in Table 101, Appendix B, are summarized below. Samples 1-4, inclusive, are listed in detail in Table I and, as previously explained, were selected with the aid of chance combinations of figures taken from logarithmic tables. Sample 5 was selected by taking each tenth relative price in Table 101, beginning with the first; sample 6 by arranging the relative prices in order of their

---

[1] See G. U. Yule, *Introduction to the Theory of Statistics,* pp. 279-281, for discussion of bias in sampling.

size and taking each tenth item, beginning with the fourth, from the lower end of the distribution. The reader will find it interesting to make his own selection of samples from this table by various methods and to compare his results with those given below and with the arithmetic average of the complete list of 307 relative prices, which is 216.6 per cent.

TABLE II

AVERAGES OF RANDOM SAMPLES FROM TABLE 101

Number of the sample	Number of cases in sample	Arithmetic average (per cent)
No. 1	25	203.0
No. 2	25	221.7
No. 3	25	212.1
No. 4	25	218.7
No. 5	31	210.0
No. 6	31	216.7

The fact that substantially accurate estimates may be obtained by sampling often enables the statistician to reach important conclusions in circumstances where a complete enumeration is impracticable. The principles of sampling have been introduced, in this elementary way, somewhat earlier than is usual in textbooks on statistical method, in the hope that the reader will be stimulated to begin immediately to watch for applications of the sampling process in the economic and social life with which he is familiar.

REFERENCES

1. BOWLEY, A. L., *Elements of Statistics,* 4th ed., pp. 277-284, 329-337. (The reader who is unfamiliar with the mathematical symbols used by Bowley will find it necessary to read more than the portions stated to follow his reasoning.)
2. —— *Elementary Manual of Statistics,* chap. vii.
3. CHAPIN, F. S., *Field Work and Social Research,* pp. 112-125.
4. KING, W. I., *Elements of Statistical Method,* pp. 28-31.
5. PEARL, RAYMOND, *Introduction to Medical Biometry and Statistics,* pp. 255-262, "Practical Problems of Sampling."
6. SECRIST, H., *Readings,* pp. 62-64, 111-124.
7. YULE, G. U., *An Introduction to the Theory of Statistics,* chap. xiii. "Simple Sampling of Attributes," and the following chapters.

CHAPTER III

CLASSIFICATION AND TABULATION

The Nature of Classification

CLASSIFICATION, or the arrangement of items into groups according to common characteristics, is the first essential step in scientific analysis. The biologist groups plants and animals according to genus and species; the chemist talks of sulphates and carbonates; the sociologist classifies populations; and the economist designates the factors in production as labor, land, capital, and entrepreneur. Likewise the statistician finds it necessary to divide his data, his working materials, into groups or classes before he can readily discover their full import.

Types of classification.[1] We may even find it profitable to characterize the types of classification. In the first place, a scientific classification is *exclusive,* in the sense that there is no overlapping of subclasses. A classification of the residents of a city as males and females would be exclusive; but a classification as women, children, and the gainfully employed would be unscientific, for not all men are gainfully employed and many of the persons so employed are women and children.

Statistical data may be subjected to either historical classification or cross-section classification of the *geographical, qualitative,* or *quantitative* type. That is, statistical facts may be classified on a chronological basis, such as the growth of population during a decade, price changes, wage fluctuations, the "ups and downs" of the stock market (see Table VII, Appendix A,[2] stubs) or the

---

[1] See Dr. Franz Žižek, *Statistical Averages,* pp. 7-24, for discussion of the "Classification of Statistical Series with Reference to the Problem of Averages."

[2] Tables V-XII are grouped, in order of number, in Appendix A to this chapter. The other tables mentioned are in the general text or in Appendix B, near the close of the book.

division may be some basis irrespective of time. The enumeration of the total population in each of the several states is geographical classification. If the basis of cross-classification is the possession of different characteristics, we may speak of a classification by attributes or a qualitative classification. The basis may be marital condition, cause of death, race, sex, nationality, religious faith, political adherence, etc., etc. Thieves may be distinguished as porch-climbers, pickpockets, safe-blowers, etc., and we have a qualitative classification.

If, however, the classification merely separates the data into groups according to the degree or quantity of some attribute, measurable in numerical terms, then we have a classification by magnitude or *size*. Thus in Table VI (Appendix A) the population is arranged in groups according to age—according to the degree possessed of the single attribute age. Such a table is known as a *frequency table*. Frequency tables of wages, incomes, age at death, and of many similar social facts are important aids in statistical studies. (See discussion later in this chapter.)

When distinctions are carefully made, "collections of units which differ from other collections by characteristics which cannot be expressed in figures" are termed *sections or classes;* for example, the divisions of a population according to sex or according to states. "Collections of units which differ from other collections by characteristics which can be expressed in figures are called groups." When the classification is by attributes, we have *classes;* when it is by size or quantitative variation of any kind, we have *groups,* but this distinction is not closely followed.[1]

THE MECHANICS OF CLASSIFICATION [2]

In a well-planned statistical investigation the scheme of classification is determined upon before the work of gathering data is commenced,[3] and the allocation of the items to the various

[1] Cf. G. C. Whipple, *Vital Statistics,* p. 39.
[2] See discussion of the relative merits of the "writing method" and the "checking method" of compiling original data, H. O. Rugg, *Statistical Methods Applied to Education,* pp. 60-64.
[3] For the dependence of the schedule on the scheme of tabulation, see Bailey and Cummings, *Statistics,* pp. 26-44.

classes may be partly accomplished in the process of obtaining the information. Ordinarily, however, the items must be systematically sorted and the numbers in the classes counted or tallied before the process of classification is complete. The information which the statistician wishes to tabulate is usually contained in questionnaires or schedules which have been gathered in field surveys or by correspondence. The necessary tallying of the items from these schedules may be done by hand or by the use of tabulating machines.

Mechanical tabulation. In a large statistical organization, sorting and counting is done by Hollerith or Powers tabulating machines. In Plates I-IV are shown pictures of the Hollerith machines and of special cards used. The data on the original schedules, or on listing cards, are transcribed to tabulating cards similar to the one represented below, by punching holes for each item on the schedule in accordance with a code prepared for the particular data. There are forty-five columns on the card, and these are divided into "fields." In Plate I, the first column is the Month "field" and the last six columns are the Cost "field." The punching is done with a "key punch" (Plate II), which is operated like a typewriter. There is also a "gang punch," which is adapted to punching holes through several cards at once and is useful when part of the data is similar on many cards. When punched, the cards are run through the "sorter" (Plate III), which can be set to sort on the basis of any one of the forty-five columns. Suppose it is set for Column 1, then the cards will be sorted according to months. Then the cards for January, for example, may be put into the "tabulator" (Plate IV) and the data in the Selling Price "field" totaled. In fact, as indicated in Plate IV, several "fields" may be totaled simultaneously. In similar manner any other desired sorting and totaling may be quickly accomplished. The essential mechanical principle of the process is the establishment of electrical contact through the punched holes.

The requisition tabulating card in Plate IV illustrates the combination type, suitable for use in making pen entries directly upon the tabulating card.

PLATE I
HOLLERITH SALES TABULATING CARD

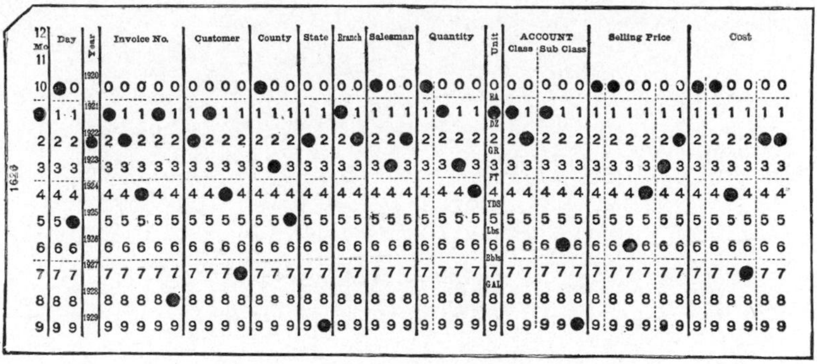

Courtesy, The Tabulating Machine Co.

PLATE II.—KEY PUNCH

PLATE III
HOLLERITH SORTER

Courtesy, The Tabulating Machine Co.

PLATE IV

HOLLERITH REQUISITION CARD AND TABULATING MACHINE

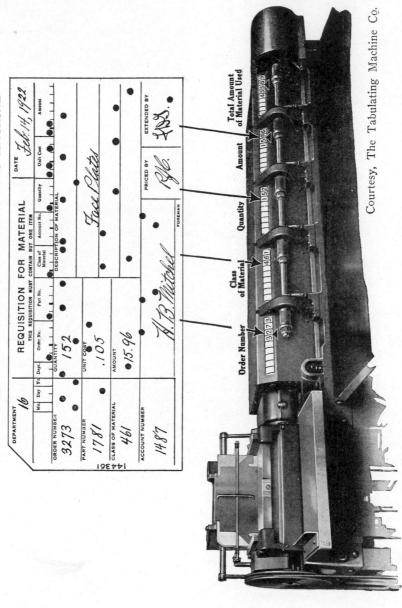

Courtesy, The Tabulating Machine Co.

Coding. The necessary transcription of the data from the original schedules to the tabulating cards may be direct from the uncoded schedules, or, if it is desired to prepare the schedules so that the task of transcription will be even more routine, they may be previously coded by marking each answer with the code number to be punched on the card.

Listing cards. If for some particular purpose, use is to be made of only a portion of the information on the schedule, it may be advantageous to transcribe this selected data to special listing cards before beginning the tabulating process. On these listing forms, explanatory material essential to the original schedule may be largely omitted; the answers given on the schedule may be translated into uniform terminology and arranged in

TABLE III

ILLUSTRATIONS OF TALLYING DEVICES
(Based on Table I)

A.—COLUMN METHOD OF TALLYING, BY CROSS-FIVES

RELATIVE PRICE	TALLY	TOTAL	RELATIVE PRICE	TALLY	TOTAL
ALL GROUPS		100	225 – 249	ʃʃʃʃ ʃʃʃʃ	9
75 – 99	ʃ	1	250 – 274	ʃʃʃʃ ʃʃʃʃ ʃʃʃ	13
100 – 124	ʃʃ	2	275 – 299	ʃʃʃʃ	5
125 – 149	ʃʃʃʃ	4	300 – 324	ʃʃ	2
150 – 174	ʃʃʃʃ ʃʃʃʃ ʃʃʃ	13	325 – 349	ʃ	1
175 – 199	ʃʃʃʃ ʃʃʃʃ ʃʃʃʃ ʃʃʃʃ ʃʃʃʃ ʃ	26	350 – 374	ʃʃ	2
200 – 224	ʃʃʃʃ ʃʃʃʃ ʃʃʃʃ ʃʃʃʃ ʃ	21	375 – 399	ʃ	1

B.—DIVISION-INTO-SQUARES, BY CROSS-TENS

TOTAL 100	75 –99 (1)	100-124 (2)	125 -149 (4)	150-174 (13)	175-199 (26)	200-224 (21)
225 -249 (9)	250-274 (13)	275-299 (5)	300-324 (2)	325-349 (1)	350-374 (2)	375-399 (1)

a more convenient and compact form, and, if desirable, they may be coded on the listing cards.

When the *counting* must be done *by hand,* it is sometimes convenient to use a *coded card,* arranged in a manner somewhat similar to those used in mechanical tabulating, as an intermediate step between the original records and the tally sheet.

Methods of tallying. There are various feasible methods of tallying. If, for example, you are counting the number of men receiving each given wage, you may list the possible wage amounts in regular sequence in a column down one edge of the paper and then enter the tallies opposite the given wage; or a sheet of paper may be ruled off into squares and each square marked with a given wage, and the tallies placed in the respective squares. If the same tabulation is repeated at frequent intervals, it is convenient to construct a special tray divided into labeled partitions into which to sort the tally cards. Illustrations of methods of tallying are given on page 27. In both examples the data tallied are the one hundred 1919 relative wholesale prices used in the discussion of sampling in the preceding chapter.

STATISTICAL TABLES [1]

When the sorting and counting are completed, the next step is the recording of the data in tabular form. Tabulation is the shorthand of the statistician, a short-cut method of expressing numerical data. A good statistical table is not a mere careless grouping of columns and rows of figures; it is a triumph of ingenuity and technique, a masterpiece of economy of space combined with a maximum of clearly presented information. To prepare a first-class table, one must have a clear idea of the facts to be presented, the contrasts to be stressed, the points upon which emphasis is to be placed, and, lastly, a familiarity with the technique of table preparation. The emphasis, contrasts, and comparisons will vary with each table, but there are certain principles

---

[1] The suggestions in this chapter relate primarily to tables for publication, but most of them can be heeded to advantage in preparing tables for less formal use. For an enumeration of the "statistical standards to which tabulation should conform," see H. Secrist, *Readings,* pp. 269-270.

of technique which are of general application. Let us first turn
our attention to the **terminology of tabulation.**

A table is an arrangement of figures in columns and rows so
placed that the significance of the figures is determined by reference to two sets of explanatory phrases, *captions* at the head of
the *columns* and *stubs* at the edge of the *rows*. Thus in Table V
(Tables V-XII, inclusive, are grouped in Appendix A, at the
close of this chapter) the word "Single" is a stub and the figures
opposite it (22,584,467—12,967,565—and 9,616,902) are spoken
of as a row; the phrase "Both sexes" is a caption and the figures
beneath this caption are a column. There is great diversity in
the arrangement of tables, but all of them consist in some combination of the four elements, captions, stubs, and columns and
rows of figures.

The **advantages** of arrangement of data in the tabular form
are so obvious as to make extended comment unnecessary. The
repetition of explanatory phrases is reduced to a minimum. In
Table V each caption suffices for six sets of figures. The visuali-
zation of relations and the process of comparison is much facilitated. In a table, it becomes an easy matter to indicate the order
of importance, and to summate or average the items. The compact and simplified form of the table materially lessens the tax
on the memory.

The number. To facilitate reference in the explanation
which accompanies them, tables should be consecutively numbered. For this purpose both Roman and Arabic numerals are in
common use. The number may be advantageously placed above
the title as in Table V. The placing of the number in the first
line of the title, as in Table VIII-B, is slightly less effective but
may save some space. When economy of space is an important
consideration, the number may be placed in the upper left corner
of the first caption, as in Table VII. In such a case the number
stands out more clearly if printed in black-face type. Ordinarily
neither number nor title should be placed beneath the table, as
the reader should note the number and read the title before
consulting the table.

The title. The preparation of a title appears simple, but this is a delusive simplicity. There are few phases of common statistical practice that afford so great a challenge to common sense, ingenuity, and care in details as the formulation of a good title. It is the sign-post of the table, designed to catch the eye of the reader, to suggest the noteworthy features, and encourage further perusal. It must also contain such important facts as are not brought out in the body of the table. *The ideal title is reasonably concise, catchy, unambiguous,*[1] *not misleading, and adequate.* Let us elaborate the significance of these terms.

The title must be as *concise* [2] as is consistent with a reasonable compliance with the other requisites of a good title. If not brief, it will not be read, or, even if read, the important points will be obscured and the table will not be so thoroughly understood. The title must be *catchy,* suggesting to the reader the pertinent facts in the table and in some instances the conclusions to be drawn, and inducing him to study the table itself. It is sometimes effective to have a short main title to catch the eye, with a somewhat longer subtitle to add the necessary detail (Table XI). In the effort to be concise, care should be taken that the title is *not* left *ambiguous,* requiring a study of the table itself to determine if possible which of two interpretations is correct. No argument is needed to sustain the suggestion that a title should *not* be *misleading,* but only faithful attention to the implications of the words used will prevent misstatements from occasionally creeping into the terse language of a title.

What is required to make a title adequate will vary with each sort of circumstance. Preferably it should be *self-explanatory,* with a minimum of reliance on explanation in the accompanying text or footnotes. The table is most effective if it is a self-sufficing unit. To be adequate the title should also be *comprehensive.* This does not mean that it should include an enumeration of all or much of the detail contained in the table,

---

[1] *Ambiguous title:* "Amounts paid to collectors arising from the proceeds of in rem actions, etc., during the fiscal year." (What does "etc." include?)

[2] *Verbose title:* "Aggregate collections made and reported to the Commissioner of Internal Revenue by the collectors of the several collection districts and by the stamp agent in the Philippine Islands during the fiscal year ended June 30, 1917."

but that it should be so worded that it does not by implication exclude any of the data actually in the table. A working test for adequacy is found in the question, Does the title answer the three queries: Where? When? What? It should be obvious to the reader, as he scans the title and glances over the table, to what period the data refer, to what geographical district they apply, and what facts are being shown. Unless the maker of the table is assured that these questions are otherwise satisfactorily answered, he should see that the information appears in the title. Sometimes the nature of the text in which the table appears will indicate clearly the territory to which the data apply, or the necessary information may be given in the captions or stubs, and require repetition in the title only when emphasis on the facts in question is especially desired.

The **unit of expression** should always be clearly indicated, in either the title, subtitle, or captions. Two methods of indication are illustrated in Tables VI and VII.

Lettering. In general, the size of type or lettering used in the title, subtitle, captions, and stubs should be graduated in accordance with their relative importance. Usually captions and stubs should be in smaller type than the title, and subcaptions in still smaller type. The title should be centered horizontally above the table and the captions centered within the caption space. The inverted pyramid arrangement of the title, as in Table V, is a favorite form and usually gives a well-proportioned appearance.

Ruling. The essential purpose of ruling is to increase the attractiveness of a table and particularly to bring out more clearly the relations of its several parts. Some tables are unruled (Table VI, also Tables 102 and 103 in Appendix B), but this practice is to be avoided in complicated tables as not conducive to an orderly and effective arrangement of the data. The ruling in Table V (also Tables VIII-XI, inclusive) is of the open-side or semi-box type; that in Table VII, of the closed-side or complete-box type.

The main divisions of a table should be set off by double lines. The detailed interpretation of this rule rests, of necessity, with the individual. The double line beneath the total figures, even when they are placed at the top, is a rather well standardized practice and should be followed unless the total is emphasized by printing it in black-face type (Table VI).

The student will find it helpful to study the various combinations of ruling in standard statistical publications, particularly the federal census volumes.

General-purpose and special-purpose tables.[1]   A distinction should be made between general-purpose tables, which are "designed to bring together in most convenient and accessible form all the data bearing upon a given topic," and special-purpose tables, which are "intended to throw into relief relationships of special significance in a given study. The general-purpose table is an orderly presentation of statistical material; the special-purpose table, a record of the results of statistical analysis." [2] The tables appearing in the census volumes are usually of the former type; [3] those used in books to illustrate or prove a given point, are of the latter. The general-purpose table is determined in form and arrangement largely by considerations of space and convenience of entry and transcription; the special-purpose table, largely by considerations of effective presentation to the reader of the facts and relations which the author wishes to stress. Many of the suggestions given below apply to both types, but are designed primarily with reference to the special-purpose table.

The distinction between complete and partial cross-classification.   A *complete cross-classification* is one which indicates for each subclass of any one of the two or more classifications, the apportionment of the given subclass on the basis of any one of the other classifications appearing in the table. Tables VIII-B, VIII-C, and VIII-D are complete cross-classification tables. For example, in Table VIII-D, there are four classifications—by age, sex, marital status, and color—and the table gives the apportionment of each subclass of each of the four classifications among

---

[1] Professor Rugg uses the terms "original and secondary tabulations" in his *Statistical Methods Applied to Education,* p. 59.

[2] Cf. E. E. Day, "The Standardization of the Construction of Statistical Tables," *Quar. Pub. of the American Statistical Association,* vol. 17, pp. 59-66.

[3] On the other hand, the small tables appearing in the descriptive portions of the census volumes are usually of the special-purpose type.

the subclasses of the other three classifications. For example, of the single persons, we are given the number who are under sixteen years, the number of these who are white, and the number of those white who are males.

Table IX, on the other hand, presents a *partial cross-classification,* in that while the table classifies workmen by year, union status, sex, and color, it does not indicate the number of women who are union members, or, again, the number of men who are non-union. This table is also incomplete in that totals are not shown.

Another common type of table is the *partially subclassified* table illustrated by Table XI. The classification by race is comprehensive, embracing all subdivisions of the total, but the classification by age gives the data only for adult males.

Statistical tables exhibit great diversity in form, but in most of their features they are but variations of the several types discussed in this chapter. The student who wishes a thorough command of the technique of table preparation will find it helpful, and not altogether uninteresting, to scrutinize the tables found in his reading for possible modifications conducive to an increase in accuracy and effectiveness.

Arrangement of table contents. In determining the particular arrangement to be given to the stubs and captions in a table, the compiler must first determine his order of emphasis. He must decide just what comparisons he wishes to make and which of the desired comparisons are to be stressed. This decision made, certain recognized principles of table technique can be readily applied. For example, it is generally conceded that the easiest comparison is between sets of figures arranged in vertical sequence—that is, adjacent in the same column. Hence, if one wishes to list a simple comparison between the subclasses of one class, it is arranged in one column, as in Table VIII-A. The next easiest comparison is between adjacent columns, with the figures to be compared in the same row, as between the "Male" and "Female" columns in Table VIII-B. However, if a third comparison is to be made, it is impossible to set the figures to be compared immediately adjacent, for the adjacent positions have been utilized in the primary and secondary comparisons. The next, or third best, position is considered to be in the same column, with the figures to be compared separated by intervening figures (alternating in column), as the comparison between "Married" and "Single" in Table VIII-C.

If still a fourth comparison is to be made, the next best position is in alternate columns, or, in other words, alternating in the same row, as in the comparison between the "White" and "Colored" columns in Table VIII-D.[1] The choice may not be great between the first and second positions, or between the third and fourth, but there is some margin of advantage to the vertical comparison, especially when it is necessary for the eye to jump as in the third and fourth comparisons.

To summarize, the most effective arrangement of sets of figures to be compared is as follows:

First—or primary comparison—adjacent in the same column.

Second—or secondary comparison—adjacent in the same row.

Third—alternating in the same column.

Fourth—alternating in the same row.

Space considerations. Obviously, it will often be necessary to modify the above arrangements because of considerations of space. They are standards to be kept in mind, and only modified for cause; but, for example, if crop yields are to be classified by states for five or six years in one table, it is ordinarily more convenient to put the states in the stubs rather than in the captions, even though it may be desired to give primary emphasis to the comparison between years.

When the wording for one classification is considerably longer than that for the other classification, it is usually a saving of space to place the longer terms as stubs.

Grouping of stubs. When the stubs are numerous, it is convenient to arrange them in single-spaced groups of five or six, thus keeping the table compact and at the same time avoiding the confusing effect of long, unbroken columns of figures.

---

[1] For another example of the four-classification, or "quadruple," type, with a ruling somewhat different from that in Table VIII-D, see H. Secrist, *Introduction to Statistical Methods,* p. 131.

As a primary principle, let us reiterate, one should keep in mind that *figures to be compared should be brought as close together as possible.* If it is desired to compare percentages, in a composite table having both absolute numbers and percentages, the percentage columns or rows should be together (see Table X). As a rule, *complex tables should be avoided,* for the ease of interpretation decreases rapidly with an increase in complexity.

Arrangement of subclasses. The arrangement of major classes is determined primarily, as we have seen, by the desired emphasis. Within the classes there may be no particular order of emphasis in mind, but the *stubs or captions should be arranged in a series*—that is, in some *logical order.* The basis of arrangement may be *alphabetical, chronological,* according to *size, customary,* as in the practice of naming the geographical divisions of the United States from east to west, or some other fairly obvious order of importance. In any event, the arrangement of items should not be indiscriminate. In chronological sequences, the more common practice is to place the earlier date at the left or top, but the Census publications frequently reverse the order, putting the most recent date at the top, as the latest date is of greatest interest. In some instances, the most recent date is repeated, appearing both at the beginning and end of the sequence.

Location of totals. We are so accustomed to the location of totals at the foot of a column when using tables for computation purposes, that our first thought is to place them at the bottom in tables designed for presentation purposes. However, many leading statistical bureaus are coming to place totals at the top of columns and at the left end of rows. This brings them into the most prominent place in the table, where the eye catches them immediately after reading the captions and stubs. Frequently the reader is interested only in the totals or at least wishes to compare them with the particular detail which is significant to him. Hence it is urged that the lead of the Census Bureau in this practice be followed so that the reading public will become accustomed to finding the total in the most convenient place.

Subtotals. There is no clear uniformity of practice in the location or ruling for subtotals. Often they may be omitted without substantial loss. One method of ruling is indicated in Table VIII-C. Often the subgroups and their totals can be conveniently indicated by the spacing between stubs.

Miscellaneous and exceptional items. Frequently it is not desirable to make a classification so complete as to enumerate specifically all the subclasses, in which case the *unnamed* groups should be included in a column designated by the words "all other" or some similar phrase, with such additional explanation as may appear necessary to make the meaning clear. Exceptional items, such as those below the limit of expression, may be indicated by numerals or other marks referring to explanatory footnotes. Thus in a table classifying population in terms of millions, one subclass may have a population of only 400,000, which fact may be indicated in a footnote.

Source of information. The source of the data from which a table is taken should always be given. Where the source is especially significant it should appear in the title, or, more often, in a subtitle. Otherwise it may be placed in a footnote, identified by a reference numeral or figure inserted after the number of the table, or at the close of the title, as in Table VI.

Numbering of columns and stubs. The practice of numbering stubs and columns helps to locate them when reference is made in the body of the text, and is to be encouraged. It is somewhat more common to number the rows with Arabic numerals and the columns with letters or Roman numerals (Table VIII-D). When the column numbers are used in explaining mathematical computations, letters are preferable to Roman numerals (Table XXXVIII in Chapter IX).

Location of table on page. If possible, the table should be placed upon the page so that it can be read from the same direction as the general text.

Frequency Distributions

A characteristic which presents more than one numerical value is, in statistical terminology, a *variable*. The several values which the characteristic presents are the *variate values,* or, considered in the aggregate, a *series*. The number of times a given value appears is the *variate frequency*.   If the variate values are grouped into classes, the number of observations in each class is the *class frequency,* and the distribution of the observations over the several classes is the *frequency distribution*.   A table showing the frequency distribution—that is, designating the classes and giving the frequencies of each—is a variate frequency table, or, as it is more commonly called, a *frequency table*.

Neither sex nor religion nor political affiliation is a variable in the sense just mentioned, for none of these are characteristics capable of presenting quantitative variations.   But age, wages, death rates, and interest rates are variables.

The range of variate values included in a given class is the *class interval,* and the *class limits* are the upper and lower extremes of a given class.   A distinction may be made between the *expressed limits* as stated in the table and the *actual limits* which are implied by the expressed limits.   In Table IV the "expressed limits" of the first group are 50 and 149, but the "actual limits" are 49.5 and 149.4.

For illustrations of the several somewhat abstract terms in the above paragraphs, let us hark back to the relative prices listed in Table I, p. 20.   Each of these relative prices, it will be recalled, represents the 1919 price of a different commodity expressed as a percentage of the 1913 price of the same commodity.   As "relative price" has many different numerical values, it is a "variable" as defined above.   The "variable values" are the one hundred relative prices listed in Table I.   In Table III, earlier in this chapter, these variate values were counted and the number or "frequency" in each "class" recorded.   Table IV below contains the frequencies for classes with a "class interval" of one hundred.

IV.— FREQUENCY TABLE

Relative Price (Class interval)	Number in the given class (Frequency)
50—149	7
150—249	69
250—349	21
350—449	3

Continuous and discontinuous variation.[1] It will help to clarify the subsequent discussion of the methods of analyzing and graphing frequency distributions if we first note the distinction between strictly continuous, strictly discontinuous, and approximately continuous series.

In a *strictly continuous series* there is an infinite number of possible values to the variable. The transition from one value to another may be by insensible gradations. Thus, if the height of the shortest man is forty inches, and the tallest eighty inches, it is possible for other men to be of any height between forty and eighty inches. In fact, in series in which the variate values are determined by measurement, it is impossible to determine the exact size of any one item. We may measure height to the nearest inch, the nearest tenth of an inch, or to some still smaller fraction of an inch, but there is always a still finer degree of measurement which is conceivable even if not yet attained.

On the other hand, a *discontinuous* or discrete series has breaks or gaps in the variate values. We have such a series whenever the variate values are obtained by counting rather than by the measuring process or whenever there is a definite lower limit to the unit of measurement. A frequency distribution of residences classified according to the number of rooms would show some residences with one room, some with two, some with three, and so on, but none with 3.75 rooms.

Many *economic and social series* are to some extent discontinuous. Thus all series which rest on values in monetary terms have a minimum fraction of variation. Variances in wages are seldom less than one cent; stocks are quoted on the stock exchanges in minimum units of one-eighth of a dollar per share; wheat, in the Chicago pit, in fractions of one-eighth of a cent per bushel.

[1] Note the distinction made by Professor Secrist between continuous and discrete series. "By continuous series are meant those in which measurements are simply approximations to an absolute value and which differ by small gradations. That is, they are series in which measurements are only approximations, within the limits set up, to an absolute but indeterminate measurement. By discrete or broken series, on the other hand, are meant measurements which are determined by the nature of the units in which expressed. . . ." (*Introduction to Statistical Method,* p. 148.)

However, some social and economic series are continuous and others are approximately continuous. All age classifications, depending as they do upon the time element, which is impossible of exact measurement, are fundamentally continuous. Also any series, such as death rates, which is obtained by the process of division, may present an almost infinite number of decimal values between any two limits, though the actual practice is usually to express death rates in terms of an integral number per 1,000 or per 100,000. Series of this latter type may be called artificially or *approximately continuous*. The relative price series we have previously considered is continuous in this sense.

Series of the discontinuous type frequently exhibit a *round-number* tendency; for example, a tendency to cluster around the fives or tens.

Problems in the arrangement of frequency distributions.[1]

In the determination of frequency distributions or the construction of the frequency tables which present them, the chief *problems* are (1) the determination of the number of classes, or, what amounts to the same thing, the choice of the *class interval*, and (2) the location and method of expressing the *class limits*. If the interval is taken too large, the members of the class will not be sufficiently homogeneous to justify treatment as one class, and hence the midpoint cannot be safely used as typical of the group. Also, the important features of the frequency distribution will be obscured. On the other hand, if the interval is taken too small, the classification will be unwieldy and in the fineness of the detail the main tendencies will be obscured. Yule[2] suggests that in a continuous series, or one with small discrete steps, usually it is best to have fifteen or twenty-five classes. In a discrete series with steps which are large in comparison with the total range, the nature of the series often determines the class intervals. Thus, in the classification of residences according to the number of rooms, the minimum class interval would be one room.

---

[1] See G. C. Whipple, *Vital Statistics*, pp. 43-46, for an illuminating discussion of grouping and group designations.

[2] Yule, *op. cit.*, p. 79.

A uniform class interval is highly desirable. It facilitates accurate and ready comparison of the class-frequencies; it facilitates the use of the class interval as a unit of measurement in computing the average of the series,[1] and it makes it easier to construct a graph giving a true representation of the series. These criticisms do not apply with equal validity to the practice of subdividing some of the classes into smaller, equal-sized intervals in that part of the range where the variation in frequency is great. For example, in a classification of incomes with a class interval of $5,000, it may be desirable to divide the class from $1,000 to $5,000 into five subclasses, in order to study the distribution among the smaller income classes.

The use of unequal class intervals is, however, very common and may be justified in part at least by considerations of space and time. Also, in official statistics, considerations of secrecy sometimes require the consolidation of classes with small frequencies in order to conceal the facts concerning individuals in the classes, and unequal intervals are sometimes necessitated by the fact that the classification is by statute provisions divided into unequal groups.

In this connection it should be noted that the practice of using an indefinite lower or upper limit for the extreme classes in a distribution increases the difficulty of approximating the arithmetic average of the distribution. If the lower class in a wage distribution is given as "Under $25," the reader has little clew as to the probable average wage of the class. Likewise, if the highest class is stated as "$50 or more."

The class limits. After the number of classes and the size of the class intervals have been decided, there still remains the problem of the location of the class limits and the best method of expressing these limits. In general, the limits should be so placed (1) that either the limits or the midpoint of the class will be integers; (2) so that the limits are unambiguous; and (3) so that they do not fall at points of round number concentration. The placing of the limits on integral numbers simplifies their

---

[1] See discussion of "step-deviation" method of computing the arithmetic average in H. Secrist, *An Introduction to Statistical Methods,* pp. 251-253.

expression. Locating them so that the midpoint is an integer facilitates the process of computing the average of the distribution when the midpoint is taken as typical of the class.

In a distinctly discontinuous series, ambiguity may be easily avoided by having no common class limits (see Table VI). In the following classifications of families according to the number in the family, Distribution B is ambiguous, but the class limits in Distribution A are entirely clear.

DISTRIBUTION A   DISTRIBUTION B

Persons per family	Number of families	Persons per family	Number of families
1	10	1–2	10
2	25	2–3	25
3	35	3–4	35
4	50	4–5	50
5	45	5–6	45

For purposes of classification, the use, as in Table VI, of *non-overlapping limits,* is to be recommended, though for purposes of popular presentation it may be advisable to express the limits in round numbers. A classification of incomes may well be expressed in terms of $1,000-$2,000, $2,000-$3,000, etc., even though in the original tabulation the class limits were taken as $1,000 to $1,999, etc.

Even where the limits do not overlap the statistician will ordinarily have to determine *actual limits* in addition to the expressed limits. Thus, if incomes are calculated to the cent but classified only to the nearest dollar, the expressed limits may be $1,000 and $1,999, $2,000 and $2,999, as above, but if an item of $1,999.49 is counted with the $1,000-$1,999 class and an item of $1,999.50 is counted with the $2,000-$2,999 class, then the actual limits are $1,999.49 and $1,999.50, respectively, and so on for the other classes. The meaning of the class *limits* becomes *more obvious if the accuracy to which the original measurements are read is stated.*

Occasionally the class limits are expressed merely by giving the *midpoint* of the class or, as in Table XII-E, by giving merely the *lower limit* of the class. In the latter case, if length is measured to the nearest tenth-inch, the class 2 – includes all measurements read from 2.0 inches up to 2.9 inches, inclusive. An item 2.96 inches long would be read as 3.0 inches and fall into the next class, designated as 3 –.

If an item apparently falls *on the boundary line of two classes,* ambiguity can usually be avoided by calculating the size of the item to one more decimal place or by establishing limits where no items occur.

The class *limits should be entered* in the table *for all classes* between the extremes even if there are no frequencies for some of the classes.

Simple and cumulative frequency tables. A *simple frequency table* gives the number of items in each class, considered separately from the other classes (Table IV). If the table gives the number in each class plus the frequencies of all lower classes, that is, the number in or below the given class, we have a cumulative frequency on the "less than" basis, which means that the cumulative frequency set opposite each class includes all items the size of which does not exceed the upper limit of the designated class. If the table shows the number in the given class plus all items with higher values, it is a cumulative frequency on the "more than" basis.

In Table XII-A, we have first a simple frequency of the number of fires in each class; then the cumulative frequency on the "less than" basis; and, in the last column, the cumulative frequency on the "more than" basis.

In a later chapter (V), we shall examine the methods of graphically representing these various types of frequency distributions.

NOTE.—The tables referred to in the above chapter are, with a few stated exceptions, grouped in Appendix A, following. The student may find it profitable to examine also the tables which appear in general Appendix B near the close of the book and in subsequent chapters. A list of all tables is given at the front of the book.

APPENDIX A—CHAPTER III. TABLE TYPES.

TABLE V

MARITAL CONDITION OF PERSONS FIFTEEN YEARS OF AGE AND OVER IN THE
UNITED STATES IN 1920 [1]

Marital Condition	Both Sexes	Male	Female
Total..........................	72,098,178	36,920,663	35,177,515
Single	22,584,467	12,967,565	9,616,902
Married	43,168,199	21,849,266	21,318,933
Widowed	5,675,933	1,758,308	3,917,625
Divorced	508,588	235,284	273,304
Marital condition not reported..	160,991	110,240	50,751

[1] Adapted from Fourteenth Census of the United States (1920), vol ii, p. 388.

Study suggestions.—Note the following features of Table V, above; Number placed at top; title centered, in inverted pyramid form; open side or semi-box type of ruling; totals at top and left; source of data given in footnote, with key numeral referring thereto; captions approximately centered at top, bottom, and sides; and figures likewise centered in column. These are *standard characteristics* which most tables should possess.

Study suggestions.—Note the following features of Table VI: (1) absence of ruling; (2) method of indicating that the numbers are expressed in thousands; (3) the class limits do not overlap; (4) stubs are bunched in groups of five or six to increase ease of reading the table.

Which of these methods are to be recommended for general adoption?

TABLE VI

DISTRIBUTION BY AGE PERIODS OF THE POPULATION OF THE UNITED STATES

Age Period	Number of Persons (000 omitted)	
	1910	1920
All ages................................	91,972	105,711
Under 5 years..........................	10,631	11,573
5 to 9 years..........................	9,761	11,398
10 to 14 years..........................	9,107	10,641
15 to 19 years..........................	9,064	9,431
20 to 24 years..........................	9,057	9,277
25 to 29 years..........................	8,180	9,086
30 to 34 years..........................	6,972	8,071
35 to 39 years..........................	6,396	7,775
40 to 44 years..........................	5,262	6,346
45 to 49 years..........................	4,469	5,764
50 to 54 years..........................	3,901	4,735
55 to 59 years..........................	2,787	3,549
60 to 64 years..........................	2,267	2,983
65 to 69 years..........................	1,680	2,068
70 to 74 years..........................	1,114	1,395
75 to 79 years..........................	667	857
80 to 84 years..........................	322	403
85 to 89 years..........................	123	157
90 to 94 years..........................	33	40
95 to 99 years..........................	7	10
100 years and over.....................	4	4
Age unknown	169	149

[1] From the Fourteenth Census of the United States: 1920, vol. ii, p. 154.

Study suggestions.—Note the following features of Table VII: (1) Boxed type of ruling; (2) Insertion of table number within the caption space, which is frequently done in the census volumes, with the number emphasized by the use of black-faced type; (3) method of indicating that the figures are given in terms of millions; (4) the order of arranging the years, designed to give emphasis to the later years.

NET GOVERNMENTAL-COST PAYMENTS[1]
In millions of dollars

Table VII Year	Federal Government	The 48 States	Cities having a population of over 30,000
1919	15,740	635	1,202
1918	9,312	561	1,145
1917	2,406	513	1,082
1916	1,048	505	1,044
1915	1,048	491	1,057

[1] Census Bureau: *Financial Statistics of States*, 1919, p. 30.

COMPLETE CROSS-CLASSIFICATION TABLES

The four tables immediately following give forms suitable for complete cross-classifications of a group of persons. In Table VIII-A, the simplest form possible, the classification is only by age; in VIII-B, it is by age and sex; in VIII-C, by age, sex and marital status; in VIII-D, by age, sex, marital status, and color. According to the principles stated in the foregoing pages, the order of emphasis in these tables is (1) age, (2) sex, (3) marital status, and (4) color.

TABLE VIII-A. ONE CLASSIFICATION

AGE	NUMBER OF EMPLOYEES
All ages	1,000
Under sixteen years........	100
Sixteen or over...........	900

TABLE VIII-B. TWO CLASSIFICATIONS

AGE	SEX		
	Both sexes	Male	Female
All ages	1,000	600	400
Under sixteen years	100	90	10
Sixteen or over....	900	510	390

TABLE VIII-C. THREE CLASSIFICATIONS

MARITAL STATUS	AGE	SEX		
		Both Sexes	Male	Female
Married and Single	All ages	1,000	600	400
	Under sixteen years.........	100	90	10
	Sixteen or over..............	900	510	390
Married	All ages	601	500	101
	Under sixteen years.........	1	0	1
	Sixteen or over..............	600	500	100
Single	All ages	399	100	299
	Under sixteen years.........	99	90	9
	Sixteen or over..............	300	10	290

TABLE VIII-D. FOUR CLASSIFICATIONS [1]

AGE AND MARITAL STATUS	A	B	C	D	E	F	G	H	I
	SEX AND COLOR								
	White and Colored			White			Colored		
	Both Sexes	Male	Female	Both Sexes	Male	Female	Both Sexes	Male	Female
1. Total: all ages......	1,000	600	400	800	450	350	200	150	50
2. Under sixteen years	100	90	10	50	45	5	50	45	5
3. Sixteen or over....	900	510	390	750	405	345	150	105	45
4. Married: all ages....	601	500	101	470	400	70	131	100	31
5. Under sixteen years	1	...	1	...	...	...	1	...	1
6. Sixteen or over....	600	500	100	470	400	70	130	100	30
7. Single: all ages......	399	100	299	330	50	280	69	50	19
8. Under sixteen years	99	90	9	50	45	5	49	45	4
9. Sixteen or over....	300	10	290	280	5	275	20	5	15

[1] Modifications in the form of this table can be made without affecting its essential plan of arrangement. The caption "Sex and Color" and the column numbers may be omitted, and additional horizontal ruling may be used, as in Table VIII-C.

TABLE IX
PARTIAL CROSS-CLASSIFICATION TABLE
Workmen in the Victory Automobile Tire Factory
(Hypothetical data)

Year	Union Status		Sex		Color	
	Union	Non-union	Male	Female	White	Black
1923	300	500	600	200	700	100
1924	1,000	400	900	500	1,200	200
1925	1,500	500	1,200	800	1,700	300

Study questions

1. What total columns might appropriately be added to above table?
2. What additional data are needed to make it possible to show a complete cross-classification?
3. What classification is given the primary emphasis?

TABLE X

NUMBER AND PER CENT OF STORES REPORTING CLASSIFIED AMOUNTS OF ADVERTISING PER $100 OF TOTAL NET SALES, BY SIZE OF CITY:[a]

1919

Amount of Advertising per $100 of Total Net Sales	Stores in Cities of Different Size			
	Number		Per Cent of Total Number	
	Population under 40,000	Population 40,000 or more	Population under 40,000	Population 40,000 or more
Total.........	276	91	100.0	100.0
Under $0.50.....	26	4	9.4	4.4
$0.50 to $1.00....	81	9	29.4	9.9
$1.00 to $1.50....	74	11	26.8	12.1
$1.50 to $2.00....	38	13	13.8	14.3
$2.00 to $2.50....	29	16	10.5	17.6
$2.50 to $3.00....	16	14	5.8	15.4
$3.00 to $4.00....	7	10	2.5	10.9
$4.00 to $5.00....	5	8	1.8	8.8
$5.00 to $6.00....	—	6	—	6.6

[a] Adapted from the Northwestern University School of Commerce Bureau of Business Research: *Clothing Survey,* vol. iv, p. 315.

Study questions for Table X.

1.   What criticisms, if any, would you make of the class limits?

2.   To what comparisons have the positions of primary and secondary emphasis, respectively, been given?

3.   Do the title, captions, and stubs meet the test of adequacy, answering the questions: What? Where? When?

TABLE XI

A PARTIAL SUBCLASSIFICATION TABLE

Classification of the Total Population and Adult Males in the United States in 1920, according to Race or Color [1]

Class of Population	Total Population	Males twenty-one years of age and over	
		Number	Per cent which males are of given class
Total	105,710,620	31,403,370	29.7
White	94,820,915	28,442,400	30.0
Negro	10,463,131	2,792,006	26.7
Indian	244,437	61,229	25.0
Chinese	61,639	46,979	76.2
Japanese	111,010	53,411	48.1
All other	9,488	7,345	77.4

[1] Data from Fourteenth Census of the United States, vol. iii, pp. 18-19.

Study questions

1.   Why is the above table designated as a partial subclassification table? What should be added to make it a complete subclassification?

2.   What principle of arrangement has been followed in the stubs? What other logical sequences might be used?

HYPOTHETICAL FREQUENCY DISTRIBUTIONS ILLUSTRATING METHODS AND FAULTS IN THE ARRANGEMENT OF CLASS INTERVALS

Study Suggestions.—Test the following arrangements of class intervals for: (1) uniformity; (2) definiteness of limits. Note carefully the method by which the last two columns in Table XII-A are derived from the "In given grade" column.

TABLE XII-A

DISTRIBUTION OF FIRE LOSSES

(Hypothetical data)

Amount of loss	Number of fires		
	In given grade	In grade or below	In grade or above
Total.......	200	200	200
$100–199	110	110	200
200–299	60	170	90
300–399	20	190	30
400–499	10	200	10

Table XII-B Age in years	Table XII-C Weekly wage in dollars	Table XII-D Price in cents	Table XII-E Length in inches
Under 5	5–10	Under 5	2–
5 to 6	15–20	5 to 9	3–
7 to 9	20–25	10 to 14	4–
10 to 14	25–30	15 to 19	5–
15 to 25	35–40	20 to 29	6–
		30 to 39	

REFERENCES

1. BAILEY AND CUMMINGS, *Statistics,* chap. v.
2. BOWLEY, A. L., *Elements of Statistics,* 4th ed., chap. iv.
3. DAY, E. E., "Standardization of the Construction of Statistical Tables," *Quar. Pub. of Amer. Stat. Assoc.,* vol. 17, pp. 59-66.
4. KING, W. I., *Elements of Statistical Method,* chap. ix, and pp. 97-107, 117.
5. PEARL, RAYMOND, *Introduction to Medical Biometry and Statistics,* chap. iv.
6. RUGG, H. O., *Statistical Methods Applied to Education,* chap. iii.
7. SECRIST, H., *Business Statistics,* pp. 41-50.
8. —— *Readings,* chap. v.
9. —— *An Introduction to Statistical Methods,* chap. v.
10. WATKINS, G. P., "Theory of Statistical Tabulation," *Quar. Pub. of Amer. Stat. Assoc.,* Dec., 1915, pp. 742-757.
11. WHIPPLE, G. C., *Vital Statistics,* pp. 20-22, 39, 43-48, 53-55.
12. YULE, G. U., *An Introduction to the Theory of Statistics,* pp. 75-84, "The Frequency Distribution."
13. ŽIŽEK, FRANZ, *Statistical Averages,* pp. 7-25, on classification; pp. 80-91, on frequency grouping.

CHAPTER IV

GRAPHIC PRESENTATION—1: BAR CHARTS AND MAPS

EACH day millions of persons attend moving-picture shows in preference to reading an equally good or better story in printed form; and magazines are filled with pictorial illustrations used by the advertiser to catch the attention and stir the imagination of the reader. Diagrams and graphs represent the effort of the statistician to utilize this attention-attracting power of visual presentation. By translating dry figures into graphic forms he hopes to command the interest of the reader and at the same time to give him a correct impression of essential facts. For a detailed account of the forms and uses of statistical diagrams, reference must be made to the special treatises on the subject, but any worker with statistical methods, or anyone who expects to be under the necessity of presenting facts, should be familiar with the underlying principles and with the more common types of charts. It should also be noted that diagrams, particularly the line graph, to which the next chapter is devoted, may be used for purposes of analysis and determination of previously unknown facts, as well as for presentation purposes. (See the discussion of "Interpolation" in Chapter V and of the use of the ratio chart for computation purposes in Chapter VI.)

CLASSIFICATION OF STATISTICAL DIAGRAMS [1]

Statistical diagrams may be classified according to their form, purpose, circumstances of use, or type of comparison to be made. In this chapter the primary basis of classification is form, but it should be noted that the determination of suitable form is conditioned by the character of the data to be presented, the circumstances under which the chart is to be used, and the purpose. Some types of diagrams are peculiarly appropriate for chrono-

[1] For further detail concerning classification of diagrams, see Appendix A, at the close of this chapter.

logical data, others for portraying frequency distributions. Charts may serve for illustration, for analysis, or for computation. Some of them are wall charts for use in lecture or exhibit, or desk or pocket charts for use of the investigator or executive; others are to be published in a book or pamphlet.

Obviously the rules of construction are not identical for all these forms and uses. A chart designed for illustrative purposes should be constructed with particular attention to an effective and truthful presentation; one for use in statistical analysis or computation, for example in estimating the population of a country between intercensal years, must be drawn with more than usual attention to precision of construction.[1] A wall chart for lecture purposes should include only the major features, with the explanatory detail to be added by the lecturer; a desk chart may be varied to conform to the personal preferences of the user; while a published chart should conform to standardized practices. The suggestions in this and the following chapters refer primarily to charts intended for publication or for use under conditions essentially similar to publication.

General Standards of Diagrammatic Presentation

It will be helpful to distinguish between certain fundamental principles which should be kept in mind in the preparation of any form of chart, and the various rules or suggestions which aid in the application of the general principles to particular forms of charts. The general object of the use of diagrams is scientifically and effectively to present numerical facts. To gain these ends:

(1) A chart should convey a *truthful message*. It is quite possible, without introducing any direct numerical inaccuracy, so to construct a graph that a false impression is conveyed. The diagram should be so drawn that the impression which will be received by a reasonably intelligent reader will correspond to the data on which the chart is based.

(2) It should be *clear*. It should be easily and quickly interpreted. One great advantage of the chart is that it mini-

[1] Cf. classification per use in W. C. Marshall, *Graphic Methods*, p. 13.

mizes the strain upon the intellectual alertness of the reader.
If the chart is not clear, not comprehended in a glance, this
advantage is largely lost.

(3) It should be in *appropriate form*—that is, in a form
adapted to the subject matter, the place of presentation and
the audience. We shall see presently that the use of certain
types of charts for showing particular types of facts or comparisons has become more or less customary. As to place of
presentation, the rules that will hold for a printed chart to
be placed in a book will necessarily be modified somewhat for
a wall chart or one to be used on the desk of an executive.
Before a technically trained audience, one might use the
ratio chart to good advantage; one will use it charily in
popular presentation.

(4) The chart should be *verifiable by the reader*. It is usually
impossible in a chart to represent the numerical facts with a
high degree of precision or completeness; and either on the
chart or in the accompanying text or tables there should
be given the numerical data on which the chart is based, so
that the reader may, if he wishes, verify the impression he
has received from it and satisfy the desire for additional
information which the chart has aroused.

To summarize, the good diagram will be truthful, clear, appropriate in form, and verifiable by the reader.

WORKING RULES FOR THE HORIZONTAL BAR CHART (Chart 1)

Let us see what devices are needed to carry out the general
standards just presented when use is made of the horizontal bar
chart. This type is one of the simplest and most useful of the
varied forms which are coming into such extensive use in popular
and scientific presentation. In Chart 1 we have a sample of a
simple bar chart with the constituent elements designated. This
chart does not conform to all the specifications suggested below,
but will serve as a convenient basis of discussion. The following
working rules should be observed in the construction of a bar
chart, or, if not observed, there should be some good reason for
the non-conformity.

CHART I

SAMPLE HORIZONTAL-BAR CHART

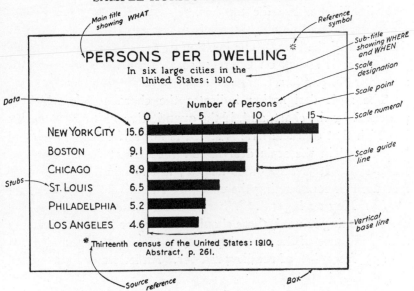

(1) **Title.** Each chart should be provided with a title complying with the standards suggested for table titles—that is, that they be concise, catchy, adequate, unambiguous, and not misleading (cf. Chapter III).

There is no uniformity in practice in the location of the title. In some cases it is placed beneath the chart; in others, above; or it may be inserted within the chart (see subtitles to Charts 6 and 7). Where space is a consideration and the arrangement of the diagram permits, the inserted title may be used effectively; otherwise the title is preferable at the top, where it will be seen first as the eye travels down the page.

If the title tends to be long, the device of splitting it into a main title and a subtitle is helpful, as in Chart 1. This is particularly true where several charts have all but one feature in common. The varying feature should then appear in the main title.

(2) **Number.** All charts should bear a number, preferably at the top. The designations *Chart, Plate,* and *Fig.* are common.

(3) **Scale elements.** The *scale points* on a horizontal bar diagram are usually placed on the top bar, or on an independent scale line just above the top bar, with a few scale *guide lines* dropped at round-number intervals to facilitate the estimation of the length of the bars. The location of the scale points and scale guide lines is shown on Chart 1, as also are the *scale numerals* and *scale designation.*

The scale designation indicates the characteristic which is presented by the chart, and, if the quantitative *unit of expression* in which that characteristic is stated is not self-evident, it should be included in the scale designation (see Chart 2, "Millions of Dollars"). It is sometimes helpful, also, to indicate the *space unit* used in constructing the chart, as 1 mm. = $1,000,000, etc.

(4) **Key or legend.** Where more than one kind of line or cross-hatching is used, there should be a key or legend to indicate the significance of the several types (see Charts 2, 3, 4, and 8).

(5) **Location of reading matter.** All letters or figures used

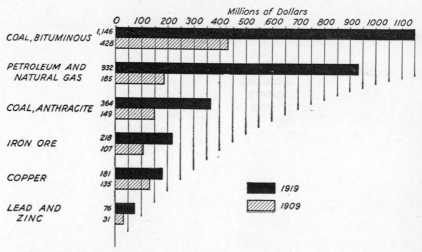

CHART 2

HORIZONTAL-BAR CHART FOR TWO PERIODS

VALUE OF PRODUCTS IN LEADING MINING INDUSTRIES IN THE UNITED STATES: 1909 and 1919*

* Numerical data in Table XIII.

should be so placed that they can be easily read from the bottom or from the right-hand side of the sheet.

The designations of the separate bars will ordinarily be placed as "stubs" to the left of the bars.

TABLE XIII

VALUE OF PRODUCTS IN LEADING MINING INDUSTRIES IN THE
UNITED STATES: 1909 and 1919 [a]

Industry	1909	1919
Bituminous coal............	$427,962,464	$1,145,977,565
Petroleum and natural gas..	185,416,684	931,973,423
Anthracite coal.............	149,180,471	364,084,142
Iron ore....................	106,947,082	218,217,905
Copper	134,616,987	181,258,087
Lead and zinc.............	31,363,094	75,579,347

[a] Fourteenth Census of the United States, 1920, vol. xi, p. 23, table 8.

CHART 3 *

SUBDIVIDED BAR CHART FOR COMPARISON OF COMPONENT PARTS.

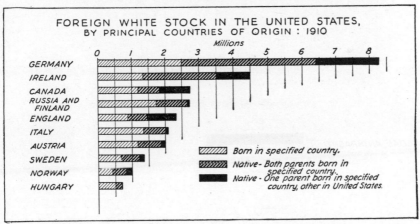

FOREIGN WHITE STOCK IN THE UNITED STATES,
BY PRINCIPAL COUNTRIES OF ORIGIN : 1910

* Adapted from the *Thirteenth Census of the United States: Abstract*, p. 194. See Table XIV.

TABLE XIV

FOREIGN WHITE STOCK IN THE UNITED STATES, BY COUNTRY OF ORIGIN, 1910 [a]

A	B	C	D	E
			Native white of foreign or mixed parentage	
Country of origin	Total foreign stock	Born in specified country	Both parents born in specified country	One parent born in the United States, and the other in specified country
Germany	8,282,618	2,501,181	3,911,847	1,869,590
Ireland	4,504,360	1,352,155	2,141,577	1,010,628
Canada	2,754,615	1,196,070	638,267	920,278
Russia and Finland	2,752,675	1,732,421	949,316	70,938
England	2,322,442	876,455	592,285	853,702
Italy	2,098,360	1,343,070	695,187	60,103
Austria	2,001,559	1,174,924	709,070	117,565
Sweden	1,364,215	665,183	546,788	152,244
Norway	979,099	403,858	410,951	164,290
Hungary	700,227	495,600	191,059	13,568

[a] Thirteenth Census of the United States, Abstract, p. 194.

CHART 4

PERCENTAGE DISTRIBUTIONS

COLOR OR RACE, NATIVITY, AND PARENTAGE IN URBAN AND RURAL COMMUNITIES OF THE UNITED STATES: 1910 *

Per cent

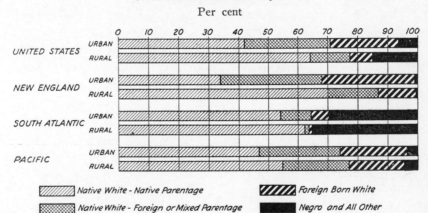

     Native White - Native Parentage   Foreign Born White

     Native White - Foreign or Mixed Parentage   Negro and All Other

* Based on data in Table XV.

TABLE XV

POPULATION OF URBAN AND RURAL COMMUNITIES CLASSIFIED BY COLOR OR
RACE, NATIVITY, AND PARENTAGE: 1910 [a]

Per cent of the total population of the given community

Nativity and parentage	United States		New England		South Atlantic		Pacific	
	Urban	Rural	Urban	Rural	Urban	Rural	Urban	Rural
Native white, native parentage..	41.9	64.1	33.9	69.8	54.2	62.2	46.9	54.8
Native white, foreign or mixed parentage	29.0	13.3	34.2	17.0	10.1	1.4	27.2	22.4
Foreign born white	22.6	7.5	30.7	12.6	6.2	1.1	22.2	18.4
Negro and all other	6.5	15.1	1.2	0.6	29.5	35.3	3.7	4.5
Total..........	100.0	100.0	100.0	100.0	100.0	100.0	100.0	100.0

[a] Computed from Thirteenth Census of the United States, Abstract, p. 92, table 18.

(6) **Data.** To insure compliance with the general requirement that a chart be verifiable, the data upon which it is based should, if convenient, appear directly on the chart, either at the base or end of each bar (Chart 1), in the bar itself (Chart 6), or in an inserted table (Chart 7). Otherwise, the original data should appear in an accompanying table (Charts 3 and 4).

(7) **References.** The chart should be accompanied by a clear statement of the source of the information upon which it is based, which is usually placed in a footnote (Chart 1), or in the subtitle. If placed in a footnote, a reference symbol (Chart 1), number, or letter should follow the chart number or title to call attention to the source reference.

(8) **Box.** The use of the box, as in Charts 1 and 3, is a matter of discretion. In Chart 2, for example, the box is not used. A table or title inserted within the area defined by the axes of the chart should be boxed (see Charts 6 and 7).

(9) **Location of the bars.** All bars or lines to be compared in length should, if practicable, start from the same base line.

(10) **Width of bars.** All bars should be of equal width, the

usual purpose of this type of chart being to show only one size comparison, by means of varying lengths of bars. The exact width is a matter both of available space and of visually effective proportioning. The bars should ordinarily be separated slightly.[1]

The Vertical Bar Chart

The vertical bar chart is particularly suitable for portraying frequency distributions (Chart 7), and for showing time variation (Charts 5 and 6). The bar chart is an alternative arrangement

CHART 5

SIMPLE TIME GRAPH

PER CENT OF THE TOTAL POPULATION OF THE UNITED STATES IN URBAN COMMUNITIES: 1880-1920 *

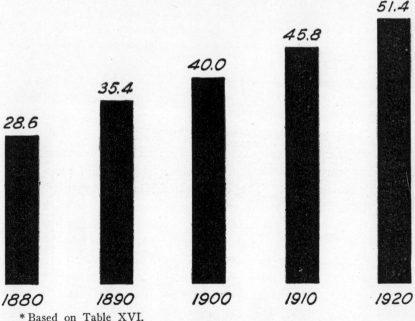

* Based on Table XVI.

[1] In a bar chart portraying a frequency distribution with unequal class intervals, the width of the bars may appropriately be proportioned to the width of the class intervals. This exception applies particularly to the vertical bar type, that form being more suitable for showing frequency series. Cf. R. P. Falkner, "Income Tax Statistics," *Quar. Pub. American Statistical Association*, vol. xiv, pp. 521-549, especially p. 537.

for the use of the graph for these two purposes, and if the vertical bar chart is used, the similarity to the arrangement of the graph is greater than if the horizontal bar chart is used. (For example, in Chart 20, Chapter V, the smoothed line graph is evolved from a vertical bar chart.)

TABLE XVI

URBAN AND RURAL POPULATION OF THE UNITED STATES: 1880-1920 [a]

Year	Number of persons			Per cent		
	Total	Urban	Rural	Total	Urban	Rural
1880	50,155,783	14,358,167	35,797,616	100.0	28.6	71.4
1890	62,947,714	22,298,359	40,649,355	100.0	35.4	64.6
1900	75,994,575	30,380,433	45,614,142	100.0	40.0	60.0
1910	91,972,266	42,166,120	49,806,146	100.0	45.8	54.2
1920	105,710,620	54,304,603	51,406,017	100.0	51.4	48.6

[a] Fourteenth Census of the United States, vol. 1, p. 43, table 26.

CHART 6*

COMBINATION OF VERTICAL BAR CHART WITH LINE GRAPH

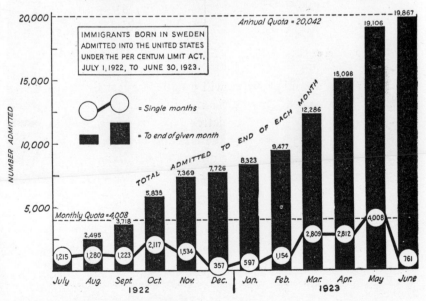

* Based on data in Table XVII.

TABLE XVII

July 1, 1922, to June 30, 1923 [a]

Monthly quota=4,008   Annual quota=20,042

Year and month	Admitted in given month	Admitted from July 1, 1922, to end of given month
1922		
July	1,215	1,215
Aug.	1,280	2,495
Sept.	1,223	3,718
Oct.	2,117	5,835
Nov.	1,534	7,369
Dec.	357	7,726
1923		
Jan.	597	8,323
Feb.	1,154	9,477
Mar.	2,809	12,286
Apr.	2,812	15,098
May	4,008	19,106
June	761	19,867

[a] Compiled from U. S. Bureau of Immigration, *Weekly Bulletin.*

With such few changes as will readily suggest themselves, the rules set forth above for horizontal bar charts can be applied to vertical bar charts. In the latter type, the scale numerals and designations usually appear at the left and bottom.

Examples of vertical bar charts. In Chart 5 we have a diagram illustrating the use of the vertical bar for representing a simple chronological series. The date is shown on the horizontal axis and the quantities are represented by the height of the bars. Note the method for giving the numerical data.

A relatively complicated combination of the bar chart and line graph is presented in Chart 6. It indicates, by a series of circles, the number of persons born in Sweden who were admitted into the United States during each month from July, 1922, to June,

CHART 7

VERTICAL BAR CHART SHOWING A DISCRETE FREQUENCY DISTRIBUTION

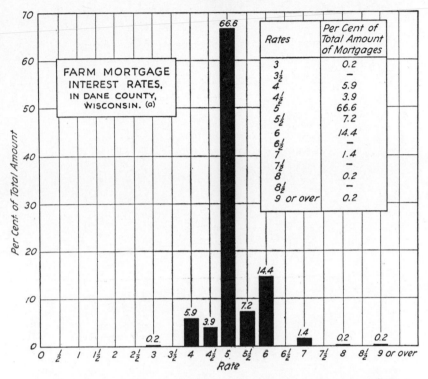

FARM MORTGAGE INTEREST RATES, IN DANE COUNTY, WISCONSIN. (a)

Rates	Per Cent of Total Amount of Mortgages
3	0.2
3½	–
4	5.9
4½	3.9
5	66.6
5½	7.2
6	14.4
6½	–
7	1.4
7½	
8	0.2
8½	–
9 or over	0.2

^a B. H. Hibbard and Frank Robotka, *Farm Credit in Wisconsin*, Bulletin 247, Table II, p. 13, Agriculture Experiment Station of the University of Wisconsin, January, 1915.

1923, and, by the full height of the bars, the cumulative number admitted to the end of each respective month. This chart illustrates the similarity in construction of the vertical bar and the time graph, and the consequent logical basis for using the vertical rather than the horizontal form of bar for representing time series.

Chart 7 shows the use of the vertical bar chart in representing a frequency distribution of a strictly discontinuous type with a round-number tendency. It will be noticed that there is a marked concentration at the rates expressed in even percentages. The bar chart, rather than the graph, is usually to be recommended for a series of this nature.

STATISTICAL MAPS OR CARTOGRAMS [1]

When geographical location becomes of significance, the statistical map is a simple and effective means of presenting data. The map is a device familiar to all readers and is easily adapted to the portrayal of relative density of population, the geographical distribution of an industry, or similar data (see the *Statistical Atlas,* the *Abstract of the Census,* and Charts 8, 9, and 10). Most statistical maps are of three types: *cross-hatch, colored,* and *dot* maps.

CHART 8

CROSS-HATCH STATISTICAL MAP*

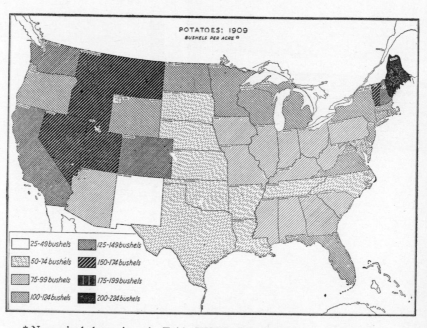

POTATOES: 1909
BUSHELS PER ACRE

25-49 bushels
50-74 bushels
75-99 bushels
100-124 bushels
125-149 bushels
150-174 bushels
175-199 bushels
200-224 bushels

* Numerical data given in Table XVIII, Column III.
[1] Cf. H. Secrist, *Introduction to Statistical Methods,* pp. 176-191.

CHART 9

MULTIPLE-DOT MAP

1909 POTATO ACREAGE*

Each Dot Represents 2,000 Acres

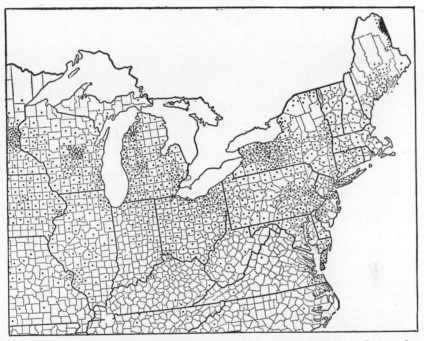

* Adapted, with permission, from V. C. Finch and O. E. Baker, *Geography of the World's Agriculture*, p. 69, U. S. Department of Agriculture. In order to bring out the detail clearly, only a section of the original map, which covers the entire United States, is here reproduced.

CHART 10

QUARTERED-DOT STATISTICAL MAP *

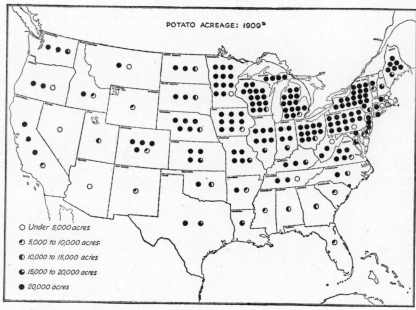

POTATO ACREAGE: 1909 ᵇ

O Under 5,000 acres

◑ 5,000 to 10,000 acres

◐ 10,000 to 15,000 acres

◕ 15,000 to 20,000 acres

● 20,000 acres

* Based on numerical data in Table XVIII, Column II.

TABLE XVIII

ACREAGE AND AVERAGE YIELD PER ACRE OF POTATOES IN THE UNITED STATES
IN 1909 [a]

State	Acreage	Bushels per acre	State	Acreage	Bushels per acre
I	II	III	I	II	III
Alabama	14,486	78	Nebraska	111,151	73
Arkansas	29,719	71	Nevada	4,864	158
Arizona	1,151	84	New Hampshire.	17,370	136
California	67,688	145	New Jersey.....	72,991	110
Colorado	85,839	137	New Mexico.....	6,230	47
Connecticut ...	23,959	112	New York......	394,319	123
Delaware	9,703	91	North Carolina..	31,990	74
Florida	8,509	101	North Dakota...	54,067	103
Georgia	11,877	75	Ohio	212,808	96
Idaho	28,341	166	Oklahoma	32,295	59
Illinois	138,052	88	Oregon	44,265	109
Indiana	99,504	90	Pennsylvania ...	262,013	83
Iowa	169,567	87	Rhode Island....	4,649	119
Kansas	79,025	72	South Carolina..	8,610	91
Kentucky	55,750	92	South Dakota...	50,052	69
Louisiana	19,655	60	Tennessee	40,963	71
Maine	135,799	210	Texas	36,092	62
Maryland	39,299	88	Utah	14,210	170
Massachusetts .	24,459	120	Vermont	26,859	154
Michigan	365,483	105	Virginia	86,927	101
Minnesota	223,692	120	Washington	57,897	132
Mississippi	8,342	77	West Virginia...	42,621	96
Missouri	96,259	81	Wisconsin	290,185	110
Montana	20,710	156	Wyoming	8,333	112

[a] Thirteenth Census of the United States, 1910, vol. v, Agriculture, General
Report and Analysis, pp. 653, 656.

Cross-hatch maps. Chart 8, showing the production of potatoes per acre in 1909, illustrates several types of cross-hatching.
The usual principle is for the heavier shades to represent a cor-
respondingly greater density or magnitude of the factor portrayed. A similar principle holds for colored maps with varying
shades of the same color, in that the darker shades are used to

represent the greater magnitudes. Where practicable, it is desirable to have the group intervals equal, as in Chart 8, where there is a variation in the cross-hatching for each twenty-five-bushel interval.

Colored maps. In this type of cartogram we may use varying shades of the same color or distinct colors for representing the varying frequencies or densities in the several districts.[1] Usually color printing is too expensive to recommend it for use in published charts, particularly since equally good results can be obtained by the cross-hatch or dot types.

Dot maps. Two forms of dot maps are illustrated by Charts 9 and 10, respectively. In Chart 9 the dots are all of the same size and shading, but the relative acreage in each district is shown by the density of the dots. This type of map lends itself more readily than the others to the representation of relative densities without regard to fixed territorial divisions.

A second type of dot map (Chart 10), which we may call the *quartered-dot* type, is used in some of the census publications. Chart 10 is based upon the same data as Chart 9, except that the latter chart applies to only a portion of the United States, but in Chart 10 quantity is represented by the shading as well as by the number of the dots. For example, a solid dot represents 20,000 acres of potatoes; a three-quarter dot, 15,000 to 20,000; a half, 10,000 to 15,000; a quarter dot, 5,000 to 10,000; and an unshaded circle, under 5,000 acres. On the whole, the quartered-dot map is not as flexible as the multiple dot type illustrated by Chart 9.

AREA AND VOLUME CHARTS

As a rule, diagrams in which the unit of measurement is a given area or volume are to be avoided. The eye cannot readily appraise the relative magnitudes of surfaces or volumes. If surfaces are used, the area, not merely one dimension, of the figure should be proportioned to the data to be represented. Of the various area charts, the most useful is the **"pie,"** or **circle chart** (Charts 11 and 12). This type is popular for the representation

[1] The 1900 *Statistical Atlas of the United States* contains many examples of colored shaded charts.

of the distribution of a dollar of expense, taxes, or family budget and is quite appropriate for that purpose. However, even in such cases the same facts could probably be shown with equal ease and clarity by the ordinary bar diagram. The *open-face* type of circle chart is shown in Chart 11 and the *cross-hatch* type in Chart 12.

CHART 11

OPEN-FACE CIRCLE CHART

Percentage Distribution of Persons Ten Years of Age and Over Engaged in Gainful Occupations in the United States: 1920 *

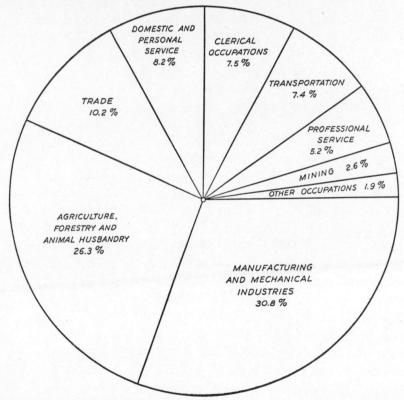

* Based on Table XIX, second column.

CHART 12
CROSS-HATCH CIRCLE CHART
Percentage Distribution of Males Engaged in Gainful Occupations in the
United States: 1920 *

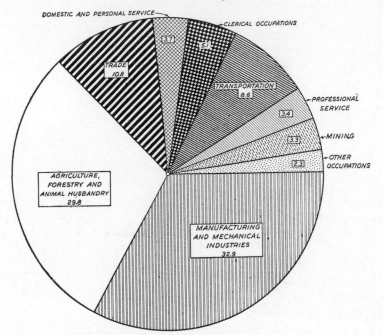

* Based on Table XIX, fourth column.

The criticisms just made of area charts apply with even
greater force to charts with a unit of cubic content as the basis
of measurement.

Emblematic pictograms.   The emblematic pictogram attempts by means of pictures to suggest not only the relative
magnitudes involved, but also the nature of the items whose
magnitudes are under consideration.   We have all probably noticed, in popular articles, charts utilizing men of different sizes
to portray the relative size of standing armies or ships of varying
sizes to represent the respective navies, etc.   Usually, from the
point of view of accurate statistical presentation, the emblematic
pictogram is to be condemned.   It is subject to the same weaknesses as the ordinary surface or volume chart, plus the additional
complexity introduced by the irregularity of outline.   If the

TABLE XIX.—OCCUPATIONS OF THE GAINFULLY EMPLOYED

NUMBER AND PERCENTAGE DISTRIBUTION OF PERSONS TEN YEARS OF AGE
AND OVER GAINFULLY EMPLOYED IN THE UNITED STATES: 1920 [a]

Occupation	Both sexes		Males	
	Number	Per cent of total	Number	Per cent of total males
All occupations	41,614,248	100.0	33,064,737	100.0
Agriculture, forestry, and animal husbandry..............	10,953,158	26.3	9,869,030	29.8
Extraction of minerals........	1,090,223	2.6	1,087,359	3.3
Manufacturing and mechanical industries	12,818,524	30.8	10,888,183	32.9
Transportation	3,063,582	7.4	2,850,528	8.6
Trade	4,242,979	10.2	3,575,187	10.8
Public service (not elsewhere classified)	770,460	1.9	748,666	2.3
Professional service..........	2,143,889	5.2	1,127,391	3.4
Domestic and personal service..	3,404,892	8.2	1,217,968	3.7
Clerical occupations..........	3,126,541	7.5	1,700,425	5.1

[a] Fourteenth Census of the United States, 1920, Abstract of Occupation Statistics, p. 482.

pictogram form is used, special care should be taken to see that the original data are on the chart or readily accessible. An effective use of this type of chart is obtained by combining the emblematic pictogram with the horizontal-bar chart, the pictogram to show the quality of the thing represented and the bar chart to represent the numerical data.

The problem of determining what form of chart is best for various purposes is discussed in the following chapter.

APPENDIX A—CHAPTER IV

CLASSIFICATION OF CHARTS ON VARIOUS BASES WITH REFERENCES TO ILLUSTRATIONS IN THIS AND FOLLOWING CHAPTERS

I. General form:
  1. Bar charts:
    a. Horizontal bars (Charts 1-4).
    b. Vertical bars (Charts 5, 6, and 7).
  2. Statistical maps or cartograms:
    a. Cross-hatch (Chart 8).
    b. Dot: Multiple (Chart 9); quartered (Chart 10); graduated size.
    c. Shaded and colored.
  3. Surfaces:
    a. Circle charts (Charts 11, 12).
    b. Square and rectangular areas.
  4. Volumes:
    a. Cubes.
    b. Spheres.
    c. Emblematic pictograms, irregular shape.
  5. Line graphs:
    a. Natural scale (*e.g.*, Charts 13-21).
    b. Ratio charts, with logarithmic vertical scale (Charts 22 and 23).

II. Classification by certain detail of form:
  1. Dimensions by which the statistical quantities are represented:
    a. One dimension (Charts 1-7).
    b. Two dimensions (area charts, Charts 11 and 12).
    c. Three dimensions (volume charts).
  2. Number of scales:
    A chart may be a two-dimension or three-dimension chart and have only one scale, the scale unit being a stipulated unit of area or volume. The ordinary graph, on the other hand, is a one-dimension chart, in that quantities are represented by vertical distances only, but the graph has two scales—a horizontal scale for time and a vertical scale for quantity. In fact, a graph may have two or more vertical scales (Chart 38).
  3. Method of differentiating the several parts:
    a. Open face with inserted or contiguous legend (Chart 11).
    b. Cross-hatch (Charts 8, 12, and 14).
    c. Shades of one color (Statistical Atlas, 1900).
    d. Multiple colors (Statistical Atlas, 1900; National Industrial Conference Board, *Graphical Analysis of*

> *the Census of Manufactures of the United States,*
> *1849 to 1919).*
>> e. Differentiated lines : solid, dotted, broken, etc. (Charts
>> 13, 38, and 41).
> 4. Principle upon which graph curves are drawn :
>> a. Angular graphs (Chart 13)—data points connected
>> by straight lines.
>> b. Smoothed graphs (Charts 18, 19, 20, 25, 26, 28-32).

III. Classification by purpose :
1. Illustration (Charts 1-14).
2. Analysis (Charts 18-21).
3. Computation (see chapter VI).

IV. Circumstances under which used :
1. Wall chart.
2. Desk chart.
3. Book chart.

V. Type of comparison to be made :
1. Simple comparisons of magnitude (Chart 1).
2. Simple comparisons involving time.
   a. Chronological element subordinate (Chart 2).
   b. Chronological comparison primary (Chart 5).
3. Component parts (Charts 3, 4, and 14).
4. Frequency distributions :
   a. Discrete (Chart 7).
   b. Continuous (Chart 20).

REFERENCES

1. BRINTON, W. C., *Graphic Methods for Presenting Facts.*
2. Bureau of the Census, *Abstract of the Census,* 1910.
3. ——— Statistical Atlas, 1900 and 1914.
4. HASKELL, A. C., *How to Make and Use Graphic Charts.*
5. ——— *Graphic Charts in Business,* chaps. xiii, xiv.
6. KARSTEN, KARL G., *Charts and Graphs.* (See table of contents.)
7. MARSHALL, W. C., *Graphical Methods.*
8. SECRIST, HORACE, *Statistics in Business,* chap. v.
9. ——— *Introduction to Statistical Methods,* chap. vi.
10. ——— *Readings and Problems in Statistical Methods,* pp. 273-277.
11. WARNE, F. J., *Chartography in Ten Lessons,* 1919.
12. ——— *Elementary Course in Chartography,* 1917.
13. ——— *Warne's Book of Charts,* 1913.

CHAPTER V

GRAPHIC PRESENTATION—2: LINE GRAPHS

OF the many forms of diagrams or charts used for statistical presentation and analysis, the well-known graph is by all means the most important. It is particularly useful both in the presentation and in the analysis of historical series, which play so large a part in economic statistics. Government reports, private commercial papers, and books are profusely illustrated with graphs. They are extensively used in business administration as well as in scientific study, and the student of economic problems must at least be able quickly to appraise and interpret a graph if he is to have an up-to-date equipment for the study of modern economic literature.

The characteristic feature of the graph is the representation of data by reference to *two scales,* one vertical, the other horizontal, and each representing consecutive quantitative variations of time or number or other magnitude.

TYPES OF GRAPHS

The following classification of graphs may help us to keep in mind the distinctions between the several forms:

(1) Classified **per data** represented:

   (a) *Historical,* presenting a series of data for periods of time. The chronological graph may represent only the *simple* amounts for each given date or period (Chart 13) or the amounts *cumulated* from the beginning to each respective date.

   (b) *Frequency.* Frequency graphs portray the data of a frequency distribution and may be either *simple* frequency graphs (Charts 20, 21) or *cumulative* frequency graphs representing cumulations on either the "more than" or the "less than" basis [1] (Chart 24 in Chapter VII).

(2) Classified according to the **spacing of the vertical scale divisions.**

   (a) *Arithmetic.* Most graphs are arithmetic—that is, based on ordinary natural numbers, with *equal divisions* on the chart to represent equal quantities.

   (b) The *ratio* chart, however, is based upon the logarithms of the quantities to be represented and the vertical divisions between the co-ordinates are not equal-spaced. Discussion of this type of chart is postponed until Chapter VI.

(3) Classified per the type of **graph line.**

   (a) The *straight-line,* unsmoothed or angular, graph is formed by connecting known or plotted points with straight lines (Chart 13; curve A of Chart 19).

   (b) The *smoothed graph* is formed from the angular graph by drawing curved lines between or among the plotted points (see Curve B, Chart 19, and the discussion of "smoothing" in the latter part of this chapter).

Where not otherwise indicated, the discussion of rules of construction applies particularly to the ordinary arithmetic, angular graph for historical data.

STRUCTURAL ELEMENTS (See Chart 13)

The usual structural elements in a graph are as follows:

Number, title, axes, point of origin, co-ordinate lines, scale units, scale points, scale numerals, and scale designations, plotted points, connected lines, key or legend, box (at discretion), original data, source reference, reference symbol or numeral.

The horizontal base line and the left vertical line are usually the primary axes. The horizontal axis is known as the *X-axis,* and the vertical as the *Y-axis.* The co-ordinate lines are the hori-

[1] The meaning of the terms "more than" and "less than" is explained in the closing paragraph of chap. iii.

CHART 13
SAMPLE GRAPH WITH EXPLANATORY LEGENDS *

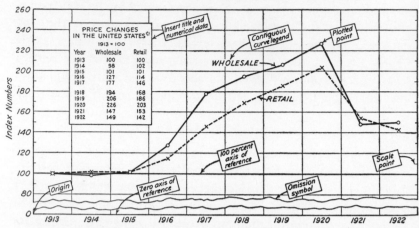

PRICE CHANGES IN THE UNITED STATES* 1913 = 100		
Year	Wholesale	Retail
1913	100	100
1914	98	102
1915	101	101
1916	127	114
1917	177	146
1918	194	168
1919	206	186
1920	226	203
1921	147	153
1922	149	142

* United States Bureau of Labor Statistics, *Monthly Labor Review,* Mar. 3, 1923, pp. 71, 112.

zontal and vertical rulings drawn parallel to the axes to assist in carrying the scales across the diagram, and the *co-ordinates* of a plotted point are its abscissa, or distance from the Y-axis measured parallel to the X-axis, and its ordinate, or perpendicular distance from the X-axis.

The *origin* of the scale is usually taken at the lower left corner, where the primary axes intersect (Chart 13), though where values of less than zero appear, the origin will be at the intersection of the zero line and the vertical axis (Chart 15).

The *scale unit* is the portion of a scale line taken to represent a given number or quantity of the characteristic to be shown. The complete statement of the scale unit often does not appear in a printed graph, but may to advantage be indicated, particularly for use while the original draft is being constructed. (Examples: ½ inch equals one year; 20 mm. equal 10 per cent, etc., etc.)

The term "scale unit" is also used to designate the *unit of expression,* or the quantitative unit in which the data are recorded, such as "thousands of tons," "millions of bushels." Where the nature of this unit is not obvious, it should invariably be stated in the scale designation.

The *scale points* are inserted to indicate the divisions of the scale line and thus facilitate the reading of the graph. The *scale numerals* give the numerical values represented by the scale points, and the *scale designation* explains the significance of the scale numerals in terms of the characteristic shown. In Chart 13 the figures 80, 100, 120, etc., are the scale numerals on the vertical scale, and the phrase "Index Numbers" is the scale designation. The meaning of the other terms used should be self-explanatory.

GENERAL STANDARDS FOR GRAPH CONSTRUCTION

The principles stated in the previous chapter for diagrammatic presentation in general apply also to the particular form of diagram we are now considering. The graph should convey a truthful message, be clear, in appropriate form, and verifiable by the reader. Standardization has proceeded somewhat further for graphs than for other forms of diagrams, and the following suggestions should be adhered to unless clear reason for the exception appears.

WORKING RULES [1]

Where the principles involved are identical with those discussed for horizontal bar charts, they are merely mentioned below and the reader is referred to the previous discussion, Chapter IV, for further detail.

The general arrangement

1. The *general arrangement* on the chart should proceed from *left to right,* and ordinarily from *bottom to top,* and all lettering should be so placed as to be readable from the bottom or right-hand side of the chart, preferably from the bottom.

The scale elements

2. *The scale units should be uniform* (see exception for ratio charts, Chapter VI) and be so chosen as to maintain *suitable proportions* between the two dimensions of the graph. The scale

[1] These rules are largely an adaptation from those given by W. C. Brinton in *Graphic Methods for Presenting Facts,* pp. 361-363, and subsequently modified by the Joint Committee on Standards for Graphic Presentation.

unit should not be smaller than the eye can conveniently distinguish, nor smaller than the accuracy with which the data were measured or determined. If the figures are accurate only to the nearest million, the quantity represented by the scale unit should not be less than one million.

The beginner usually errs in choosing too large a scale unit for the vertical scale, with the result that the vertical fluctuations are unduly exaggerated. No hard-and-fast rule can be given for the choice of scale units. It will be found helpful to examine a considerable number of printed graphs and note the typical proportions between the vertical and horizontal scales. It may be taken as a rough working rule that the scales should be so chosen that the height of the chart will be not greater than its width, and usually a better appearance will be obtained if the height is less than the width.

3. *Scale points* should be placed at intervals to which scale numerals apply and which are not marked by a distinct co-ordinate line, and at such other regular intervals as may help in the easy reading of the chart (cf. Charts 13, 14).

4. *The scale numerals* should be placed at round-number intervals along the bottom and left side. Where the chart is large or complicated, duplicate sets of scale numerals along the top and right-hand side are helpful.

5. *The scale designations* should *include the unit of expression,* as "Price in thousands of dollars," "Production in millions of tons," "Population in millions." An exception may be made where the unit is obvious. Thus in Chart 13 it is scarcely necessary to state that the horizontal-scale numerals refer to years or the vertical-scale numbers to percentages of the base price.

The scale designation is ordinarily *placed* below the horizontal-scale numerals and to the left of the vertical-scale numerals, but may sometimes advantageously be placed at the top of the column of scale numerals (Chart 17).

The axes of reference

6. The *axes* should be *heavier lines* than the other co-ordinate lines on the paper. This applies not merely to the *zero line,* but

also to the *hundred-per-cent line* (Chart 13), to the *par line* in a foreign-exchange graph, and to any other similar line of reference.

7. As a general rule, the vertical scale should be so selected that the *zero line* will be shown *on the chart*. Violation of this rule is apt to give the reader an exaggerated idea of the fluctuations portrayed (Chart 17).

8. *If it is necessary to eliminate part of the vertical scale, to save space, the break should be indicated by a wave line (see Chart 13).* This serves as a warning signal of the omission and may in part overcome the error mentioned in Rule 7.

The data and plotting

9. If the numerical data cannot conveniently be set forth on the chart (as in Charts 13, 18), then it should be shown in an accompanying table (Charts 15, 16).

10. The plotted points should be indicated by small crosses or circles so that they will not be obscured by the connecting lines (Chart 13).

Adherence to this rule is not so important if there is a co-ordinate line for each plotted point, and no unused lines, or where the points lie close together (see Chart 15 for illustration of the latter situation).

11. In a chronological graph, the data should be plotted at the midpoints of the periods to which they refer, particularly if the graph is to be used for interpolation between the plotted points (Charts 18, 19).

Identification aids

12. There should be a *number* and a *title* conforming to the standards of conciseness, clarity, adequacy, and advertising appeal previously set forth for tables and diagrams (Chapters III and IV).

13. *A key or legend* should clearly identify the various curves.

Where the chart is not crowded the legend may be placed contiguous to the curve (Charts 13 and 20) or as an inserted boxed legend. Otherwise it is placed just above or below the main chart.

14. The *source of information* should be shown in title, subtitle, or in a footnote with reference symbol therefor (Charts 13 and 14).

Obviously no set of rules can be given to cover every case. "Whenever the vividness and accuracy of the statistical picture is not sacrificed by so doing, the conventional and generally accepted ways should be followed," but the statistician should always keep in mind that the primary purpose of a graph is not to conform to set rules, but to present the data in the most effective and accurate manner possible.

SPECIAL TYPES OF CHARTS

The charts in this chapter are varied in general form and in detail of construction, with a view to providing illustrations of common charting terminology and practices. Illustrative references have been made to these charts in the preceding paragraphs, but, in addition, it may be helpful to note other features peculiar to each chart.

Chart 13, which appears earlier in this chapter, is a *"sample" graph* with explanatory labels to call attention to specific features.

CHART 14
COMPONENT-PARTS BAND CHART

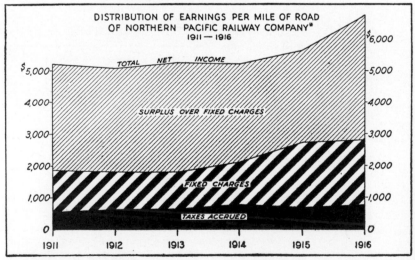

* Based on Table XX.

TABLE XX

DISTRIBUTION OF EARNINGS OF THE NORTHERN PACIFIC RAILWAY PER MILE
OF ROAD: 1911-1916 [a]

Year ended June 30	Total net income	Taxes accrued	Fixed charges	Surplus over fixed charges
1911	$5,206	$554	$1,315	$3,337
1912	5,080	621	1,197	3,262
1913	5,262	639	1,178	3,445
1914	5,220	795	1,318	3,107
1915	5,649	692	2,044	2,913
1916	6,755	780	2,037	3,938

[a] Moody's *Analysis of Investments—Steam Railroads—*1921, p. 247.

Chart 14, sometimes designated as a *"band" chart,* illustrates one method of showing chronological variations in the components of a total. The "band" chart is an effective device for conveying a general impression of the apportionment of a total; but a vertical bar chart, similarly differentiated by cross-hatching, would be somewhat more precise in its meaning. Also, if the relative proportions of the components are to be stressed, the data should be reduced to percentages before plotting.

CHART 15
SILHOUETTE EXCESS-AND-DEFICIT CHART

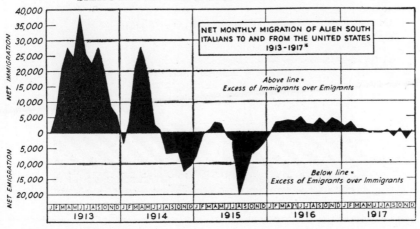

* Based on Table XXI.

The *silhouette* type of graph illustrated in Chart 15 gives a vivid impression of the changes from period to period, and is useful where there is but one series to depict. It is, however, not well adapted to more complicated charts because the movement of a second curve is obscured whenever it enters the silhouette. The "excess-and-deficit" device illustrated by Chart 15 may be applied in charting annual net profit or loss over a period of years.

TABLE XXI

NET MONTHLY MIGRATION OF ALIEN SOUTH ITALIANS TO AND FROM THE
UNITED STATES: 1913-1917 [a]

(+) = Excess of immigrants over emigrants
(—) = Excess of emigrants over immigrants

Month	1913	1914	1915	1916	1917
Jan.	— 472	— 3,033	— 7,215	— 330	+ 1,744
Feb.	+ 6,888	+ 3,054	— 365	+ 3,072	+ 3,177
Mar.	+ 20,119	+ 20,903	+ 730	+ 3,498	+ 858
Apr.	+ 27,562	+ 27,683	+ 3,315	+ 3,899	+ 727
May	+ 24,426	+ 18,503	+ 2,874	+ 3,382	— 309
June	+ 38,496	+ 2,736	— 1,212	+ 4,724	— 246
July	+ 25,597	+ 843	— 2,736	+ 2,515	— 282
Aug.	+ 22,290	— 6,498	— 20,320	+ 2,232	+ 378
Sept.	+ 27,484	— 6,445	— 14,047	+ 4,352	— 1,493
Oct.	+ 19,448	— 6,316	— 7,059	+ 2,353	+ 1,104
Nov.	+ 8,456	— 12,298	— 5,999	+ 4,204	— 2,346
Dec.	+ 5,724	— 10,825	— 3,156	+ 3,531	+ 45

[a] Computed from numbers of immigrants and emigrants given in the 1913-1917 monthly issues of the *Immigration Bulletin,* published by the U. S. Bureau of Immigration. These figures cover only persons contemplating a relatively permanent change of residence and hence do not include persons entering the United States for a sojourn of less than a year, returning from a similar temporary visit abroad, or leaving after a temporary sojourn in the United States.

In Chart 16 we have a device frequently used in the *Survey of Current Business* for comparison of recent monthly data with annual data for previous years. The left portion of the chart shows the curve for average monthly production of bituminous coal for each year, 1913-1922; the right section of the chart, the curve for production in each month, January to October, 1923. This *duplex chart with a common vertical scale* enables the reader to see the details of the recent movement and, at the same time, the general features of the movement over a longer period.

CHART 16

YEAR-MONTH CHART

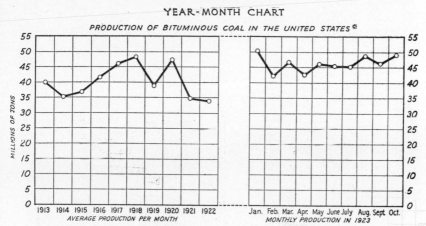

PRODUCTION OF BITUMINOUS COAL IN THE UNITED STATES *

MILLIONS OF TONS

AVERAGE PRODUCTION PER MONTH   MONTHLY PRODUCTION IN 1923

* Based on Table XXII.

TABLE XXII

BITUMINOUS COAL PRODUCTION IN THE UNITED STATES
Thousands of short tons

Average monthly production in given year [a]		Monthly production in 1923 [b]	
1913	39,870	Jan.	50,178
1914	35,225	Feb.	42,160
1915	36,885	Mar.	46,802
1916	41,877	Apr.	42,564
1917	45,983	May	46,076
1918	48,282	June	45,490
1919	38,822	July	45,126
1920	47,389	Aug.	48,864
1921	34,660	Sept.	46,216
1922	33,991	Oct.	49,171

[a] Computed from data given in table 102, Appendix B.
[b] U. S. Geological Survey—Weekly Bulletins Nos. 298, 302, 306, 313.

Chart 17, a "Comparison of Complete and Abbreviated Vertical Scales," is designed to illustrate the misleading exaggeration of fluctuations which arises from omitting a portion of the vertical scale and the consequent desirability of giving some warning of such omission. The break in the lower part of Fig. B is introduced to call attention to the omission of most of the scale below 30,000.

CHART 17

COMPARISON OF COMPLETE AND ABBREVIATED VERTICAL SCALES

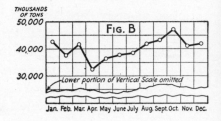

AVERAGE AMOUNT OF BITUMINOUS COAL PRODUCED IN THE UNITED STATES IN THE PERIOD: 1913-1922 (BY MONTHS).*

* Based on Table XXIII.

TABLE XXIII

PRODUCTION OF BITUMINOUS COAL IN THE UNITED STATES BY MONTHS: 1913-1922 [a]

Thousands of short tons

January	42,703	July	38,572
February	37,770	August	41,910
March	41,778	September	43,353
April	32,490	October	47,356
May	36,571	November	41,136
June	37,952	December	41,990

[a] Computed from data given in table 102, Appendix B.

Adjusted scales. Occasionally it becomes desirable to plot two curves on the same chart, although the numerical data are in different units or vary so widely in magnitude as to make plotting on the same scale impracticable. For some purposes the representation of such series is best accomplished by means of the ratio chart discussed in the following chapter; but if it *is* desired to use natural scales, reasonably satisfactory results may be obtained by using a different vertical scale for each series, the scale units being adjusted in exact or approximate proportion to the averages of the two series.[1] If the reader will turn to Chart 38, in Chapter XV, "Cotton Production and Price," he will note that the scales are adjusted in the ratio of 500 to 1, which is, in round numbers, the ratio of the respective averages of the two series; that is, the vertical distance which represents one thousand million pounds production of cotton represents two cents in price.

Zee-charts. In the charting of historical data, particularly for the use of a business executive, it is often helpful to use a composite chart showing on the same sheet, for example, the original monthly data, a cumulative total from the beginning of the year, and a moving total for the twelve months ending with the given month. The "Zee-chart" derives its name from the rough similarity of its three curves to the letter "Z." For effective showing of the three curves, two vertical scales are required, one for the original monthly data, and a smaller scale for the cumulative and moving totals.[2]

THE SMOOTHING OF CHRONOLOGICAL CURVES (Charts 18, 19)

Smoothing consists in removing the angles or sharp turns in a graph by substituting curves for straight lines connecting the plotted points. Its object is to obtain a graph which is more truly representative of the facts portrayed than the crude or angular graph. More specifically stated, the smoothing of an historical graph has as its object either interpolation or the determination of a general trend.

Determination of a general trend. The irregular curve obtained by taking prices of a given commodity at frequent dates may be smoothed to give an indication of the general trend. The methods of accomplishing this smoothing are discussed in Chapter XIII, on long-time and seasonal trends.

[1] For discussion of the various methods of scale conversion see H. Secrist, *Statistical Methods,* pp. 222-227.
[2] Cf. Karl G. Karsten, *Charts and Graphs,* chap. xxii.

Interpolation. In discussing interpolation on chronological graphs it will be helpful to distinguish between those which show little or no fluctuation other than a general trend and those which have a marked oscillatory movement. Chart 18 illustrates the non-oscillating type; Chart 19, the more erratic curve. The results of interpolation are more apt to be reliable on the non-oscillating curve.

CHART 18

SMOOTHING A NON-OSCILLATING CHRONOLOGICAL GRAPH *

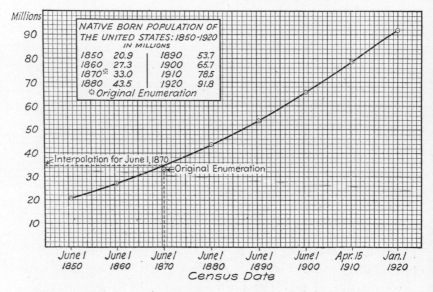

* The data given in table inserted in chart are from: *Census of the United States,* 1910, Vol. I, p. 129, and 1920, Vol. III, p. 15.

In Chart 18 a smoothed curve has been drawn through plotted points representing the numbers of native born in the United States at each census from 1850 to 1920, except 1870. The results of the 1870 census appear out of line with the general trend and have been ignored in drawing the smoothed curve. In fact, the Census Office later decided that some 1,250,000 persons had been omitted in the Southern States in 1870. The Census Office made its estimate by assuming that the proportional rate of growth was the same for the two decades 1860-1870 and 1870-

1880.[1] Another method of estimating the correct number of the native born in 1870 is by interpolation on a smoothed curve as in Chart 18. A perpendicular erected at June 1, 1870, intersects the smoothed curve at a point representing approximately 34,500,000 persons. The census estimate was 34,251,220. If we make, in our estimate, some allowance for the probability that the increase was not quite regular between 1860 and 1880 because of the retarding influence of the Civil War, the two estimates are brought still closer together.

To interpolate on the curve for any intercensal year—1917, for example—it is only necessary to read the ordinate value of the curve at the selected date.

Interpolation becomes less accurate when applied to an oscillating curve, unless the oscillations have a high degree of regularity. Let us experiment with a curve of the oscillating type. Table XXIV gives the wholesale prices of eggs in New York on

TABLE XXIV.—WHOLESALE PRICES OF EGGS

FRESH FIRSTS, AT NEW YORK, ON THE THURSDAY NEAREST
THE 15TH OF THE MONTH [a]

Date 1922	Price per dozen (cents)	Date 1923	Price per dozen (cents)
Jan. 12........	35	Jan. 18.......	39
Feb. 16......	39	Feb. 15.......	39
Mar. 16......	24	Mar. 15......	30
Apr. 13......	25	Apr. 12.......	29
May 18.......	27½	May 17.......	27½
June 15......	25	June 14.......	25½
July 13.......	24	July 12.......	25
Aug. 17......	24	Aug. 16......	28½
Sept. 14......	34	Sept. 13......	36
Oct. 12.......	35	Oct. 18.......	35
Nov. 16......	50	Nov. 15......	52
Dec. 14.......	54	Dec. 13.......	46

[a] *Bradstreet's,* weekly issues.

---

[1] Eleventh Census of the United States, *Report on Population,* Part I, pp. xi-xvi.

CHART 19

SMOOTHING AN OSCILLATING CHRONOLOGICAL GRAPH *

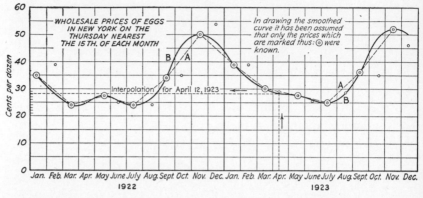

*Based on Table XXIV.

the Thursday nearest the 15th of each month in the years 1922 and 1923, represented in Chart 19 by small circles. Let us assume, however, that we have only the prices for alternate months, represented by the double circles, and wish to construct a curve which will represent the best estimate of the movement of prices between the known figures. First we will draw a straight-line or angular curve, connecting each of the bimonthly points with broken straight lines (curve "A"). This gives a fairly good representation of the movement of the prices, but is open to the objection that the changes seem to be sudden and to occur always at the dates for which data are known, that is, at the bimonthly periods. In an effort to obtain a curve which represents the more probable gradual change, curve "B" is drawn by the freehand smoothing process.[1]

In smoothing a time curve freehand,[2] one should aim to avoid abrupt turns and to maintain the maximum radius of curvature

[1] Smoothing may be done by means of mathematical formulas, particularly in connection with the smoothing of frequency curves or in the determination of a general trend (see chap. xiii), but the freehand method is ordinarily satisfactory for the approximate smoothing of frequency curves and for drawing a smoothed curve for interpolation in a time series.

Cf. discussion in C. J. West, *Introduction to Mathematical Statistics,* of the rectangle method of smoothing applied to historical data, chap. ii.

[2] A French curve is a helpful device for use in smoothing by inspection.

—that is, so to draw the curve that the circle of which any given part of the curve may be considered a segment will be relatively large.

After this smoothed curve is drawn we may interpolate for an estimate of the price on any date desired by erecting a perpendicular to the horizontal base line at the given date and noting the price corresponding to the point where this perpendicular cuts the smoothed curve. Thus the interpolation line erected at April 12, 1923, in Chart 19 intersects the smoothed curve at the point corresponding approximately to 28¼ cents. A similar reading from the intersection with the angular curve "A" gives twenty-nine cents as the price for April 12th, which is the actual price as shown by the small circle. In this particular case the smoothed curve is less accurate than the angular curve. In June, 1923, on the other hand, the smoothed curve is closer to the actual price than the angular curve.

In Chart 19 we have assumed that the plotted points for every other month were known and correct and have attempted to smooth only between these fixed points, passing the smoothed curve through every such point. However, if the plotted points represent only a sample and the purpose of the smoothing is to estimate the movement of the data for the entire "universe," the curve may pass *among* rather than *through* the plotted points.

Not all chronological data are suitable for the smoothing process.[1] There must be present a reasonable presumption of uniformity and continuity of movement between the known points according to some determinable principle. For example, it is ordinarily a reasonable assumption that there have been no erratic fluctuations in population between successive census periods, but a similar assumption for the course of the price of wheat through a decade would not be justified. Again, if a graph represents the total production of pig iron for successive months, it would be drawing a false conclusion to smooth the curve between the months and interpolate, for example, halfway between the points for January and February and call the resulting value the semi-

[1] Compare the discussion below of frequency data suitable for the smoothing process and footnote reference therefor.

monthly production for the first half of February. On the whole, although the continuous smoothed curve presents a better ap-. pearance, for most time series of economic data the angular or unsmoothed curve is a sufficient approximation to accuracy.

CONSTRUCTION OF FREQUENCY CURVES

In the chapter on Tabulation, we noted the methods of constructing frequency tables. When it is desired to translate a frequency table into graphic form, the class intervals are laid out on the horizontal axis and the frequencies are plotted vertically. They may be represented by a simple vertical bar diagram (Chart 7, Chapter IV) or a frequency graph may be constructed. A common form of frequency graph is illustrated in curve B, Chart 20. This is obtained by plotting the frequencies at the midpoint of the respective classes and connecting the plotted points with straight lines. This form is known technically as the frequency polygon or more popularly as the frequency graph (unsmoothed). Another form of diagram is shown in curve A of Chart 20. This is the rectangular histogram or frequency bar chart which may be directly used as one form of vertical bar diagram for presen-

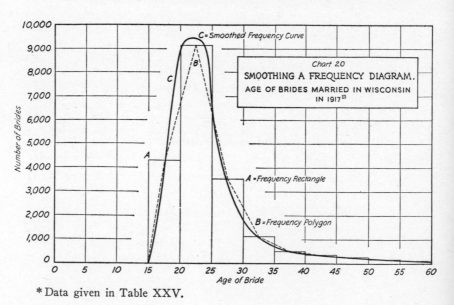

Chart 20

SMOOTHING A FREQUENCY DIAGRAM.

AGE OF BRIDES MARRIED IN WISCONSIN IN 1917[*]

C = Smoothed Frequency Curve
A = Frequency Rectangle
B = Frequency Polygon

*Data given in Table XXV.

tation or as a first step in the construction of a smoothed frequency graph.

TABLE XXV

BRIDES AND GROOMS IN WISCONSIN BY AGE GROUPS: 1917 [a]

Age Group	Brides	Grooms
Total	19,524	19,524
15–19	4,292	409
20–24	9,121	8,045
25–29	3,568	6,153
30–34	1,144	2,462
35–39	488	986
40–44	321	512
45–49	245	311
50–54	118	245
55–59	80	161
60–79	67	188
80 or over............	—	4
Age not stated.........	80	48

[a] *Report of the Wisconsin State Board of Health,* for the term ending June 30, 1918, p. 200.

Smoothing a frequency graph (Chart 20).

The *purpose* of smoothing a frequency graph may be (1) to estimate the distribution of the frequencies within a given class, or (2) to smooth out the accidental irregularities shown by the sample and thus more nearly to approximate the graph which would best represent the universe, or population, from which the sample is taken.

To illustrate *the method of smoothing a frequency graph for the purpose of estimating the distribution of the frequencies within a given class,* let us turn our attention to Chart 20, based on Table XXV. We note that over 4,000 brides are in the 15-19 group.[1] If we represent this by a frequency bar or rectangle as

[1] In locating the boundaries of the rectangles in Chart 20, it is assumed that the brides gave their age at their last birthday, so that, for example, the 15-19 age group includes all those who have passed their fifteenth birthday and not yet reached their twentieth. If ages were given to the nearest birthday, then the boundaries of the rectangles should be shifted one-half year to the left, as the actual limits of the 15-19 group would be 14.5 and 19.5.

in curve A, the apparent assumption is that the brides are evenly distributed through the 15-19 group. Obviously, however, the greater proportion are in the upper portion of this five-year group. How can we approximate the distribution within each group without recourse to the some 19,000 individual records from which the frequency table is constructed? This question we may attempt to answer from the results of smoothing, even when the data shown represent the universe rather than a mere sample.

In Chart 20 the rectangular diagram, sometimes called the rectangular histogram, is first constructed; then a frequency polygon (B) is formed by connecting the midpoints of the several rectangles and bringing the line down to the outer limits of the extreme classes. This partially smoothes the curve, and with diagram A as a guide to the area and diagram B as an aïd in determining direction of the curve, the smooth curve C is drawn. If this curve is correctly located, about two-thirds of the brides in the 15-19 age group are in the second half of the period and the largest number of brides of any one age is found to be at the age of about twenty-two years.

Professor Carl J. West [1] has suggested the following *rules to be observed in smoothing frequency curves:*

(1) "The curve should be so smoothed that the total area under the resulting curve is equal to the sum of the areas of the original rectangles."

(2) "Where possible, the areas of the individual rectangles are to remain unchanged."

(3) To the above should be added the rule that "the curve must be free from abrupt changes in direction."

These rules are designed primarily for application when smoothing a curve drawn from a sample, but apply even more rigorously to the smoothing of a frequency curve representing the complete data, as in that case Rule 2 should be strictly adhered to, for we can with such a curve legitimately make estimates only as to the distribution *within* the class.

[1] Carl J. West, *Introduction to Mathematical Statistics,* chap. ii, especially p. 19.

In smoothing a curve drawn from a sample it is customary to bring the polygon to the base line a half-class interval beyond the outside boundaries of the two end classes, on the assumption that the sample did not include the most extreme items in the universe sampled.

Special problems in smoothing.

When a smoothed curve is drawn from a frequency polygon, should the peak of the curve overtop the polygon, coincide with it, or fall short thereof?

Ordinarily the peak of the smoothed curve should overtop the peak of the frequency polygon. Let us remember that in smoothing a curve from a sample distribution, we are endeavoring to estimate the proportionate frequencies for the several values of the variable, not the actual number of frequencies. The sample may represent 400 items, and the total universe 4,000, but we use substantially the same chart for both. Now, the rectangular histogram is constructed on the assumption of equal distribution of the items through the class, whereas we know that ordinarily there is a concentration in some part of the class. In a symmetrical distribution there will be relatively more items in the central part of the middle class than near the extremes of that class, so a logical smoothing process is to lower the extremes and add to the center.

We reach the same conclusion by observing the second rule for smoothing—the maintenance of the area of individual rectangles—for when the frequency polygon is drawn it cuts off from both sides of the central rectangle and the smoothed curve likewise cuts a little off each side, so this deficiency must be added at the center to maintain the area (see Chart 20).

However, if the highest rectangle appears to be abnormally high as compared with the other rectangles, and the abnormality is probably due to inadequacy of the sample, then the smoothed curve may logically fall short of the top of the highest rectangle (Chart 21).

The freedom with which smoothing may be carried on varies

with the size of the sample and the character of the data.[1] *If the sample is small and the general tendencies of the universe from which it is drawn are well known,* it will be legitimate to smooth somewhat freely. *If the sample is large,* however, the presumption is strengthened that any irregularities which appear are true characteristics of the type of data in question and smoothing should be restricted to an attempt to approximate the distribution within each class (as in Chart 20). Also, *if the amount of information concerning the general tendencies of the universe from which the sample is drawn is limited,* then the freedom of smoothing is likewise limited, for one has no basis for assuming that the irregularities shown by the sample are not really characteristics of the universe. It is known, for example, that natural phenomena tend to be distributed in a symmetrical curve around the mode,[2] but this tendency is less pronounced in social and economic data and one is consequently less justified in assuming that the lack of symmetry is a mere "fluctuation of sampling." The lack of symmetry in the "Age of Brides" curve (Chart 20), for example, is characteristic of the data. Few women are married before the age of fifteen; but the great majority are married within the next fifteen years.

In this connection the distinction between *continuous and discrete* series should be kept in mind. In a continuous series, as we have previously noted, any value between the smallest and largest value is a possible value, whereas in the discontinuous series there are gaps. A frequency distribution of the ages of persons might conceivably begin with the infant just born, with its life measured in seconds or fractions thereof, and persons may be found at any age between that of the youngest infant and the oldest man. But if a frequency distribution of the number of persons per family were compiled the smallest number would be one, and there would be no fractional values. It would be mis-

[1] Cf. "The Theory and Justification of Curve Smoothing," in H. Secrist, *Readings, op. cit.,* pp. 278-282, quoted from G. H. Knibbs, *The Mathematical Theory of Population.*

[2] See chap. x for discussion of this symmetrical curve.

leading to smooth a curve from such data [1] and interpolate to get the number of families with four and one-half children. In a smoothed curve drawn from a sample of data of the continuous type it is possible to read the ordinate at any point on the curve, and the value thus obtained by interpolation is a reasonable, possible value.

In general, the nearer the approach to a truly continuous series, the more appropriate does the smoothing process become. In all cases, however, the economic characteristics of the series plotted must be carefully noted in interpreting a smoothed curve. For ordinary purposes the angular graph will be adequate.

Comparative frequency graphs. If two or more frequency distributions are to be compared, the similarities and differences become more evident if the series are reduced to percentages and graphs constructed therefrom. Chart 21 affords an illustration of this principle.[2] Fig. A. represents the distribution of the 307 relative prices used in the 1919 wholesale-price index of the Bureau of Labor Statistics; while Fig. B represents the distribution of a random sample of 100 selected from the complete list of 307. It is obvious that comparison between the two distributions is facilitated by the fact that they are plotted on a common scale and this scale is one of percentages rather than of absolute numbers.

It may be noted that a good comparative graph could be constructed by adding to Chart 20 a curve showing the age distribution of the grooms as shown in Table XXV. Reduction to percentages would not be necessary, inasmuch as the number of grooms is necessarily identical with the number of brides.

If several distributions are to be compared, the clarity of the comparisons will be improved by putting only two or three curves on each chart and making two or more charts, repeating one of

[1] Chart 7 (in chap. iv), showing the frequency distribution of amounts of mortgages classified by rates, indicates the fallacies which would be involved in smoothing data of the discrete type with a marked tendency to concentration at certain intervals.

[2] Strictly speaking, the sides of the rectangles in Chart 21 should be erected at the *actual* limits of the classes—that is, at 49.5, 74.5, 99.5, etc.—but the more convenient practice of placing them at the round numbers 50, 75, 100, etc., does not lead to material error unless very precise interpolation is attempted.

CHART 21

COMPARATIVE FREQUENCY DIAGRAMS

PERCENTAGE DISTRIBUTION OF THE 1919 RELATIVE PRICES OF WHOLESALE
COMMODITIES IN THE UNITED STATES[*]

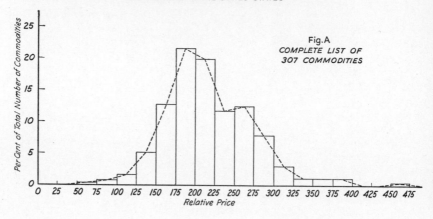

Fig. A
COMPLETE LIST OF
307 COMMODITIES

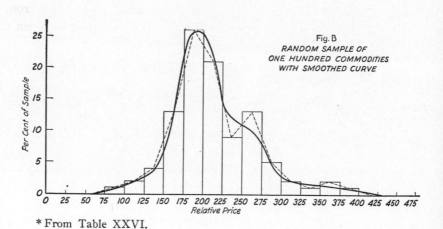

Fig. B
RANDOM SAMPLE OF
ONE HUNDRED COMMODITIES
WITH SMOOTHED CURVE

*From Table XXVI.

TABLE XXVI

COMPARATIVE FREQUENCY DISTRIBUTIONS OF A COMPLETE LIST AND A
RANDOM SAMPLE

1919 RELATIVE WHOLESALE PRICES OF COMMODITIES IN THE
UNITED STATES [a]

Relative price	Number		Per cent of total	
	Complete list	Sample	Complete list	Sample
Total	307	100	100.0	100.0
50- 74	1	0	0.3	....
75- 99	2	1	0.7	1.0
100-124	5	2	1.6	2.0
125-149	16	4	5.2	4.0
150-174	39	13	12.7	13.0
175-199	66	26	21.5	26.0
200-224	61	21	19.9	21.0
225-249	36	9	11.7	9.0
250-274	38	13	12.4	13.0
275-299	24	5	7.8	5.0
300-324	9	2	2.9	2.0
325-349	3	1	1.0	1.0
350-374	3	2	1.0	2.0
375-399	3	1	1.0	1.0
400-424	0	0	...	...
425-449	0	0	...	...
450-474	1	0	0.3	...

[a] Based on tables III and 101.

the curves on each to facilitate comparison. This principle holds for chronological as well as frequency charts.[1]

Cumulative frequency graphs. When a cumulative frequency distribution is charted, the frequencies are plotted at the upper limits of the classes if the cumulation is on the "less than" basis, but at the lower limits if it is on the "more than" basis. The cumulative frequency graph is useful in the determination of the median and other similar partition measures (see Chart 24, Chapter VII, with explanation of construction and use).

[1] Cf. the two charts showing the graphs for the groups of data which are combined to form the Harvard "Index of Business Conditions," *Review of Economic Statistics,* p. 110, preliminary vol. i.

Cumulative frequency curves may be used to advantage also in comparing or combining distributions with irregular or dissimilar class intervals, inasmuch as the validity of comparisons between cumulations to a given point is not affected by variances in the intervals of the classes the frequencies of which have been cumulated.

Irregular class intervals. When the class intervals of a frequency graph are irregular, care must be taken to see that the frequency chart is not misleading. The safest device is to reduce the frequencies of the several classes to some *common denominator*. For example, in Table XXV the class intervals are irregular in the upper portion of the distribution, in that the 60-79 interval is four times as large as the other intervals. If the frequency in this group were large enough to be significant, it could be divided by four to give the number per five-year period.[1]

CHOICE OF TYPE OF DIAGRAM OF GRAPH [2]

Graphic representation, though not fully standardized, has a certain body of tradition and practices, based partly upon mere custom and partly upon the peculiar adaptability of given types of charts to special uses. While the variations in the forms and uses of charts seem almost unlimited, the greater number are of a few major types. For the sake of increasing the uniformity of presentation, the selection of the type should conform to the following principles where there is no clear reason for other choice:

(1) For **simple comparison of size (non-chronological).**[3]
Where it is desired to represent simple comparisons of size, the horizontal bar chart is preferable. It is simple in construction, easily interpreted, and effective (Chart 1). If the items to be compared are numerous, horizontal lines may be substituted for the bars.

[1] See G. C. Whipple, *Vital Statistics,* pp. 72-75, for a good, brief discussion of the plotting of irregular groups.
[2] Cf. H. Secrist, *Readings,* op. cit., pp. 274-276.
[3] See the census for frequent use of the horizontal chart in comparing relative populations of the several states.

(2) For **comparisons of component parts.**   (Non-chrono-logical)

(a) *One total only.*[1]

Where, for example, it is desired to show the national-ities in the population of a given state, *the horizontal bar chart* may be used, with a separate bar for each nationality and, preferably, a bar showing the size of the total.

The *circle chart* (Charts 11, 12) may also be used to show component parts.   It is more difficult than the bar chart to read with substantial accuracy, but it has a certain popularity.   It finds its most suitable use in expressing the relative percentages of a total, as in showing the distribu-tion of a dollar of expenditure, income, or taxes.

(b) *Two or more totals.*

The component parts of two or more totals can best be compared by means of *horizontal subdivided bar charts* with distinctive cross-hatching for each constituent ele-ment, if but one bar is used for each total (Chart 3). *Percentage distributions.*   The application of the *subdi-vided bar chart* to the showing of the percentage distribu-tion of several totals is well illustrated by Chart 4.

If *separate bars* are used for each portion of the total, as is practicable if there are only two or three totals, then it is preferable to distinguish the totals to which the parts belong by the variation in cross-hatching (Chart 2).

(3) **Frequency distributions** (Charts 7, 20, 21).

Either the *vertical bar chart* or the *frequency graph* should be used for representing a frequency distribution. If but one distribution is to be shown, the bar chart is apt to be the most effective.   If two or more distributions are to be compared, or if it is desired to use smoothing, the graph will be found more adaptable.

(4) **Geographic variation** (Charts 8, 9, 10).

Where it is desired to show relative density of popula-

---

[1] A frequency distribution is one method of representing component parts of a total but, as noted in (3), the vertical bar chart is more suitable than the horizontal bar chart for that purpose.

tion, proportion of illiteracy, or similar ratios in the various geographical districts, the *statistical map* is best.

If contrasts are to be made for only relatively large districts considered as a whole, the cross-hatch map is adequate; but if it is desired to show the relative concentration within comparatively small parts of the total area, the dot map is more appropriate (cf. Charts 9 and 10).

If an effort is to be made to enable the reader to approximate the actual numbers shown on the map, the quartered-dot map (Chart 10) or a map with dots graduated in size according to the quantities to be represented may be used, but it is doubtful if any such method is an adequate device for showing actual amounts. They are satisfactory for approximate comparisons, but reference should be made to the original table for close estimates, or the numerical data may be recorded upon the map.

(5) **Time variation.**

(a) When data for *several years* are compared, custom suggests that the vertical bar chart or the graph be used, with time measured on the horizontal axis. The graph is better for a continuous series or where several series are placed on the same chart, and is extensively used even for a single discrete series.

(b) When *only two or three years* are to be compared, the horizontal bar chart may be used, particularly if there are several factors or component parts in each year to be compared (cf. Chart 2).

(c) For showing proportionate changes the ratio chart is best (see Chapter VI).

REFERENCES

1. BRINTON, W. C., *Graphic Methods of Presenting Facts.*
2. HASKELL, ALLAN C., *How to Make and Use Graphic Charts.*
3. ——— *Graphic Charts in Business.*
4. KARSTEN, KARL G., *Charts and Graphs* (see table of contents).
5. MARSHALL, W. C., *Graphical Methods.*
6. SECRIST, HORACE, *An Introduction to Statistical Methods,* chap. vii.
7. ——— *Readings and Problems in Statistical Methods,* chap. vi, especially pp. 273-282.

8. SECRIST, HORACE, *Statistics in Business,* chap. v.
9. WARNE, F. J., *Chartography in Ten Lessons,* 1919.
10. —————— *Elementary Course in Chartography,* 1917.
11. —————— *Warne's Book of Charts,* 1913.
12. WEST, CARL J., *Introduction to Mathematical Statistics,* chaps. i, ii, iii.
13. WHIPPLE, G. C., *Vital Statistics,* chap. iii.

CHAPTER VI

GRAPHIC PRESENTATION—3: THE RATIO CHART

THE ratio chart is a type of graphic presentation suitable for showing proportional changes, particularly when it is desired to indicate the absolute amounts at the same time. The choice between the ratio chart and the types previously discussed is chiefly determined by the purpose of the chart. If we are making a study of immigration and are interested primarily in the increase from year to year measured in thousands of immigrants, without consideration of the proportion which this increase bears to the total number, then the original data, shown on the ordinary equal-spaced or natural-scale graph, are best. If we wish to portray percentage changes from the immigration in 1900 or some other one year, a graph with immigration in 1900 shown as one hundred per cent, and the numbers for other years expressed as percentages of the 1900 immigration, is appropriate. Also, if we wish to indicate merely the percentage changes from the immigration of the immediately preceding year, without making at all obvious the relation between the present immigration and that of the more remote years, these percentage changes may appropriately be plotted on a natural-scale chart.

But if we wish to show the proportional changes from the preceding year in such a way as to make easy a comparison with proportional changes between other years, and at the same time to show the absolute numbers of immigrants, then recourse is had to the ratio chart.

The distinguishing structural characteristic of the ratio chart lies in its vertical spacing. If the reader will turn to Chart 22 and examine the lower half, he will notice that while the horizontal intervals are equal, as in the ordinary graph, the vertical spacing telescopes as we proceed toward the $100 line. The con-

CHART 22 *

RATIO CHART

A o——o = Constant Percentage Rate of Increase (50 per cent).
B x——x = Constant Amount of Increase ($50).
C ●——● = Alternating fifty per cent Increase and fifty per cent Decrease.
(Two-cycle Ruling)

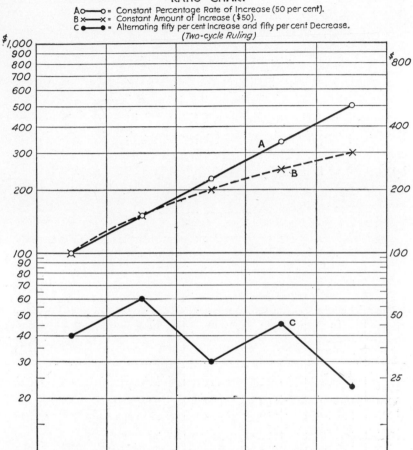

*Based on data in Table XXVII.

tinued narrowing of the spacing is obscured in the transition from the lower to the upper half of the chart because in the lower half there is a ruled line for each ten dollars, and in the upper half (or second cycle) only one line for each hundred dollars. On closer examination it will be seen that the spacing is so proportioned that a given per cent of increase is always represented by the same vertical change on the chart. This will be obvious on noting the intervals represented by the scale numerals at the right of the chart. The distance from 25 to 50 is the same as the distance from 50 to 100, or from 100 to 200, etc. Equal ratios of increase are represented by equal vertical intervals.

Let us see what is the effect of this ratio spacing on the trend of a curve plotted thereon. In Table XXVII we have three hypothetical series. Series A increases 50 per cent annually, in terms of the total of the immediately preceding year. Series B increases 50 dollars each year. Series C increases 50 per cent the first year; then decreases 50 per cent; then increases 50 per cent; and so on. These three series are represented on Chart 22 by curves A, B, and C, respectively.

TABLE XXVII

HYPOTHETICAL DATA USED IN CONSTRUCTING CHART 22

Year	Series A		Series B		Series C	
	Amount in dollars	Per cent change from preceding year	Amount in dollars	Increase in dollars	Amount in dollars	Per cent change from preceding year
1920	100.00	......	100	......	40.00	......
1921	150.00	+ 50	150	50	60.00	+ 50
1922	225.00	+ 50	200	50	30.00	— 50
1923	337.50	+ 50	250	50	45.00	+ 50
1924	506.25	+ 50	300	50	22.50	— 50
1925	759.38	+ 50	350	50	33.75	+ 50

It will be noted that Curve A, representing a constant proportional rate of increase of fifty per cent, plots as a straight line, and any other line of constant ratio of increase will be a straight line on a ratio chart.

Curve B would be a straight line on an ordinary chart, for it represents increases by equal absolute increments and hence equal vertical rises on a natural scale. On the ratio chart, inasmuch as the fifty-dollar increase represents a constantly decreasing percentage of the preceding year, the slope of the curve is concave to the base line.

On examination of Curve C it will be noted that the lines of fifty-per-cent increase are parallel with each other and with Curve A, and that the lines of fifty-per-cent decrease are parallel with each other. In general, on a ratio chart the slope of the line at any given point indicates the proportionate rate of increase or of decrease at that time; and consequently equal ratios of increase or of decrease for equal intervals of time—that is, equal proportional rates of change—will be represented by parallel lines.

CHART 23

NATURAL AND RATIO SCALES

BANK CLEARINGS IN NEW YORK CITY AND THE PACIFIC SECTION: JULY TO DECEMBER, 1920 *

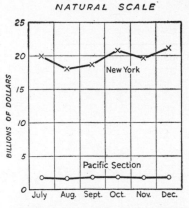 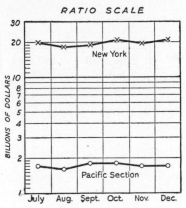

* Numerical data in Table XXVIII.

In Chart 23 we have a comparison of the results obtained by plotting on natural and ratio scales two series differing widely in their absolute amounts but with somewhat similar percentage fluctuations. As shown on the natural scale, the relative increases and decreases in the New York City clearings are fairly obvious, but the clearings line for the Pacific section is so nearly straight that it is difficult to determine with the eye the direction and extent of the change. Does this natural-scale chart give a true representation of the relative movements in the two series? On examination of the per-cent change for each period, we note that in some months there is a substantial similarity in the relative changes in the clearings of the Pacific section as compared with the New York City clearings, the Pacific section change even exceeding for the August to September comparison the percentage change in the New York clearings. The same data are plotted in the ratio chart to the right, and the similarity between the curves is much more obvious. This characteristic of the ratio chart makes it particularly useful whenever it is desired to compare the relative fluctuations of two series differing widely in their absolute amounts, as often occurs when a part is compared with a total.

TABLE XXVIII

BANK CLEARINGS IN NEW YORK CITY AND THE PACIFIC SECTION
JULY TO DECEMBER, 1920 [a]

Month	New York		Pacific Section	
	Billions of dollars	Per cent change	Billions of dollars	Per cent change
July	19.8	.....	1.7	.....
Aug.	17.9	— 9.6	1.6	— 5.9
Sept.	18.6	+ 3.9	1.8	+ 12.5
Oct.	20.7	+ 11.3	1.8	No change [b]
Nov.	19.4	— 6.3	1.7	— 5.6
Dec.	21.0	+ 8.2	1.7	No change [b]

[a] Review of Economic Statistics: 1920, 241, 342; 1921, 26.
[b] Less than one-tenth of one per cent change.

METHODS OF CONSTRUCTION

Ratio charts may be constructed either by the use of paper with ratio ruling [1] or by plotting the logarithms of the data to be represented. Technically, ratio chart paper is known as semi-logarithmic paper, in contrast with double logarithmic paper, which is ratio-ruled in both directions. Semi-logarithmic paper ordinarily comes in one, two, three, four, or five-cycle ruling, each

[1] Special papers with vertical or semi-logarithmic ruling are sold, for example, by the Codex Book Co., Inc., New York, and the Educational Exhibition Co., Providence, R. I.

cycle adapted to accommodating the range between two successive powers of ten. For example, in Chart 22 we have a two-cycle ruling covering the range from 10 to 1,000. This would serve equally well to cover a range from 10 million to a billion.

The relation of logarithms to the ratio chart.

It is not absolutely necessary that one understand logarithms in order to construct and employ ratio charts. With the use of prepared paper the ratio chart can be plotted as easily as the ordinary graph. However, inasmuch as ratio ruling rests upon logarithms, a brief review of their nature may help to insure a clear grasp of the nature of the ratio chart.

A logarithm is the power to which ten must be raised to obtain a given number. The logarithm of ten is one; of 100, two; of 1,000, three, etc. For numbers intervening between the even powers of ten the logarithm is a fraction, composed of an integral called the characteristic and a decimal fraction known as the mantissa. A short table of logarithms is given in Appendix D. More elaborate tables may be found in the references listed under "Aids in Computation," Appendix A. Also, they may be computed with a Fuller slide rule. The following list will afford a basis for illustrating some of their important characteristics:

Number	Log	Number	Log	Number	Log
1	0.0000	5	0.6990	30	1.4771
2	0.3010	8	0.9031	50	1.6990
3	0.4771	10	1.0000	100	2.0000
4	0.6021	20	1.3010	1,000	3.0000

An examination of the above logarithms will reveal the following principles:

1. The logarithm of the product of two numbers is the sum of their separate logarithms. For example:

   The log of $8(4 \times 2) = 0.9031$ (0.6021 plus 0.3010)
   The log of $4(2 \times 2) = 0.6021$ (0.3010 plus 0.3010)[1]

2. The logarithms of the numbers resulting from successive multiplication by the same number are found by successively adding the logarithm of that number, as illustrated

[1] The discrepancy of 0.0001 is due to fractions lost in computing the log of 2 to only four decimal places.

by the logarithms of 2, 4, and 8 above. Note also that the logarithm of each power of ten is one more than the logarithm of the next lower power. The log of 10 is 1, the log of 100 (10 x 10) is 2, and so on.

Hence the logarithms of a series with a constant rate of increase will, if plotted, give a curve with a constant vertical rise equal to the logarithm of the rate of increase. In other words, a chart of the logarithms of numbers is a ratio chart.

Rules for the Interpretation of Ratio Charts

To afford a convenient reference, let us summarize the mechanical and mathematical characteristics of the ratio chart:

1. It has a natural horizontal scale and a logarithmic vertical scale (natural x, log y).
2. It has no zero line.
3. A geometric progression plots on a ratio chart as a straight line—that is, a straight line represents a constant proportional rate of change. If the curve is *ascending in a straight line,* the series it represents is increasing at a uniform rate; if *descending* in a straight line, it is decreasing at a uniform rate.

   Corollaries: If the curve *bends upward from a straight line,* the rate of growth is increasing; if *downward,* the rate of growth is decreasing.
4. *Equal vertical rises* represent equal proportional increases; *equal falls,* equal proportional decreases.
5. Equal slopes of two curves or of two segments of the same curve, indicate equal percentage rates of change.

   Corollaries: If two curves on the same ratio chart vary in slope, the steeper curve is changing at a faster percentage rate.

   The slope of the imaginary straight line between any two points on a ratio curve represents the average rate of change between those points.
6. If we are interested only in the relative fluctuations of two or more curves and not in the absolute numbers which they represent, they may, after they are drawn, be *shifted*

up or down vertically until the curves to be compared are brought close together.

SUMMARY OF THE USES OF THE RATIO CHART

Because of its structural characteristics just enumerated, the ratio chart is particularly useful for the following purposes :

1. *For comparison of proportional rates of change,* on the several segments of the same curve. On an ordinary chart an increase of $5 from a $1,000 base occupies as much room as a $5 increase from a $10 base ; on a ratio chart a $500 increase from $1,000 has the same effect as a $5 increase from $10.

2. *For comparison of fluctuations in two or more series differing widely in their absolute values.* The ratio chart gives a faithful picture in a comparatively small compass of the relative fluctuations of a part as compared with its total. Thus a producer can readily compare the fluctuations in his business with that of the industry as a whole. The greater vertical capacity of the ratio chart enables the plotting of several widely differing values without jumbling the small curves together and obscuring their relative oscillations.

3. *For easy forecasting of future movements when a constant rate of change can be assumed.* In Chart 22 let us assume that the data are known only for the beginning of 1921, 1922, and 1923, then the amount for January, 1924, can be readily estimated by projecting the straight line to the ordinate representing the beginning of that year, and reading the resulting values on the vertical scale. The business man frequently assumes a constant rate of increase in estimating his future business.

4. *For computation when constant rates of change are present.* For example, a chart can be readily constructed on the ratio basis which will show the result of compounding a dollar at the several rates of interest for any desired number of years. The compound interest lines plot as

straight lines, their respective slopes varying with the rate of interest.

The use of the ratio chart has been increasing rapidly in recent years. The price charts in the special bulletins of the Bureau of Labor Statistics on retail prices (No. 315) and whole-sale prices (No. 320) are drawn on the ratio scale. It must be remembered, of course, that the ratio chart should be used only when we wish to give stress to relative rates of change, and furthermore, that for popular use, the varying spacing is apt to be somewhat confusing.

REFERENCES

1. BIVINS, P. A., "The Ratio Chart and Its Application," a series of articles in *Industrial Management,* beginning July 1, 1921.
2. BOWLEY, A. L., *Elements of Statistics,* 4th ed., pp. 169-177.
3. BRINTON, W. C., *Graphic Methods for Presenting Facts,* pp. 132-137.
4. CHENEY, L. W., "Comparison of Arithmetic and Ratio Charts," in *Monthly Labor Review,* March, 1919, pp. 20-34.
5. EGGLESTON AND ROBINSON, *Business Costs,* pp. 425-441
6. FISHER, I., "The Ratio Chart," *Quar. Pub. Amer. Stat. Assoc.,* 1917, pp. 577-601.
7. HASKELL, ALLAN C., *How to Make and Use Graphic Charts,* chaps. iii, iv.
8. ———— *Graphic Charts in Business,* chaps. v, vii, x, xi.
9. KARSTEN, KARL G., *Charts and Graphs* (see table of contents).
10. MARSHALL, W. C., *Graphical Methods,* chap. ii, for illustrations of specially ruled papers, pp. 44-46.
11. SECRIST, H., *Readings and Problems in Statistical Methods,* pp. 282-305.

CHAPTER VII

AVERAGES

The need for summarizing expressions. Types and averages are summary expressions designed to give a concise picture of the characteristics of a group. If the human mind were capable of grasping and keeping in its proper relations an unlimited amount of detail, the most satisfactory way to describe a group of items would be to describe the characteristics of each individual member of the group. But, presented with a great mass of facts, we fail to grasp the significant general tendencies; we are lost in the maze; we "cannot see the forest for the trees." As a matter of economy of intellectual effort there is need of some "single expression which gathers into itself all the significant characteristics of complex data," some means of crystallizing into a single concept the truth about a mass of detail.

This need becomes especially imperative when problems of comparison arise. "For the focusing of judgment which comparison requires, concentrated or summary expressions are necessary." If we wish to compare the sales made by two salesmen, we may note each single order, but it is much more suggestive of the real relations to state that the average sales of one are $500 per day and of the other, $1,000.

There are *four kinds of summarizing expressions* commonly used in statistical practice to elucidate the characteristics of a series or to facilitate comparison between aggregates: (1) *averages;* (2) *measures of dispersion,* which express the degree of divergence or spread from the average; (3) *measures of skewness,* which express the lack of symmetry in the distribution; and (4) *statistical ratios,* which are primarily aids to comparisons between groups or aggregates. The present chapter deals with averages.

The need for averages is amply demonstrated by the frequency of their use in every-day discussion. We speak of average wealth, wages, prices, interest rates, and profits; of average duration of life; of average rainfall, average crops, average temperature. The uses of types and averages may be summarized as follows: [1]

(1) To give a concise picture of a large group.

(2) To facilitate the comparison of different groups by means of these simple pictures and particularly to enable the formulation of a mathematical statement of the relationship between groups.

Even a superficial examination of the various meanings to which the term average is applied soon reveals a considerable diversity among them. Sometimes the word is used in the sense of the *modal item,* or the magnitude which occurs most frequently in the group; more commonly it signifies the *arithmetic average,*— that is, the quotient obtained by dividing the sum of all the items by their number; again, it may mean the size of the item which divides the total number into two groups, equal in number, all of the members of the one being larger, those of the other smaller, than the dividing item, or *median.* In each case the presumable intention of the user of the term is to select the item which will best typify the group. What are the considerations which determine the type or average that may most appropriately be chosen?

Points of view from which each type may be considered. In determining whether to use the mode, median, arithmetic average, or other type, the statistician must know

(1) The special characteristics of the group of data which he wishes to represent;

(2) The characteristics of the various averages.

It is only by relating these two considerations that he is enabled to make the best choice of the average to be used. It is not possible to establish an invariable rule which can be blindly followed, but the basis for intelligent judgment is laid by familiarizing oneself with the nature of the various types and averages. To this end each of the more commonly used averages will be discussed from the threefold point of view of

[1] Cf. W. I. King, *Elements of Statistical Method,* p. 121.

1. Definition,
2. Methods of computation,
3. Characteristics (merits and weaknesses).

The Arithmetic Mean

The simple arithmetic average or arithmetic mean, the most familiar of all the averages and types, is the result obtained when the sum of the magnitudes of a group or series is divided by the number of items in the group. It is usual to speak of the arithmetic mean simply as the mean, and in the subsequent discussion when the term *mean* is used without a qualifying adjective it refers to the arithmetic average.

Methods of calculation.

If the size of each individual item is known, simple summation and division by the number of items gives the arithmetic average. If the data are presented in the form of a frequency table, it is customary to assume that the midpoint of the class represents the average of the class, and hence that the total sum can be obtained by multiplying the midpoint of each class by the respective frequency, and then summating the products. The sum thus obtained divided by the number of items is assumed to represent the average.

Short-cut method. It is often convenient to use the short-cut method of calculating the arithmetic average. The steps in the process are:

1. *Assume an average.* In most instances it is preferable to select a number from which deviations can be easily expressed and computed. If the data are in a frequency table, the midpoint of a class provides a convenient assumed average.
2. *Calculate and average the deviations from the assumed average.*
3. *Add the resulting average deviation to the assumed average* algebraically—that is, if the deviation is negative, subtract it from the assumed average; if positive, add it. The result is the true arithmetic average.

This process rests upon the principle that the deviations from the arithmetic average, taken with their proper + or — signs, total zero,[1] hence the average deviations from any other value will be greater or less than zero by the amount of difference between the true and the assumed average.

The short-cut method may be stated in algebraic terms by the following formula:

$$A = E + \frac{\Sigma (m - E)}{n} \dots\dots\dots\dots\dots (Formula\ 3),$$

where A is the correct arithmetic average;

E, the estimated or assumed average;

m, the size of any single item;

n, the total number of items; and

Σ, the sign for summation. This is the Greek capital S, called sigma, and is used generally in formulas to indicate that the aggregate of quantities like those following the symbol Σ, is to be taken.

If the data are given in the form of a frequency table, as is more often the case, we may modify the above formula to read:

$$A = E + \frac{\Sigma f (V - E)}{n} \dots\dots\dots\dots\dots (Formula\ 4),$$

where f is the frequency of each respective class, and

V is the value of the class, usually taken as the midpoint.

In Table XXIX we have an illustration of the computation of the mean by the short-cut method. The student should thor-

---

[1] For algebraic proof of this statement, see W. I. King, *Elements of Statistical Method*, pp. 133-136, or the following brief explanation quoted from H. L. Moore, *Forecasting the Yield and the Price of Cotton*, p. 19:

"Theorem I. The algebraic sum of the deviations of a series of magnitudes from their arithmetical mean value is zero.

"Let the magnitudes be $x_1, x_2, x_3, \dots x_n$, N in number, and let their arithmetical mean value be $\bar{x}$. Then, by the definition of the arithmetical mean, we have $\bar{x} = \dfrac{x_1 + x_2 + x_3 + \dots + x_n}{N}$".... (Formula 1)

"therefore $\qquad N\bar{x} = x_1 + x_2 + x_3 + \dots \quad x_n$

and $\quad (x_1 - \bar{x}) + (x_2 - \bar{x}) + (x_3 - \bar{x}) + \dots \quad (x_n - \bar{x}) = 0$".... (Formula 2).

"But the quantities on the left-hand side of the equation are the deviations of the magnitudes from the arithmetical mean of the magnitudes, and the sum of these deviations is proved to be zero." (It will be noted that the last step is accomplished by subtracting $\bar{x}$, or the mean, N times from both sides of the equation.)

oughly master the procedure involved, as he will find it convenient in statistical practice. In this computation the assumed average, or E, is taken as 202, in order that the deviations of the midpoints [1] of the classes therefrom will be in round numbers.

TABLE XXIX

COMPUTATION OF THE ARITHMETIC MEAN BY THE SHORT-CUT METHOD

One hundred 1919 relative wholesale prices

(Based on Table XXVI)

Relative price group	Number in group	Midpoint of group [a]	Deviation from assumed average (E = 202)	Product of deviation and frequency
	f	V	(V–E)	f(V–E)
Totals	100	—	—	+ 1,125
75– 99	1	87	— 115	— 115
100–124	2	112	— 90	— 180
125–149	4	137	— 65	— 260
150–174	13	162	— 40	— 520
175–199	26	187	— 15	— 390
200–224	21	212	+ 10	+ 210
225–249	9	237	+ 35	+ 315
250–274	13	262	+ 60	+ 780
275–299	5	287	+ 85	+ 425
300–324	2	312	+ 110	+ 220
325–349	1	337	+ 135	+ 135
350–374	2	362	+ 160	+ 320
375–399	1	387	+ 185	+ 185

[a] In computing the relative prices, they were read to the nearest integer, and, consequently, the *actual limits* of the first class are 74.5 and 99.5. This group would include a relative price of 74.6 but not 99.6. Hence the mean of 74.5 and 99.5, or 87, is taken as the midpoint.

The aggregate of the positive deviations from the assumed average is + 2590; of the negative deviations, — 1,465. Hence the net total deviations are + 1,125. Substituting this in the

[1] It is customary, in making calculations from frequency tables, to use the midpoint of the class as representative of the entire class. This assumes an equal distribution through the class and is, accordingly, not quite accurate, but the error involved is ordinarily not large enough to be material.

following formula: $A = E + \dfrac{\Sigma \, f(V-E)}{n}$,

we have $\qquad\qquad A = 202 + \dfrac{1{,}125}{100}$, or 213.25 per cent.

The use of the short-cut method is an appreciable saving of effort when the data are in the form of a frequency table or when one or more digits are common to all or a considerable number of the items.[1] Also, in later chapters we shall see that in the computation of certain formulas for the measurement of variation and correlation, in which the arithmetic mean is a factor, the validity of the short-cut method of computing the mean materially lessens the laboriousness of the computations involved.

For a frequency table with equal class intervals, the computation of the mean may be shortened still further by assuming the midpoint of one class as the mean and expressing the deviations therefrom with the *class interval as a unit*. When the average net deviation from this assumed mean is found, it is converted to the correct units by multiplying by the class interval.[2]

Characteristics: Advantages and disadvantages.[3]

In analyzing the several types under consideration in this chapter, let us marshal the considerations involved with the following queries in mind for each type or average:

1. Is its *meaning readily comprehended* by the typical reader?

---

[1] Illustrations of series suitable for the short-cut method:

Common initial digits		Common final digits	
Series A	Series B	Series C	Series D
100,375	87	100.55	9.73
106,454	85	13,200.55	11.73
100,459	83	187.55	25.73

Series of the C and D type are apt to result whenever one is computing deviations from an average expressed to one or more decimal places.

[2] See description of this "step-deviation" method in H. Secrist, *Introduction to Statistical Methods,* pp. 251-253; or G. U. Yule, *op. cit.,* 6th ed., pp. 110-113.

[3] Yule suggests the following tests to determine a good average (not quoted verbatim): Is it rigidly defined, or left to mere estimation? Is it based on all the observations made? Is its general nature readily comprehensible? Is it calculable with reasonable ease and rapidity? To what extent is it affected by fluctuations of sampling? Does it lend itself readily to algebraical treatment?—*Op. cit.,* p. 108.

2. Is it always or usually a size which actually occurs in the data? In what other respects is it *typical of the series?*

3. To what extent is it *influenced by extreme items?*

4. What *information* is *required* for its determination?

5. How much *effort or technical skill* is *needed* for its determination?

6. Does it *lend itself to algebraic treatment,* such as is involved in combining averages of two or more series?[1]

7. What other peculiar or important characteristics does it have?

Applying the above questions to the arithmetic mean, we note the following features affecting its usefulness:

Advantages.

1. The meaning and method of computation of the arithmetic mean are familiar to the ordinary reader even if he has no special mathematical or statistical training.

2. It gives weight to extreme deviations, and to all other deviations, in direct proportion to their size, which under some circumstances is a desirable characteristic.

For example, whenever the significant fact to be shown is per-capita consumption, or production, or wealth, regardless of its distribution, then the average is most appropriate which gives weight directly in proportion to size.

3. Information is not needed as to individual items to determine the arithmetic average. The per-capita consumption of sugar can be determined from a knowledge of the total population and the total production of sugar. It is the only average which can be readily computed in many cases of similar character.[2]

4. The process of computation is simple, if the data are available in numerical, rather than graphic, form.

5. The numerical total can be determined from the average by simple multiplication.

---

[1] Yule places susceptibility to algebraic treatment as "by far the most important desideratum."—*Ibid.,* p. 108.

[2] Cf. H. Secrist, *Readings,* pp. 334-341, average tariff rates.

6. It can be combined with other arithmetic averages without introducing mathematical inconsistencies.[1]

Disadvantages.

That the arithmetic average is not always a satisfactory type, however, becomes evident from a little reflection upon its characteristics.

1. Frequently the mean is not represented in the actual data. The census gives the average size of the family in 1920 as 4.3 persons, although obviously no family has 4.3 members.[2]

2. The emphasis it gives to extremes makes it liable to distortion from the occurrence of a few unusually large or unusually small items.

3. For accurate determination of the arithmetic average, it is necessary to know the size of the extremes.

4. If the data are presented in the form of a graph, the arithmetic average cannot be readily determined.

5. It cannot be used to advantage in the study of characteristics not capable of numerical measurement.

The Weighted Arithmetic Average [3]

Weighted arithmetic averages are of two types. Either they are merely attempts to approximate the arithmetic average which would be obtained if all the items were known and a simple arithmetic average taken, or they are what may be called interpretative weighted averages. If one member of the family earns $40 a week, another $30, and a third $20, the apparent simple arithmetic average is $30; but if we ask how many weeks each is employed and weight each weekly wage by the number of weeks

[1] For discussion of the relative usefulness of the mean in the computation of index numbers, see W. C. Mitchell, *Index Numbers,* 1921 ed., p. 73.

[2] *Fourteenth Census of the U. S.,* 1920, vol. ii, p. 1266. Also, it may be noted that in some distributions, the mean, or any other single measure, even though it is represented in the data, may not be truly representative of the group. For example, an arithmetic average of the age at which persons become blind might indicate that the average is in the prime of life, whereas, in fact, relatively more persons lose their vision either in infancy or in old age. Cf. Table 105, Appendix B.

[3] See Yule, *op. cit.,* pp. 220-225, for discussion of weighted averages, especially page 225 for meaning of weighted medians, modes, and geometric means.

worked in order to find the real average weekly earnings during the year, this weighted average is merely one device for calculating or estimating the true simple arithmetic average.

On the other hand, if a student in averaging his grades in several courses, all three-credit courses, were to count one grade twice because it was in a subject which he thought was of particular importance to him, then the result would be an interpretative weighted average.

Most weighted averages are of the first type, that is, they represent efforts to determine the average which would result if the full numerical details were known and utilized in the computation.[1]

Bowley has said [2] that the discussion of proper weights "has occupied a space in statistical literature out of all proportion to its significance, for . . . given certain conditions, the same result is obtained with sufficient closeness whatever logical system of weights is applied," and he accordingly draws the conclusion that one should "in calculating averages give all care to making the items free from bias, and . . . not strain after exactness in weighting." However, it is not the intention of the writer to suggest that the accuracy of an average is not increased by the use of a logical system of weights; and in Chapter XI, "The Construction of Index Numbers," we shall see that statisticians favor a weighted average for price index numbers.

THE MODE

Definition. The mode is the size of item which occurs most frequently. The modal wage is the most common wage; more workmen receive it than any other wage. In many popular uses of the term average, the mode is the type which is implied. We speak of the average reader,[3] the average student, or the

[1] The formula for the weighted average may be stated as

$$(\text{WA}), \text{ the weighted average} = \frac{\Sigma\,(\text{W m})}{\Sigma\,(\text{W})}. \ . \ . \ . \ (\text{Formula 5}),$$

where Σ is the summation sign; W the respective weight applicable to m, the size of the item; and Σ (W), the total aggregate of weights.

[2] Bowley, A. L., *Elements of Statistics*, 4th ed., pp. 87, 94.

[3] Jay E. House, column writer on the Philadelphia *Ledger,* in discussing his method of writing says, "I aim at the average human being, he being by far the most numerous of his tribe."

average meal, meaning usually the kind that occurs in the largest numbers.

In a frequency table, the *modal class* is the class with the largest frequency (see 175-199 class, Table XXIX).

It may be helpful to distinguish between the *apparent* mode, the *estimated* mode, and the *true* mode. If we have a sample of the wages received by workmen in the carpentry trade, the wage occurring most frequently in the sample is the apparent mode. Now, if we attempt to adjust the sample [1] in such a way as to make the result an even better representation of the total than the sample itself, then the resulting mode will be the estimated mode; whereas, assuming our approximation is inexact, the true mode itself, the wage which actually occurs the most frequently in the total group, may be still different.

Calculation of the mode.[2]

(1) *Inspection.* If the individual items are all known, the mode can be determined by simple count or inspection.

(2) By *interpolation in a frequency table.* If the data are only available in the form of a frequency distribution, one must rest content with the designation of the modal class or in some way estimate the point within the modal class at which the mode falls. Let us assume the following frequency distribution:

TABLE XXX

Wage in dollars	Number receiving given wage
$10.00–$19.99	10
20.00– 29.99	20
30.00– 39.99	60
40.00– 49.99	30
50.00– 59.99	20

[1] See the method described in chap. v of smoothing a graph representing a sample in order to approximate the true distribution.

[2] Cf. W. I. King, *Elements of Statistical Method*, p. 124, and G. U. Yule, *op. cit.*, pp. 120-122. In moderately asymmetrical distributions the following relation holds approximately:

$$\text{Mode} = \text{median} - 2 \ (\text{mean} - \text{median}). \ \ldots \ (\text{Formula } 6);$$

hence if the mean and median are known, the mode may be approximated from their magnitudes.

The modal class is \$30.00 to \$39.99 and the size of the mode may be estimated from the formula,[1]

$$Mo = L + \frac{Cf_2}{f_2 + f_1} \dots\dots\dots\dots\dots\dots \text{(Formula 7),}$$

where

Mo = the size of the mode
L = the lower limit of the modal class (\$30.00)
C = the class interval (\$10 in this case)
f_2 = the frequency (30) of the adjacent class *above* (in amount of wage) the modal class
· f_1 = the frequency of the adjacent class just below the modal class.

Substituting from above table we get

$$Mo = \$30.00 + \frac{\$10 \times 30}{30 + 20} = \$36.00.$$

If the reader will turn to Table XXXI, page 122, he will find a series of relative prices, or percentages, arrayed in order of magnitude. By simply counting the items to see which percentage occurs most frequently, the apparent mode is found, in this instance, to be somewhat indefinite, being either 190.7, 194.3, or 194.7, as each of these values occurs three times.

Applying the modal formula to the simple frequency distribution in Table XXIX, page 113, we have

$$\text{Mode} = 175 + \frac{25 \times 21}{21 + 13} = 190.4$$

The reader will note that this formula merely gives an estimate based on the assumption that the location of the mode within the modal class is determined by the relative size of the adjacent classes. If the two adjacent classes are equal, the mode will be calculated as falling in the middle of the modal class; if the upper class is twice as large as the class below the modal class, the mode will be pulled two-thirds of the way up from the lower limit. The accuracy of this formula is greatest when applied to continuous data which obey closely the normal frequency law.[2] When applied to discrete data of somewhat irregular tendencies, great care must be taken in interpreting the results of the inter-

---

[1] Cf. W. I. King, *op. cit.*, p. 124.
[2] The normal frequency law refers to the tendency in certain types of data to a symmetrical distribution about the mode. It is more fully stated and discussed in chap. x.

polation. If wages are always paid to the nearest five dollars, an interpolation which gives $26 as the modal wage is misleading. The best estimate would be $25.

(3) *By grouping.* If the modal class is not easily determined, because the classes are small and no one stands out clearly as the mode, the character of the distribution may become clearer if the class intervals are widened. If the frequency distribution is only a sample and made up of small classes, the process of experimental grouping is sometimes tried in an effort to approximate the true modal class, and then the modal item is assumed to be at the midpoint of the modal class.[1]

(4) *By interpolation on a smoothed simple frequency graph.*[2] When a smoothed curve has been drawn from a frequency histogram or from a frequency polygon, by the methods described in Chapter V, the estimated mode is represented by the abscissal value of the maximum ordinate of the graph—that is, by the scale reading at the foot of the highest ordinate of the graph. In the "Age of Brides" chart in Chapter V the maximum ordinate in the smoothed curve corresponds to about 22 on the horizontal scale, hence we conclude that the best estimate obtainable by the smoothing process is that the modal age of Wisconsin brides in 1917 was twenty-two years.

(5) *By interpolation on a smoothed cumulative frequency graph.* On a smoothed cumulative frequency graph, the mode lies at the abscissal value of the point where the curve is steepest,[3] for at that point frequencies, measured on the vertical scale, are increasing faster per unit of horizontal movement than at any other point on the curve. In Chart 24, later in this chapter, the

---

[1] For fuller description of this method, see W. I. King, *Statistical Method,* pp. 122-124; and A. L. Bowley, *Elements of Statistics,* 4th ed., pp. 97-98. H. Secrist, *Statistical Methods,* pp. 272-275, gives a special method for finding the mode by grouping in an historical series.

[2] G. U. Yule, *op. cit.,* p. 120, defines the mode as "the value of the variable corresponding to the maximum of the ideal frequency-curve which gives the closest possible fit to the actual distribution."

[3] The steepest point can be approximated by finding the point at which a ruler held tangent to the curve will be most nearly vertical; also it will be at the point where a ruler kept tangent to the curve will change its direction of movement as it is moved along the curve,—that is, at the point of inflection.

slope of the "less than" curve is steepest in the 175-199 interval and it is estimated that the steepest point and the point of inflection, where the direction of the curve changes, is at 194 per cent.

For the somewhat irregular type of distributions characteristic of economic data, this method of finding the mode is usually too indefinite to be satisfactory.

Advantages of the mode.

1. Its meaning is readily comprehended.
2. It is, if correctly determined, always represented by actual items; in fact, it is the item or term which is most common.
3. Extreme items, either large or small, have no influence on its location, hence
4. No information about extremes is necessary except that their number is so few that the mode cannot be among them.

Disadvantages of the mode.

1. A clearly defined mode does not always exist. In the salary list of a business concern, no two salaries may be identical in amount.
2. In circumstances where it is important to give influence to all items, the fact that the mode is influenced not at all by the relatively large or relatively small items, noted above as an advantage, is in such cases to be reckoned as a disadvantage.
3. It cannot be determined when only the total and the number of items are known.

THE MEDIAN

Definition. The median is the middle-sized item. If the several values of a variable are arranged according to magnitude, as in Table XXXI, the median is the item which divides the array into two equal parts. There is the same number of items with values less than the median, as there are items with higher values. If the daily wages of five men are respectively $3, $4, $5, $6, and $7, the median wage is $5. If we add a sixth man with a wage of $8, the median falls between $5 and $6. In such cases it is customary to express the median as the mean of the two central

items, or $5.50 in the above case.   If the two middle items are
equal in size, the median coincides with them.

TABLE XXXI.—AN ARRAY

THE ONE HUNDRED RELATIVE PRICES IN TABLE I ARRANGED IN ORDER OF
THEIR MAGNITUDE

Rank	Relative price	Rank	Relative price	Rank	Relative price	Rank	Relative price
1....	95.0	26....	186.7	51....	200.5	76...	248.4
2....	108.7	27....	186.7	52....	206.6	77...	253.9
3....	121.1	28....	187.1	53....	209.4	78...	255.4
4....	131.4	29....	188.0	54....	209.4	79...	256.4
5....	132.7	30....	188.0	55....	211.6	80...	256.4
6....	142.3	31....	188.6	56....	212.3	81...	257.2
7....	146.7	32....	189.0	57....	213.8	82...	258.1
8....	150.9	33....	190.1	58....	213.8	83...	260.0
9....	153.5	34....	190.7	59....	214.6	84...	260.1
10....	153.5	35....	190.7	60....	215.1	85...	260.1
	— D_1ᵃ						
11....	160.4	36....	190.7	61....	215.5	86...	261.8
12....	162.7	37....	191.1	62....	215.9	87...	262.4
13....	163.7	38....	193.0	63....	216.7	88...	269.0
14....	164.5	39....	193.6	64....	217.1	89...	273.8
15....	165.6	40....	194.3	65....	219.9	90...	286.1
16....	165.6	41....	194.3	66....	221.9	91...	288.2
17....	169.5	42....	194.3	67....	223.3	92...	290.9
18....	169.5	43....	194.7	68....	225.2	93...	293.8
19....	171.6	44....	194.7	69....	227.9	94...	296.7
20....	174.4	45....	194.7	70....	228.8	95...	301.0
21....	178.1	46....	198.2	71....	233.3	96...	315.6
22....	179.3	47....	199.5	72....	234.2	97...	336.0
23....	181.2	48....	199.5	73....	236.6	98...	359.6
24....	183.1	49....	199.7	74....	246.0	99...	360.9
25....	185.3	50....	200.5	75....	246.0	100...	382.8
	— L Q		— Mi		— U Q		

ᵃ For explanation of the meaning of D_1 (first decile), LQ (lower quartile),
and UQ (upper quartile), see section later in this chapter on "Interpolation on
a Cumulative Frequency Graph."

Calculation.

(1) *Inspection or count.* If the individual values are known
and arrayed, the median may be determined by counting from

either end until the middle item is reached and noting its size. It is the $\frac{n+1}{2}$ item . . . (Formula 8); that is, if to the total number of items we add 1 and divide the result by 2, we have the rank of the median item. Then its size can be determined by inspection of the array.

Let us turn again to the array in Table XXXI. There are one hundred items, hence the median is taken as the mean of the 50th and the 51st item. Counting down the array, we find that both the 50th and the 51st item have the value 200.5, hence the median is 200.5 likewise.

(2) *By interpolation in a frequency table.* If the data are in the form of a frequency table, the median can be readily approximated by the following process. First, by use of the $\frac{n+1}{2}$ formula we determine the *rank* of the median item in the series. It then remains to determine the *size* of this median item. Let us assume the following frequency distribution:

TABLE XXXII

Wages in dollars	Number in class
Total	**9**
$10–19	1
20–29	2
30–39	5
40–49	1

As there are nine items in all, the median item is the fifth item. How can we approximate the size of the fifth item? First, by counting up from the lower limit of the distribution we find that the fifth item in the distribution is the second item in the $30–39 class. Let us assume that the items within the median class are distributed at equal intervals. Then we find the approximate size of the median from the following formula:[1]

[1] The formula given by W. I. King, in *Elements of Statistical Method,* page 129, is, in the symbols used in this book,

$$Mi = L + \frac{C(2i-1)}{2f} \quad \ldots \ldots \text{(Formula 11)}.$$

This formula gives a value of $33 for the distribution in Table A and is a

$$\text{Median (Mi)} = L + \frac{Ci}{f} \dots\dots\dots\dots\text{(Formula 9)},$$

$$\text{or, Mi} = \$30 + \frac{\$10 \times 2}{5} = \$34$$

In Formula 9

    Mi = the size of the median
     L = the lower limit of the class in which the median falls
     C = the class interval
     i = the rank of the median item (second in this case) in the class
          in which it falls
     f = the frequency of the median class

Inasmuch as it is necessary before using the above formula to find the value of (i) by the $\frac{n+1}{2}$ formula, we might rewrite it thus:

$$\text{Median} = L + C \left[\frac{\left\{\frac{n+1}{2}\right\} - \left\{\begin{array}{c}\text{Sum of frequencies in} \\ \text{classes below L}\end{array}\right\}}{f} \right] \quad \text{(Formula 10)}$$

Applying Formula 10 to the simple frequency distribution in Table XXIX, page 113, we have

$$\text{Median (Mi)} = 200 + 25 \left\{ \frac{\left\{\frac{100+1}{2}\right\} - 46}{21} \right\} = 205.4.$$

---

somewhat more logical formula, in that it assumes that the first item in the class is located only half an interval from the limit; thus in the median class we have the following distribution in which $30 is the lower limit of the median class and $40, the lower limit of the class next above the median class.

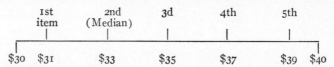

The formula given in the text above assumes that the first item is a complete interval up from the lower limit, thus placing the median item at $34. This tendency to exaggeration is lessened somewhat if L is taken to represent the actual limit ($29.50) rather than the expressed limit ($30).

For further discussion of the inaccuracies which are apt to arise in the use of the median formula see C. Alexander, *School Statistics and Publicity*, pp. 128-138.

(3) *By interpolation on a cumulative frequency graph.*[1] The median cannot be readily determined from a simple frequency graph, on which, if the graph is smoothed, the median bisects the area. However, on a smoothed cumulative frequency graph, the median is easily approximated by drawing the horizontal line which bisects the ordinate representing the total frequency, and dropping from the point on the graph cut by this horizontal line a perpendicular to the horizontal axis. The reading at the foot of this perpendicular indicates the estimated magnitude of the median.

TABLE XXXIII

CUMULATIVE FREQUENCY DISTRIBUTIONS [a]

RANDOM SAMPLE OF 100 FROM 307 RELATIVE WHOLESALE PRICES

I	II	III
	Cumulative frequency	
Relative price	Total number in given group and all lower groups (See curve A, chart 24)	Total number in given group and all higher groups (See curve B, chart 24)
75– 99	1	100
100–124	3	99
125–149	7	97
150–174	20	93
175–199	46	80
200–224	67	54
225–249	76	33
250–274	89	24
275–299	94	11
300–324	96	6
325–349	97	4
350–374	99	3
375–399	100	1

[a] Computed from table XXVI.

[1] The determination of the median from a smoothed frequency curve may be more accurate than by formula, as "it does not involve the crude assumption that the frequency is *uniformly* distributed over the interval in which the median lies."—G. U. Yule, *op. cit.,* p. 119.

CHART 24

INTERPOLATION ON A SMOOTHED CUMULATIVE FREQUENCY CURVE FOR MEDIAN,
QUARTILES, AND FIRST DECILE

SAMPLE OF 100 FROM 307 RELATIVE WHOLESALE PRICES IN THE UNITED STATES IN 1919[a]

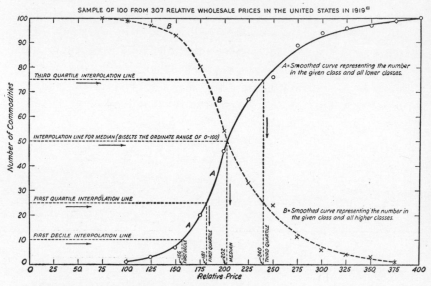

* Numerical data in Table XXXIII.

In Chart 24, based on Table XXXIII, we have an illustration
of this interpolation method. For the sake of the comparison two
curves have been drawn on this chart, but only the "less than"
curve—that is, the curve based on column II in Table XXXIII,
giving the frequencies "in given group and all lower groups," is
used in the interpolation. To approximate the median, a horizontal line is drawn from 50 on the vertical axis (bisecting the
range 0-100). From the point where this interpolation line cuts
curve A, a perpendicular is dropped to the base line and the value
at its foot, 202, is taken as the estimated median for the "universe" from which this sample is derived. It will be noted that
curves A and B intersect at the median and hence that the same
result would be obtained by interpolation on curve B as on
curve A.

In this instance, as in all interpolation, the statistician must
consider the degree of discontinuity in the data when reading the
resulting values.

As is indicated on Chart 24, the quartiles and other similar partition measures, such as the deciles and percentiles, can be located by an interpolation process similar to that used for the median. Thus the first or lower quartile is the item which divides the series into two groups, with one group containing one-fourth of the total number, all smaller than the lower quartile, and the other group containing three-fourths, all larger than this quartile. It can be located by bisecting the distance from the base line to the median item. Likewise, the third quartile bisects the upper half of the distribution. The first decile sets off the first tenth of the distribution; the median is the fifth decile, etc. If many of these "'iles" or partition measures are to be located, the smoothed cumulative curve affords the simplest method.[1]

The median of an historical series.

In an historical series, the term median may be used to indicate the item which is the middle item when the annual amounts, for example, are arrayed by size irrespective of the time to which they apply. In this case the median is found by the same method as that discussed for medians in general. Also the median is sometimes used to indicate the period which is the midpoint in time or, again, the midpoint in an historical series cumulated in order of time.

The following hypothetical series will illustrate these three meanings of the term median as applied to historical data:

Month	Tons of steel produced
January	30
February	35
March	15
April	20
May	100

The median period is March; the median amount produced is 30 tons, produced in January; the midpoint in the cumulated production, the point at which half of the total was reached, was the end of April. To avoid confusion, the term median is used in these chapters in the sense of the median amount produced; and

[1] An arithmetical method of estimating the quartiles is suggested in chap. ix, in the section on "Numerical Measures of Dispersion."

the midpoint in time or the midpoint in the cumulated production are designated by self-explanatory phrases other than median.[1]

Characteristics of the median.

The *median* is *typical* of the members of the series *in that the sum of the deviations from it, all considered positive, is a minimum*—that is, they aggregate less than the deviations from any other value in the series; it is closer in size to the items in the series than is any other item. Thus in the series 3, 4, 5, 6, 7, the total of the deviations from 5 is 6, while that from 4 or 6 is seven, and from 3 or 7, ten. References to algebraic proof of this proposition are given in the footnote.[2]

It is *best adapted to series in which the central items at least lie fairly close together,* though perhaps with few duplicated values. Thus, in the following series, 9, 10, 10, 12, 13, 14, 15, 16, 16, 17, 18, there is no definite mode, but the median, 14, is easily determined. In many such series the median is more definite in position than the mode.

The general location of the median can never depend upon a small number of items. The addition, for example, of two 18's to the above series will make 18 the mode, but only change the median from 14 to 15.

Also, the median is not distorted in position by a few exceptional items. If the observations are liable to present occasional greatly outlying values, due either to errors or to causes whose influence one wishes to eliminate, the median is, in this respect, more useful than the mean.

This latter characteristic of the median led to its choice for the average best representing typical seasonal variation in the construction of an index of business conditions by the Harvard Committee on Economic Research.[3] For example, the typical

[1] Cf. H. Secrist, *Statistical Methods*, pp. 264-269, with explanation of a graphic method of finding the midpoint in the cumulated production.

[2] Algebraic proof of the proposition that the sum of deviations from the median is a minimum is given in W. I. King, *op. cit.*, p. 128; and in C. J. West, *Introduction to Mathematical Statistics*, p. 47. This principle may also be stated as : "The mean deviation from the median is a minimum." For if the total deviations are a minimum, the average deviation will also be a minimum. Cf. illustration in A. L. Bowley, *Elements of Statistics*, 4th ed., p. 104.

[3] See *Review of Economic Statistics*, Preliminary vol. i, p. 26.

relation between the February and January production of pig iron was determined by dividing the production for each February by the production for the preceding January, and then taking the median of the resulting ratios, and so on for the other months. This process minimized the influence of any exceptional ratios due to non-seasonal causes such as the outbreak of the war or the panic of 1907.

It follows from the last-mentioned consideration that it is *not necessary, in calculating the median, to know the sizes of the exceptionally large or exceptionally small items.* Knowledge of their number is sufficient. This fact makes the median a convenient average for use when, as often happens, the data are available in the form of a frequency table with an indefinite limit to either or both of the extreme classes.

The median is relatively easy to determine. If the sizes of the individual items are known, it can be determined by inspection of a rough array with a close scrutiny of the central items only. If the data are given in a frequency table, the interpolation formula can be easily applied, and the median can also be readily located on a cumulative frequency graph.

Despite its considerable advantages, the median has not come into extensive popular use, though widely employed in the field of educational statistics. It is *not so well known as the arithmetic average. It cannot be determined when only the total and number of items is known;* nor can the total be obtained by multiplying the median by the total frequency.

The median may become somewhat *indefinite in a discontinuous series when there are many items with the same value.* Thus in the following series 3, 4, 5, 6, 6, 6, 7, 7, 7, 7, 8, the size of the $\frac{n+1}{2}$ item is 6, but there are only three items smaller and as many as five larger than 6, hence 6 does not conform closely to the concept of the median as the item which has as many values smaller than it as there are values larger.[1]

Again, the median may be located at a point in the array where there are few or no items. Thus in the series, 3, 4, 6, 7, 7, 7, 7, 7,

[1] Cf. Example in G. U. Yule, *op. cit.,* top of page 117.

11, 12, 13, 13, 14, 16, 17, 18, the median, as usually calculated, is the mean of 7 and 11, or 9. An approach to this situation is possible whenever there is a tendency to a bimodal concentration. *In fact in all series with an even number of items the median,* calculated by taking the mean of the two central items, *falls on a value which does not appear in the sample,* and in some cases *may* be a value which *never appears in the universe* from which the sample is taken. In the case of a discrete variable, such as the number of rooms per house in a group of houses, the median may be calculated at 4.5 rooms. An *exception* to this difficulty arises when the two central items are of the same magnitude.

The median *does not lend itself to algebraic treatment* such as is involved in the combination of two or more series.[1] The arithmetic average of several series may be found from the respective averages of the separate series, if total frequencies are known, but the median of two series cannot be calculated from their separate medians.

For example: In Series A: 3, 4, 5, 9, 10, the median is 5.

In Series B: 11, 12, 13, 14, 15, the median is 13.

And the median of these two medians is 9; but if we combine the items in series A and B, we have 3, 4, 5, 9, 10, 11, 12, 13, 14, 15, of which the median is 10.5.

THE GEOMETRIC MEAN [2]

The mean, mode, and median are of most common use in statistical practice, but the statistician will find it convenient to know the meaning and method of computation of the geometric mean, the quadratic mean, and the harmonic mean.

The geometric mean of two items is the square root of their product. In general it is the nth root of the product of n factors. Thus the geometric mean of 10, 100, and 1,000 is the cube root of their product:

$$G = \sqrt[3]{10 \times 100 \times 1000} = 100.$$

[1] For a fuller statement of the algebraic limitations of the median see Yule, p. 119.

[2] Cf. Yule, *op. cit.,* 6th ed., pp. 123-128, with bibliography, p. 130.

It is calculated by means of logarithms. The logarithm of the geometric mean of a series is the arithmetic average of the logarithms of each member of the series. Thus in the series 10, 100, 1,000:

$$\text{Logarithm of } G = \frac{\log 10 + \log 100 + \log 1000}{3} = \frac{1 + 2 + 3}{3} = 2.$$

But 2 is the logarithm of 100, hence $G = 100$. A short logarithmic table is given in Appendix D, and more detailed tables may be found in compilations of tables for computers (see bibliography in Appendix A).

As to the *characteristics of the geometric mean,* it is always less than the arithmetic mean of the same series; its value is always determinate except where zero or negative values occur; its computation is somewhat difficult and its abstract mathematical character lessens its usefulness for popular presentation. It lends itself readily to the algebraic manipulation required in the combination of series. For example, it can be determined from the geometric means of the sub-series.

Uses of the geometric mean.

Where a uniform percentage of increase is assumed, the geometric mean is useful for estimating values at a point in time intermediate to points at which values are known. If the census of a city was 100 in 1900 and 10,000 in 1910, the estimated population in 1905, assuming a uniform percentage rate of increase, would be the geometric mean of 100 and 10,000, or 1,000.

$$\text{Log } G = \frac{\log 100 + \log 10,000}{2} = \frac{2 + 4}{2} = 3. \text{ Therefore } G = 1,000.$$

Professor E. E. Day uses a weighted geometric mean in his unadjusted indexes of physical production and states that "This mean is adopted for two reasons: [1] (1) it reduces somewhat the influence of extreme items . . . and (2) it makes it possible to

---

[1] *Review of Economic Statistics,* Preliminary vol. ii, p. 247. A good illustration of the use of the weighted geometric mean to reduce the influence of extreme items is found in the index numbers of foreign exchange rates calculated by the *Statist* and the *Federal Reserve Bulletin,* the geometric mean being used to lessen the influence of the extremely depreciated currencies, such as that of Germany. *Federal Reserve Bulletin,* July, 1921.

shift the base of the index freely without recalculation of the averages." [1]

THE HARMONIC MEAN [2]

The harmonic mean is the reciprocal of the arithmetic average of the reciprocals of a series of quantities. Thus H (the harmonic mean) of 2, 3, and 4 is found by dividing the sum of the reciprocals ($\frac{1}{2} + 1/3 + \frac{1}{4}$) by 3, giving 13/36, and then finding the reciprocal of $\frac{13}{36}$, that is, $\frac{36}{13}$ or $2 \frac{10}{13}$.

THE QUADRATIC MEAN

The quadratic mean, otherwise known as the *"root-mean-square,"* is the square root of the arithmetic average of the squares of the separate items. We shall have occasion in Chapter IX (page 156) to explain the computation of a quadratic mean of importance—that is, the standard deviation, used as a measure of dispersion. The quadratic mean tends to emphasize the exceptional items.

LIMITATIONS OF THE USE OF AVERAGES

Despite their very important uses, it must be recognized that there are essential limitations to the application of averages. An average is a generalizing term. It obscures detail for the sake of conciseness. It is most useful when it is deduced from relatively homogeneous data. The measures of dispersion and skewness discussed in Chapter IX represent an effort to supplement the use

---

[1] Wesley C. Mitchell, *Index Numbers,* p. 70, 1921 edition, discusses the adaptability of the geometric average for the conversion of an index number from one base to another.

[2] Cf. Irving Fisher, *The Making of Index Numbers,* pp. 30-33, for the computation of the harmonic mean and its use in the construction of index numbers; and Holbrook Working, *Factors Determining the Price of Potatoes in St. Paul and Minneapolis,* p. 10, Technical Bulletin 10, University of Minnesota Agricultural Experiment Station, for use of harmonic mean in economic statistics. Also, see G. U. Yule, *op. cit.,* p. 129; H. O. Rugg, *Statistical Methods Applied to Education;* and, for a technical discussion of the harmonic average, C. M. Walsh, *The Measurement of General Exchange Value,* p. 256 ff.

of averages with other summarizing expressions giving additional information concerning the nature of the quantities from which the averages are determined.

REFERENCES

1. ALEXANDER, CARTER, *School Statistics and Publicity,* chap. v.
2. BOWLEY, A. L., *Elements of Statistics,* 4th ed., chap. v.
3. DAVIES, G. R., *Introduction to Economic Statistics,* pp. 20-28.
4. FISHER, IRVING, *The Making of Index Numbers,* chap. ii.
5. KELLEY, T. L., *Statistical Method,* chap. iii, "The Measurement of Central Tendencies."
6. KING, W. I., *Elements of Statistical Method,* chap. xii.
7. RUGG, H. O., *Statistical Methods Applied to Education,* chap. v.
8. SECRIST, H., *An Introduction to Statistical Methods,* chap. viii.
9. ——— *Readings and Problems in Statistical Methods,* chap. vii.
10. ——— *Statistics in Business,* pp. 97-111.
11. WEST, CARL J., *Introduction to Mathematical Statistics,* chap. iv.
12. WHIPPLE, G. C., *Vital Statistics,* pp. 49-53.
13. YULE, G. U., *Theory of Statistics,* chap. vii.
14. ŽIŽEK, DR. FRANZ, *Statistical Averages,* parts I and II.

CHAPTER VIII

RATIOS AND COEFFICIENTS

THE student of the commercial and social sciences is forced to make frequent and important use of various ratios, rates, and percentages, such as death, birth, and marriage rates, tax rates, accident frequency rates, labor turnover rates, stock turnover rates, rates of interest, exchange rates, etc. The detailed discussion of these belongs to the special sciences or arts in which they are used, but it may reasonably be considered a proper function of the study of statistical method to note in turn the general nature of the various concepts designated by the terms ratios and coefficients, the manner in which they are computed, the principles which guide one in their use, and, lastly, examples of some of the more important ratios employed for the expression of social and economic facts.

DEFINITIONS

A *ratio* is a fraction. It is a comparison between facts or aggregates of facts which are considered as the denominator and numerator of the ratio fraction. For example, the ratio of sales to average stock on hand in New York department stores in 1921 was [1] 3.8, meaning that 3.8 is the value of a fraction of which the amount of annual sales is the numerator and the average amount of stock on hand is the denominator. If the reader will fix in mind this concept of the ratio as a fraction, it will pave the way to an easier comprehension of the following discussion.

A *rate* is ordinarily a ratio with a customary unit of time [2] implied. Thus death rates are ratios expressed with a double

---

[1] Federal Reserve Agent, New York, *Monthly Review of Credit and Business Conditions,* February 1, 1922, p. 9.

[2] In practice this rule is not strictly followed. Foreign exchange rates, for example, do not refer to an interval of time, but to the price of a bill of exchange at a given date.

import, meaning the deaths *per year* and *per 1,000* of population; interest rates refer to the interest per year for each dollar of loan.

In this connection, we should note the distinctions in meaning between the terms absolute increase, relative increase, absolute rate of increase, and relative rate of increase. If a population increased from 1,000 in 1910 to 1,500 in 1920, the *absolute increase* is 500. The *relative increase* is a ratio obtained by dividing the increase in population by the population in 1910, giving 50 per cent. Neither of these expressions, however, allows for the time element. The *absolute* rate of increase, or the increase per year, is 50. The *relative rate* of increase, compared with the Census of 1910, is 50 divided by 1,000 or 5 per cent a year. The unqualified term "rate" ordinarily means a relative rate, but often, particularly when expressing the rapidity of population growth, it connotes, not a percentage of a fixed base as in the illustration just mentioned, but rather a uniform *proportional rate* of increase—that is, the rate of a geometric progression, with previous increases included in the denominator of the ratio.

Types of Ratios [1]

We may classify statistical ratios as (1) rates of change, (2) distribution ratios, (3) inter-class ratios, (4) hybrid ratios, and (5) special statistical coefficients.

Rates of change are important aids in the interpretation of the dynamic aspects of social and economic life. When we compare percentage increases in population with those of wealth, or percentage variations in prices with similar changes in the volume of goods produced, we are dealing with rates of change. These may be either *constant rates,* bearing an unchanging ratio to the immediately preceding total or to a fixed base, or they may be *variable rates.* The latter are often expressed by link index numbers, giving the percentage change from the preceding day, month, or year. An illustration is found in the last column of Table A, showing the percentage change in chain store sales from April, 1921, to April, 1922.

[1] Cf. classification in Bailey and Cummings, *Statistics,* p. 57 ff.

TABLE A.—CHAIN STORE SALES [a]

IN THE SECOND FEDERAL RESERVE DISTRICT (NEW YORK)

Type of Store	Number of stores		Dollar value of sales				Per cent change in sales per store, Apr., 1921, to Apr., 1922
	Apr. 1921	Apr. 1922	Apr. 1919	Apr. 1920	Apr. 1921	Apr. 1922	
Total..........	10,360	11,676	79	110	100	114	+ 1.0
Ten cent.........	1,598	1,660	84	99	100	121	+ 16.1
Grocery	5,749	6,935	83	140	100	120	— 0.3
Shoe	199	202	74	96	100	111	+ 9.5
Apparel	368	373	60	77	100	108	+ 6.6
Cigar	2,196	2,253	68	92	100	92	— 9.9
Drug	250	253	84	94	100	97	— 4.6

[a] *Monthly Review of Credit and Business Conditions* by the Federal Reserve Agent, Federal Reserve Bank, New York, June 1, 1922, p. 10.

TABLE B.—SUMMARY OF THE POPULATION OF THE UNITED STATES BY COLOR OR RACE AND SEX: 1920 [a]

Color or race	Number	Per cent distribution	Male	Female	Males to 100 females
All classes.........	105,710,620	100.0	53,900,431	51,810,189	104.0
White	94,820,915	89.7	48,430,655	46,390,260	104.4
Negro	10,463,131	9.9	5,209,436	5,253,695	99.2
Indian	244,437	0.2	125,068	119,369	104.8
Chinese	61,639	0.1	53,891	7,748	695.5
Japanese	111,010	0.1	72,707	38,303	189.8
Filipino	5,603	(b)	5,232	371	1,410.2
Hindu	2,507	(b)	2,409	98	(c)
Korean	1,224	(b)	923	301	306.6
Hawaiian	110	(b)	75	35	(c)
Other races........	44	(b)	35	9	(c)

[a] Fourteenth Census of the United States 1920, vol. iii, *Population*, p. 11.
[b] Less than one-tenth of 1 per cent.
[c] Ratio not shown where number of females is less than 100.

Distribution ratios express the numerical relation of the parts of an aggregate to the total, and are ordinarily expressed in terms of percentages. In Table B we have in the "Per cent distribution" column, a statement, in terms of percentages, of the ratio between the total population in 1920, 105,710,620, and the number of each respective race. The whites comprise 89.7 per cent of the total; the negroes 9.9 per cent.

Inter-class ratios show the relation between one part or class of a total and another class or part of the same total. The last column in Table B gives the sex ratio for the 1920 population of the United States, showing that there were 104 males to 100 females for all classes; and for the Chinese, 695.5 males to 100 females. If it is desired to stress the direct comparison between two parts of a total irrespective of their proportions to the total, the inter-class ratio is distinctly more effective than the distribution ratio.

Hybrid ratios are comparisons between aggregates which are not parts of the same category; the numerator and denominator are diverse things. All per-capita ratios fall in this class. Per-capita income, per-capita consumption, per-capita wealth— all these ratios are comparisons between unlike factors. Likewise ratios showing the revenue per passenger or per ton of freight carried by the steam railways of the United States are of the hybrid type. Because of the diversity of the two things compared, hybrid ratios should be expressed as averages rather than percentages.

Statistical coefficients are special ratios, expressing either the ratio of one summary expression to another, or the relations of associated pairs of items in two series. In the following chapter we have an illustration of the first type in the coefficient of dispersion, which is obtained by dividing the measure of dispersion, the figure which shows the average deviation from, for example, the arithmetic mean, by the mean itself. To the second class of coefficients belong the various coefficients of correlation, analyzed in Chapter XV, which symbolize the degree of sympathetic variation between the individual pairs of two series of values, as between the weights and heights of a number of men.

Methods of Computing and Expressing Ratios

The mechanical work of computing ratios may be done with the aid of mechanical calculator, slide rule, or logarithms. For rapid and reasonably accurate work the slide rule is to be recommended. As a matter of convenience most statistical ratios are expressed as *magnified ratios*—that is, as ratios multiplied by a convenient round number, usually some multiple of ten, to reduce the quotient to a more convenient form. The ordinary percentage ratio is the most obvious example. The percentage of urban population in 1920 is calculated by the following process, sometimes designated as *percentaging:*

$$\frac{\text{Part} \times 100}{\text{Base}},$$

or, $\dfrac{\text{Urban population } (\ 54,305,603)}{\text{Total population } (105,710,620)} \times 100 = 51.37$ or 51.4 per cent.

Ordinarily percentages should, as above, be calculated to two decimal places and then reduced to one decimal place when recorded. The percentage is a ratio per 100. Ratios per 1,000 or per 100,000 are also common. The general death rate is usually expressed in terms of deaths per 1,000. Specific death rates, such as the suicide rate, are frequently quoted as rates per 100,000. The tendency is to choose a base large enough so that the resulting rate has one or more integral digits.

Principles in the Computation and Use of Ratios

(1) *Distributions aggregating less than one hundred should rarely be reduced to a percentage basis.* Not much is gained in ease of comparison, and there is danger that the smallness of the sample will be overlooked.

(2) *The limited validity of averages of ratios.* The ratios for constituent parts of a whole may not be averaged without weighting to get the rate for the total. If a student spends 50 per cent of his allowance for movie tickets and his roommate spends 10 per cent, it does not necessarily follow that the two spend, in the aggregate, 30 per cent of their combined funds for movie tickets. That is true only if the separate allowances of the two men chance to be equal. The tax rates of three cities

may be 15, 20, and 25 mills, respectively, but if the cities are of different size it does not follow that the aggregate of all property in the three cities combined is taxed twenty mills. An average of the rates of population increase in the several states does not give the rate of increase for the United States as a whole, unless we make the assumption that the states are equal in population. This error is really a fallacy arising from the use of the simple instead of the weighted average.

(3) *Distribution ratios are appropriate only when the total is reasonably homogeneous.* The items should have at least some one characteristic in common before their use as an aggregate or the division of that aggregate into percentages is significant. For example, it is suggested that "the aggregate of farm animals returned on the agricultural schedule (of the census) is an aggregate which does not possess a sufficient degree of homogeneity to justify a distribution by classes of animals, showing, for example, what percentage of the total number of farm animals are horses, mules, asses, cows, goats, swine, sheep, and poultry." [1]

(4) *A rate of increase is important only when the increase has a significant relation to the base.* "Organic increases . . . such as that of population, are naturally significant in themselves as measures of organic development or growth." [1] But where the increase or decrease is not organic, greater care must be exercised to insure a significant comparison. The amount of illiteracy [2] in Massachusetts was 5.2 per cent in 1910 and 4.7 per cent in 1920. In Mississippi it was 22.4 per cent in 1910 and 17.2 per cent in 1920. If the decrease is measured in terms of the total population it appears that the decrease was about ten times greater in Mississippi than in Massachusetts, but a more significant comparison is between the number of illiterates in 1910 and the decrease of illiteracy. The percentage decrease in Massachusetts, in terms of the total population, was low because illiteracy at the outset was such a small factor among the total number of inhabitants.

[1] Bailey and Cummings, *Statistics,* pp. 63-64.
[2] Fourteenth Census of the United States, 1920, vol. iii, pp. 436, 530.

(5) In general, *the validity of the comparison involved in a ratio rests upon a proper choice of the numerator and denominator.* Ordinarily a fact should be compared only with the facts which cause or condition it. If the numerator of the ratio in question is battle losses, the denominator should be the number of men exposed to battle risks; if the numerator is automobile theft losses, the denominator should be the number of automobiles exposed to theft. This principle, though often violated, is so obvious that it needs little comment.

(6) *Comparisons between ratios are valid only when both the denominators and the numerators of the ratio fractions are comparable.* A subtle opportunity for error arises in a comparison of two or more ratios. Two ratios may conceivably be self-consistent and apparently similar, yet on close examination it is seen that they are not strictly comparable. If ratios or percentages are to be compared, care must be taken to see that both the numerators and the denominators are comparable. This rule is fundamental to logical comparisons, and violations of it are so easy, so subtle, and often so misleading that one of the greatest tasks in statistical compilation is the maintenance of comparability between data gathered at different times or by different agencies. Various violations of the principle of comparability, designated as *fallacies of non-comparable denominators or of non-comparable numerators,* are mentioned in the following discussion of special ratios in economic phenomena.

TYPICAL COMMERCIAL, ECONOMIC, AND SOCIAL RATIOS

Among the many ratios utilized in the expression and appraisal of business conditions, those sometimes designated as *credit ratios* or credit barometers are of particular interest. Mr. Alexander Wall,[1] who has made a special study of those business ratios that are of greatest aid in determining the amount of credit which may wisely be extended, distinguishes between "static" ratios and "velocity" ratios. The former measure the status of the assets and liabilities at the time the financial statement is issued; the latter compare the sales with certain items in the assets and liabilities. The *"static" ratios* are: (1) the cur-

[1] Alexander Wall, *Analytical Credits,* chaps. viii, ix, xii.

rent ratio, or the ratio of current assets to current liabilities; (2) the ratio of receivables to merchandise; (3) the ratio of debt to net worth; and (4) the ratio of net worth to non-current assets. The *"velocity" ratios* are the ratios of sales to (1) receivables, (2) merchandise, (3) net worth, and (4) non-current assets. Tradition has set the ratio of two to one as the standard for the "current ratio," but less attention has been paid to the other credit ratios. The analysis made by Mr. Wall suggests, however, that a logical procedure in credit analysis would be to set up special standards for each particular type of business with consideration given to the other "static" and "velocity" ratios as well as to the familiar current ratio.

Of the many other commercial ratios that might appropriately be discussed, let us note two or three which afford illustrations of the possibility of fallacious comparisons.

The retail merchant often speaks of his *mark-up* rate, meaning the percentage added to the cost of goods in fixing his selling price. A *mark-down* rate is the reduction made from previously quoted selling prices when, for example, a special sale is being held. Occasionally a merchant assumes that a 20-per-cent markdown is equivalent to a 20-per-cent mark-up, overlooking the fact that the denominator for the mark-up ratio is cost, whereas the denominator for the mark-down ratio is cost plus the mark-up. This illustrates the fallacy of *non-comparable denominators*.

There are many ways of expressing the turnover of employees, or the *labor turnover rate*.[1] A common method is to divide the number of separations in a year by the average number on the payroll. The result is expressed as a per cent, thus:

$$\frac{\text{Number of separations}}{\text{Average number on payroll}} \times 100 = \text{Turnover rate.}$$

Some employers, however, use replacements rather than separations for the numerator. Others use the average attendance, rather than the average number on the payroll, as the denominator. It is not necessary to examine all the possible methods to indicate the ease with which misleading comparisons can be

[1] E. J. Benge, *Standard Practice in Personnel Work,* chap. iv.

made. If one plant uses separations as a basis and another replacements, the comparison of the turnover rates for the two plants involves the fallacy of *non-comparable numerators,* especially in periods when the labor force is being considerably increased or decreased.

Interest rates are usually quoted as the percentages of the principal payable per year as interest, regardless of the duration of the loan. For example, the quotations commonly published are those for call loans, 30-90 day paper, and 4-6 months paper. Mortgage loans are usually made for periods of from three to five years. All these rates, however, are quoted in terms of the *rate per year.*

Tax rates. Income-tax rates are usually expressed in terms of per cent of taxable income. In Great Britain the rate is given in terms of shillings per pound sterling. An English income tax of six shillings is equivalent to a 30-per-cent income tax.

Property taxes are customarily expressed, in this country, in terms of mills per dollar of assessed valuation. The 1921 Madison, Wisconsin, tax levy was 23.5 mills. If an automobile was assessed at $1,000, the tax was $23.50. A 23.5 mill tax is equivalent to a tax of $2.35 per $100 or $23.50 per $1,000 and is sometimes so expressed.

We must distinguish clearly between the nominal tax rate, determined as just described, and the estimated *true tax* rate, determined by dividing the amount of tax by the estimated market value of the taxed property. If the automobile on which the owner paid a tax of $23.50 was actually worth only $500, the true tax rate was 47 mills; if it was worth $2,000, the true tax rate was 11.75 mills. Comparisons between the nominal tax rates of two states or cities are apt to be worthless because of the fallacy of non-comparable denominators. Thus the nominal tax rate of Chicago in 1919 was 59.29; that of Omaha, Nebraska, 100.73; and that of Madison, Wisconsin, 13.50. But the estimated true rates, based upon selling values rather than assessed values, were 14.77, 18.53, and 13.50, respectively.[1]

[1] *Statistics of Cities,* 1919, pp. 319, 334, 350.

Rates in vital statistics.[1]

It is in the field of vital statistics that the expression of statistical facts in the form of standardized rate terminology has reached its most highly developed stage. The *principal rates* in vital statistics are death rates, birth rates, marriage rates, divorce rates, and morbidity rates.

The *death rate* is the ratio between the number of persons who die in a given interval of time, usually taken as a year, and the number of persons estimated to be alive at the midpoint of the period. Thus the death rate is usually calculated as the ratio between the deaths during the year and the estimated July 1st population. We may distinguish between the *crude or general death rate, specific* death rates, and a *standardized* death rate. If the total number of deaths in a given city in 1925 is 20,000 and the population on July 1st is estimated as 2,000,000, the general death rate is 10.0, or ten deaths per 1,000 persons.

If we state the deaths per 100,000 from typhoid fever, we have a specific death rate. The rate of deaths in the United States from this cause decreased from 30.8 per 100,000 in 1900 to 5.0 in 1920.[2] There are specific death rates by causes of death, sex, age group, or any other significant classification of the population. For comparative analysis they are more valuable than the general death rate.

A *standardized rate* is the general rate adjusted to allow for variances in the sex and age composition of the population. Thus the report of the Registrar-General for England and Wales gives an annual death rate "standardized to the sex and age constitution of the population as enumerated in 1901." Table C, on page 144, shows the trend of this standardized rate.

This standardized death rate is computed by determining the actual specific death rates by age and sex in the given year, and applying these rates to the population of England and Wales in 1901. This procedure amounts to determining what the general death rate would have been in 1918, for example, if the popula-

[1] G. C. Whipple, *Vital Statistics,* chaps. vi, vii, ix.
[2] U. S. Bureau of the Census, *Mortality Rates,* 1910-1920, p. 33.

TABLE C

STANDARDIZED DEATH RATE IN GREAT BRITAIN [a]

Period	Rate	Period	Rate	Period	Rate
1841–1850	21.6	1891–1900	18.1	1914	13.7
1851–1860	21.2	1901–1910	15.2	1915 [b]	14.8
1861–1870	21.3	1911	14.2	1916 [b]	13.4
1871–1880	20.3	1912	13.0	1917 [b]	13.5
1881–1890	18.6	1913	13.5	1918 [b]	17.1

[a] Annual Report of the Registrar-General of Births, Deaths, and Marriages in England and Wales (1918), p. cxiii.
[b] Civilians only.

tion had been distributed, as to age and sex, in 1918 exactly as in 1901.

The death rate from all causes in the registration area of the United States was 18.1 per 1,000 in 1918, 12.9 in 1919, and 13.1 in 1920.[1]

The infant mortality rate is computed in a special way. "The term 'Infant Mortality' is universally taken to mean the ratio which the number of infants that die in any one year bears to the number of births in that year."[2]

The *natural rate of increase* is the difference between the birth rate and the death rate. If there is no emigration or immigration, the excess of births over deaths will, of course, agree with the increase of population as revealed by the census enumerations.

In the last several decades, omitting the war period, there has been a general downward trend in the birth rates and death rates of almost all civilized countries.[3]

"The *marriage rate* is found by dividing the number of persons married in a year by the estimated mid-year population, expressed in thousands,"[4] and the divorce rate is found by a similar computation.

The field of vital statistics affords many opportunities for illustrating the danger of incorrect use of comparative ratios, particularly if the comparisons are made in terms of crude death

[1] U. S. Bureau of the Census, *Mortality Statistics*, 1920, p. 9.
[2] H. T. Ashby, *Infant Mortality*, p. 2.
[3] G. C. Whipple, *Vital Statistics*, p. 210.
[4] *Ibid.*, p. 200.

rates. A comparison of the crude death rates of New Orleans and Chicago would not give a clew to the relative healthfulness of their respective climates unless allowance were made for the difference in the racial constituencies of the two populations. The death rate "for male negroes is almost double that for male whites up to the age of sixty or thereabouts." [1] The death rate from disease in the American military forces from the beginning of the Great War to May 1, 1919, was only 15,[2] whereas the death rate in the United States as a whole was 14.2 in 1917 and 18.0 in 1918. Does this indicate that, aside from battle deaths, army life was more healthful than civilian life? By no means, for the rates quoted make no allowance for the difference in age constituency. The normal death rate for the age group found in the army is less than 10.

It may be noted that army death rates from disease have been materially reduced by modern camp sanitation. In the Mexican War the rate was 110, in the Civil War 65, in the Spanish War 26, in the American expeditionary forces in the Great War 19. On the other hand, the proportion of battle deaths in the last war (53 per 1,000) was greater than in previous wars.[3]

REFERENCES

1. BAILEY AND CUMMINGS, *Statistics*, chap. vi—especially good.
2. BAILEY, W. B., *Modern Social Conditions*, pp. 33-34, 97 ff., 136 ff., and 214 ff.
3. BENGE, EUGENE J., *Standard Practice in Personnel Work*, chap. iv.
4. Bureau of the Census: *Birth Statistics; Mortality Statistics; Abstract; Population; Financial Statistics of Cities; Mortality Rates, 1910-1920.*
5. KING, W. I., *Elements of Statistical Method*, chap. iv.
6. NEWSHOLME, ARTHUR, *The Elements of Vital Statistics.*
7. PEARL, RAYMOND, *Medical Biometry and Statistics*, chap. vii, "Rates and Ratios"; chap. ix, "Standardized and Corrected Death Rates."
8. SECRIST, H., *Introduction to Statistical Methods, pp.* 69-75.
9. ——— *Readings and Problems in Statistical Methods*, "Car-seat Mile Averages and Ratios," pp. 344-347.
10. WHIPPLE, G. C., *Vital Statistics*, chaps. vi, vii, and ix.

[1] G. C. Whipple, *Vital Statistics*, p. 230.
[2] L. P. Ayres, *The War with Germany*, pp. 124-125.
[3] *Ibid.*, p. 125.

CHAPTER IX

DISPERSION AND SKEWNESS

STATISTICS has been defined as the science of averages. A more comprehensive definition would be that statistics is the science of summaries—of facts reduced to certain abstract measures of the general characteristics of a distribution. There are three [1] classes of these abstract measures or mathematical expressions used to convey the general qualities of a group. First, we have the group of averages discussed in Chapter VII. These are terse expressions with which the statistician attempts to picture the common or typical characteristics of a group in a single phrase, a single magnitude. They represent the acme of condensation. That averages are significant and helpful for statistical study, all will admit; that they have some limitations, all should recognize. They are often too generalized; they may obscure the details too much to permit intelligent comparison. It is possible for the same average to represent widely different distributions, hence we may wish to know how the items are distributed about the average. To this end, we use (1) *measures of dispersion,* descriptive of the degree of *spread* about the average; and (2) measures of *skewness,* descriptive of the degree to which the distribution about the average lacks symmetry.

METHODS OF CHARACTERIZING THE SHAPE OF A DISTRIBUTION

The shape of a distribution, or the degree of dispersion and skewness, may be shown by frequency tables, frequency graphs, numerical measures, and by coefficients of dispersion and skewness.

Frequency tables and frequency graphs show the size of each group in the distribution, while *numerical measures of dispersion*

[1] Not including the ratios analyzed in the previous chapter, which are essentially comparisons of two or more groups rather than direct characterizations of one group.

give a concise statement of the degree of spread or scatteration
about the average, this measure being expressed in terms of the
same unit as the members of the distribution. *Coefficients of
dispersion,* on the other hand, are abstract mathematical fractions
indicating the relative dispersion as compared with the average
or type from which the dispersion is measured. Such coefficients
afford a means of comparing the dispersion of two distributions
expressed in entirely different statistical units. For example, by
means of coefficients of dispersion we can compare the variation
in earnings of wage-earners, expressed in dollars, with the variation in their period of school attendance, expressed in years.

In general, measures and other representations of dispersion
indicate the degree of spread, dispersion, or deviation around the
average. Series 1 and 2 below have the same average, but the
values of the first are closely clustered around the average, while
the items in Series 2 are more widely scattered.

Series 1	Series 2
40	10
45	20
50 (mean)	50 (mean)
55	80
60	90

Measures of dispersion, then, call attention to the variability or
differences of the separate variates in a group. If you buy
twenty-one meals a week for fifty cents each, the average is fifty
cents and the dispersion is *nil*. But if you buy a cup of coffee
for a dime and call that breakfast, surrender forty cents to the
cafeteria at noon and call that a meal, and indulge at night in
real food for a dollar, meals still average fifty cents, but the
dispersion in cost is marked.

This phenomenon of dispersion is often of great *significance
in economic data*. The student of social affairs wishes to know
not only what is the average income per capita in the United
States, but also whether this income is somewhat evenly distributed or largely concentrated in the hands of a few. Are there
a large number receiving about the average income, or are there
a few with enormous incomes and many millions with incomes
far below the average mark? The sales manager wishes to know

not only the average size of sales, but whether this average is made up of many sales of about the same amount or of many small sales and a few large ones. The student of vital statistics wishes to know not only the average death rate in cities from typhoid, but also the degree to which this differs from city to city.

THE USE OF THE FREQUENCY TABLE AND GRAPH TO SHOW DISPERSION

While not, strictly speaking, measures of dispersion, the frequency table and the frequency graph afford effective devices for showing the dispersion of a series. Particularly for presentation to readers not trained in statistical terminology, the easily interpreted device of picturing relative dispersion by means of the simple frequency graph is to be recommended.

CHART 25

SYMMETRICAL FREQUENCY CURVES WITH EQUAL MEANS BUT UNEQUAL DISPERSION *

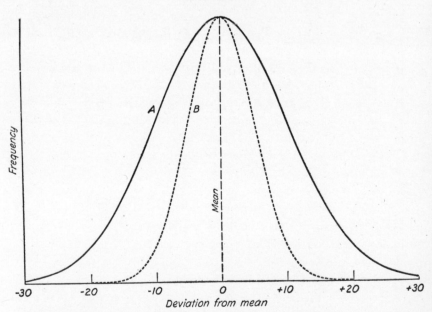

* For method of constructing these curves, see Chapter X, Table XLII and discussion of "Fitting a Normal Curve to a Distribution."

In Chart 25 [1] the means of the two distributions represented by curves A and B are identical in size and the frequencies at the mean are equal, but the reader will note that the distribution represented by curve A evidently has the greater dispersion of the two.

CHART 26

LORENZ CURVE

DISTRIBUTION OF TAXABLE INCOME AND OF THE TAX THEREON AMONG THE PERSONS ASSESSED TO WISCONSIN INCOME TAX ON INCOME OF THE YEAR 1919 *

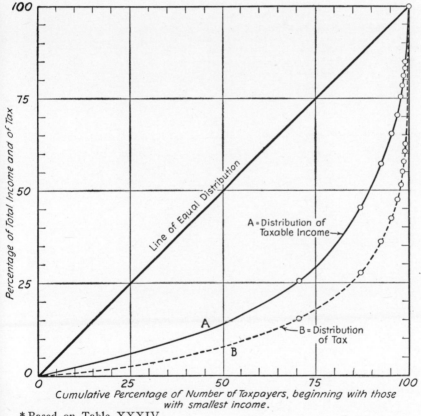

* Based on Table XXXIV.

_____

[1] For method of constructing these curves see table XLII in the following chapter.

TABLE XXXIV [a]

PERSONS ASSESSED TO THE WISCONSIN INCOME TAX ON INCOME OF THE
YEAR 1919, WITH AMOUNT OF TAXABLE INCOME AND TAX

(Columns (e) and (h) in thousands of dollars)

Size of taxable income	Number of persons			Taxable Income			Amount of Tax		
	In class	Per cent of total number		In class (000 omitted)	Per cent of total amount		In class (000 omitted)	Per cent of total amount	
		In given class	Cu-mu-lated		In given class	Cu-mu-lated		In given class	Cu-mu-lated
(a)	(b)	(c)	(d)	(e)	(f)	(g)	(h)	(i)	(j)
Total	206,626	100.0	100.0	$234,613	100.0	100.0	$3,969	100.0	100.0
Under $1,000	146,015	70.7	70.7	59,543	25.4	25.4	598	15.1	15.1
1,000 to 1,999	33,663	16.3	87.0	46,418	19.8	45.2	502	12.6	27.7
2,000 to 2,999	11,659	5.6	92.6	28,191	12.0	57.2	336	8.5	36.2
3,000 to 3,999	5,670	2.8	95.4	19,499	8.3	65.5	256	6.4	42.6
4,000 to 4,999	3,142	1.5	96.9	13,986	6.0	71.5	202	5.1	47.7
5,000 to 5,999	1,783	0.9	97.8	9,723	4.1	75.6	156	3.9	51.6
6,000 to 6,999	1,123	0.5	98.3	7,267	3.1	78.7	129	3.3	54.9
7,000 to 7,999	785	0.4	98.7	5,879	2.5	81.2	115	2.9	57.8
8,000 to 8,999	567	0.3	99.0	4,788	2.0	83.2	104	2.6	60.4
9,000 to 9,999	415	0.2	99.2	3,953	1.7	84.9	95	2.4	62.8
10,000 or more	1,804	0.9	100.0	35,366	15.1	100.0	1,475	37.2	100.0

[a] Derived from table 3, p. 33, Wisconsin Tax Commission, *Tenth Biennial Report*, 1920.

The Lorenz curve.[1] The Lorenz curve is a special type of cumulative frequency graph adapted to showing the degree to which the distribution of wealth, income, etc., deviates from equal distribution. On page 149 we have a Lorenz curve showing the distribution of taxable income and of income taxes for 1919 among the payers of Wisconsin income tax. On the horizontal axis is measured the percentage of income-tax payers, cumulated in order of size of taxable income—that is, the abscissa 50 is to be read "the 50 per cent reporting the smallest incomes." On the vertical scale is cumulated the amount of income (curve A) or the amount of the tax (curve B). If 25 per cent of the taxpayers had reported 25 per cent of the income, 50 per cent of the taxpayers 50 per cent of the income, and so on, the distribution would be shown by a straight line, marked "Line of equal distribution." However, 50 per cent of the taxpayers have reported only about 14 per cent of the income, hence the curve (A) is bowed from the equal-distribution line. The more unequal the distribution the greater the bow, as in the tax curve (B), where the higher tax rates for the higher incomes increase the inequality of distribution of the tax over that of the income. Hence, assuming interpolation on the smoothed curve B to be a sufficiently close estimation of the distribution of the tax in the lower income groups, we estimate that the poorest 50 per cent of the taxpayers were assessed only 7.5 per cent of the total tax.

The decile curve. Another special type of frequency graph for comparison of the shape of distributions results from plotting the deciles. Chart 27 is an adaptation from a diagram presented by Professor Wesley C. Mitchell in his analysis of the characteristics of price changes. In this instance the deciles are used to show the changing dispersion of a composite chronological series. A graph of the median change would show only the general tendency, while this chart indicates the extent to which individual prices vary from the general tendency. It will be noted that, although the movement of the median indicates

[1] For examples of Lorenz curves, see National Bureau of Economic Research, vol. i, *Income in the United States*, p. 141; also W. I. King, *The Wealth and Income of the People of the United States*.

that the general trend was upward, in each year one or more individual prices declined.

TABLE XXXV

DISPERSION OF PERCENTAGE CHANGES FROM PRECEDING YEAR
WHOLESALE PRICES IN THE UNITED STATES: 1914-1917 [a]

"The deciles are those points in the percentage scale of rise or fall in price which divide the whole number of price changes recorded each year into ten equal groups."

(— indicates a fall; + indicates a rise; ± o indicates "no change")

Position in the array of price changes	1914	1915	1916	1917
Greatest fall............	— 37.3	— 60.4	— 19.1	— 34.1
1st decile..............	— 12.0	— 12.0	+ 2.1	+ 8.7
2d "	— 7.4	— 5.9	+ 6.7	+ 19.4
3d "	— 4.1	— 1.9	+ 10.5	+ 25.1
4th "	— 1.3	— 0.1	+ 14.4	+ 28.6
Median	± 0	± 0	+ 18.6	+ 34.8
6th decile	± 0	+ 2.7	+ 24.0	+ 42.1
7th "	+ 1.5	+ 6.0	+ 30.1	+ 49.3
8th "	+ 5.0	+ 10.1	+ 38.7	+ 57.5
9th "	+ 9.1	+ 18.7	+ 53.4	+ 69.3
Greatest rise..........	+ 76.4	+ 172.9	+ 155.1	+ 154.2

[a] Adapted, together with accompanying chart, from W. C. Mitchell, *Index Numbers of Wholesale Prices in the United States and Foreign Countries,* United States Bureau of Labor Statistics, Bulletin no. 284, p. 14 (table), p. 14 insert (chart, 1891-1918).

NUMERICAL MEASURES OF DISPERSION

There are several methods of obtaining a numerical measure of the degree of dispersion:

1. **The range.** The most obvious measure of dispersion is the range, the spread between the smallest and the largest item in the series. This, however, is an inadequate and unreliable measure. Its magnitude depends upon only two items. The difference between the wage of the office boy and the salary of the highest paid executive in the concern is not an adequate measure of the degree to which the wages of employees vary from the average wage. For rough comparisons, the range may occa-

CHART 27

DECILE CURVE

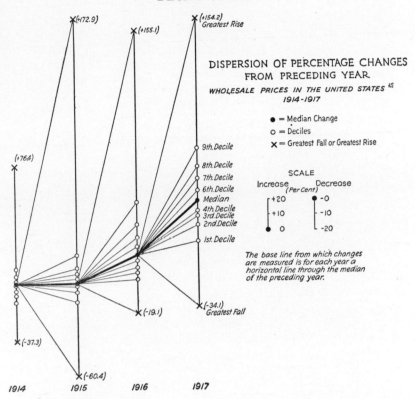

X(+172.9)

X(+155.1)

X(+154.2)
Greatest Rise

DISPERSION OF PERCENTAGE CHANGES
FROM PRECEDING YEAR

WHOLESALE PRICES IN THE UNITED STATES *
1914-1917

● = Median Change
o = Deciles
X = Greatest Fall or Greatest Rise

(+76.4)
X

9th. Decile

8th. Decile
7th. Decile
6th. Decile
Median
4th. Decile
3rd. Decile
2nd. Decile

1st. Decile

SCALE

Increase   Decrease
        (Per Cent)
+20   ● -0

+10   - -10

● 0   - -20

The base line from which changes
are measured is for each year a
horizontal line through the median
of the preceding year.

X (-19.1)   X (-34.1)
                 Greatest Fall

X (-37.3)

X (-60.4)

1914   1915   1916   1917

* Based on Table XXXV.

sionally be helpful, but it should be used sparingly, as no great
statistical significance can be attached to it. It is, however, customarily used in quoting interest rates and the degree of fluctuation in security prices.

2. **The quartile deviation,** or the semi-interquartile
range, is half of the difference between the magnitudes of the
lower and upper quartiles. The median, we have seen, is the
middle item in an array. The quartiles are the magnitudes which
divide the array into four equal groups. There are three quartiles. Below the first, or lower, quartile come one-fourth of the
cases, and above it three-fourths. The median is the second

quartile. Three-fourths of the items are smaller than the third or upper quartile and one-fourth are larger.

For example, in Table XXXI, which contains an array of one hundred relative prices, the lower quartile is located between the twenty-fifth and twenty-sixth items and the upper quartile between the seventy-fifth and the seventy-sixth.

In general, the rank of the lower quartile may be found by the formula $\frac{n}{4}$ (total number divided by 4), and the location of the upper quartile by the formula $\frac{3n}{4}$. Then their respective magnitudes may be found either by interpolation in a frequency table, or by interpolation on a smoothed frequency curve, using in both cases the same general process as used for the median. (See interpolation for lower quartile in Chart 24, Chapter VII.) This formula $(\frac{n}{4})$ is not quite exact,[1] but will answer for the approximations required in most uses of the quartile in connection with economic statistics.

The quartile deviation (Q) is found by taking half the difference between the sizes of the upper and lower quartiles. The formula for it is:

$$Q = \frac{\text{Quartile 3} - \text{Quartile 1}}{2} \text{ or } \frac{\text{U. Q} - \text{L. Q}}{2} \dots \dots \text{(Formula 12)}.$$

This gives the average deviation of the quartile from the median and is a value calculated with relative ease and yet affected by each item in the series rather than by only two items, as is the range. If the series is closely concentrated, the quartiles will be close together; if widely dispersed, the quartile range, and hence the quartile deviation, will be large.

3. **The "probable error."** The "probable error" (P. E.) is the median of the deviations from the average—that is, if the deviations are arrayed in order of size and irrespective of whether they are above or below the average, the central deviation is the "probable error." "Error" is here used in the sense

---

[1] Four different formulas, varying with the number of items in the series, are required for a precise determination of the quartile. See A. L. Bowley, *Elements of Statistics*, pp. 106-107, 4th ed.

of deviation and "probable" in the sense of equally probable—that is, if the average of a series is 50 and the probable error is 10, then half of the cases will deviate more than 10 from the average and half less; or, to put it in other words, it is an even chance, a "50-50 break," that any given case chosen at random will come within the probable-error range, that is, 50 ± 10, or from 40 to 60. In a symmetrical distribution the quartile deviation and the probable error are identical. The latter term, which is more fully explained in the following chapter, is ordinarily used under circumstances where a symmetrical curve is present or assumed. The probable error is an important dispersion measure, extensively used in expressing the degree of precision of averages and coefficients of correlation. (See Chapter X, following, on the "Theory of Probability and Error".)

4. **The average deviation** (A. D.). The average deviation is simply the arithmetic average of the deviations from the central tendency, which may be either the mode, median, or arithmetic mean. The following table illustrates its calculation from a simple distribution with a frequency of one in each class, using the median as the central tendency.

TABLE XXXVI

COMPUTATION OF THE AVERAGE DEVIATION FROM THE MEDIAN

Store	Monthly Sales	Deviation
Store A	$1,000	$500
Store B	1,200	300
Store C	1,500	0
Store D	1,600	100
Store E	2,000	500

Total deviations $1,400

Average deviation (A.D.) 280

Algebraically this process may be expressed by the formula

$$\text{A.D.} = \frac{\text{The sum of quantities like } (m - Mi)}{\text{The number of items, or } n} \quad \text{..... (Formula 13),}$$

where m is the size of each individual item; Mi, the size of the median; and n, the total number of items in the series.

If the data appear in the form of a frequency table, the only additional complexity introduced is that the midpoint of each respective class must be used as representing the magnitude of the members of that class, and the deviation of the midpoint from the mean must then be multiplied by the frequency of the class.

The reader should note that signs are ignored in calculating the average deviation.

5. **The standard deviation.** The so-called standard deviation or "root-mean-square deviation" (abbreviated as S.D. or σ, the Greek small letter "s") is found by taking the square root of the average of the squares of the deviations from the arithmetic average. Let us illustrate with a hypothetical distribution, with both class intervals and frequencies of one:

TABLE XXXVII

COMPUTATION OF THE STANDARD DEVIATION

(Mean = 6)

(m)	(d)	(d)^2
Wage per Day	Deviation	Deviation Squared
$3	3	9
5	1	1
6	0	0
7	1	1
9	3	9

The standard deviation $(S.D.) = \sqrt{\dfrac{\Sigma d^2}{n}}$ ....(Formula 14);

or $\sqrt{\dfrac{\text{Sum of squares of deviations}}{\text{Total number of deviations}}} = \sqrt{20/5} = \sqrt{4} = \$2.$

The standard deviation is useful when it is desired to give special weight to the extreme deviations. Also it has certain mathematical characteristics which recommend its use from the theoretical point of view. It is employed in an important process for determining correlation, the Pearsonian method, and hence it saves time to use the standard deviation as a measure of dispersion if it is intended to calculate subsequently the Pearsonian coefficient of correlation (see Chapter XV). It is used, also, in reducing chronological series with widely differing ranges of variation to a basis suitable for comparative plotting and analysis.[1]

The computation of the standard deviation is of sufficient importance to justify attention to a *short-cut method* of calculating it. The process is simple: (1) assume a convenient trial arithmetic mean; (2) compute the mean-square deviation from this trial average; (3) subtract the square of the difference between the true and the assumed average; and (4) extract the square root. The algebraic formula is

$$\text{S. D.} = \sqrt{\frac{\Sigma d_E^2}{n} - (A - E)^2} \quad \ldots\ldots\ldots\ldots\text{(Formula 15)},$$

where $\Sigma d_E^2 =$ the sum of the squares of the deviations from the assumed average,

$A =$ the true mean,
$E =$ the assumed mean,
$n =$ the total number of items,

or, if we wish to express the formula in such a way as to make it applicable to a frequency distribution, we substitute $\Sigma f (V - E)^2$ for Σd_E^2, V being the class mid-value and f the class frequency, and the formula becomes

$$\text{S.D.} = \sqrt{\frac{\Sigma f(V - E)^2}{n} - (A - E)^2} \quad \ldots\ldots\ldots\text{(Formula 16)}.$$

In Table XXXVIII we have the short-cut method applied to the computation of the standard deviation for the sample of one hundred 1919 relative wholesale prices in the United States which we have used in earlier computations. In the chapter on averages, we have computed the mean for this distribution, but in order to illustrate the ease with which the short-cut methods of computing the mean and the standard deviation, respectively, may be combined, we have added column g, which gives the sum of the deviations from the assumed mean or the additional data necessary for computing the correct mean.

[1] See chap. xiv, "Business Cycles and Barometers."

TABLE XXXVIII

COMPUTATION OF THE STANDARD DEVIATION BY THE SHORT-CUT METHOD

One hundred 1919 relative wholesale prices

(Based on Table XXIX)

a	b	c	d	e	f	g
Relative price (Group) (limits)	Number in group	Mid-point of group	Deviation from assumed average (212)	Deviation squared	Product of $b \times e$	Product of $b \times d$
f		V	$(V-E)$	$(V-E)^2$	$f(V-E)^2$	$f(V-E)$
Total	100				284,375	$+2050$ -1925 Net $+125$
75– 99	1	87	-125	15,625	15,625	-125
100–124	2	112	-100	10,000	20,000	-200
125–149	4	137	-75	5,625	27,500	-300
150–174	13	162	-50	2,500	32,500	-650
175–199	26	187	-25	625	16,250	-650
200–224	21	212	0	...	.....	...
225–249	9	237	$+25$	625	5,625	$+225$
250–274	13	262	$+50$	2,500	32,500	$+650$
275–299	5	287	$+75$	5,625	28,125	$+375$
300–324	2	312	$+100$	10,000	20,000	$+200$
325–349	1	337	$+125$	15,625	15,625	$+125$
350–374	2	362	$+150$	22,500	45,000	$+300$
375–399	1	387	$+175$	30,625	30,625	$+175$

Substituting in the formula, $A = E + \dfrac{\Sigma f(V-E)}{n}$, to find the correct mean, we have

$$A, \text{ or mean, } = 212 + \frac{125}{100} = 213.25, \text{ or } 213.3.$$

Substituting in the formula, $\sigma = \sqrt{\dfrac{\Sigma f(V-E)^2}{n} - (A-E)^2}$, to find the standard deviation, we have

$$\sigma = \sqrt{\frac{284,375}{100} - (212-213.3)^2} = 53.3$$

The proof for the short-cut formula, in somewhat different forms, may be found in several of the well-known treatises on statistical method and its applications.[1]

COEFFICIENTS OF DISPERSION

Chart 28 illustrates the need for some measure of relative, as contrasted with absolute, dispersion. Curves A and B are identical in shape and represent exactly the same dispersion about the respective means; but the means are not equal, hence the dispersion as compared with the magnitude of the mean is greater in curve A than it is in curve B. How can we express this difference in numerical terms?

CHART 28

FREQUENCY CURVES WITH EQUAL ABSOLUTE DISPERSION BUT UNEQUAL RELATIVE DISPERSION *

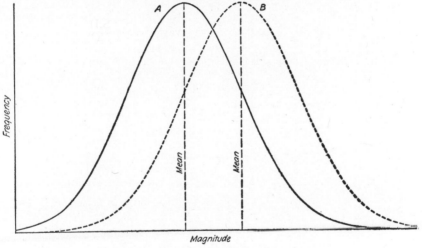

* For method of construction, see Chapter X, Table XLII.

The quartile deviation, the average deviation, and the standard deviation are all expressed in terms of some concrete unit, as dollars, for example, and do not lend themselves readily to

[1] W. I. King, *Elements of Statistical Method,* p. 151; H. L. Moore, *Forecasting the Yield and Price of Cotton,* pp. 22-23; and C. J. West, *op. cit.,* pp. 49-50.

comparison between series. An average deviation of two dollars is insignificant if it applies to monthly wages, but important if it applies to daily wages. In other words, to get a significant indication of comparative dispersion it is necessary to allow for the relative size of the items in the two series to be compared. This is done by dividing the given measure of dispersion by the average from which it is calculated.

For example, the coefficient of dispersion based on the average deviation is obtained by dividing the measure of dispersion (A.D.) by the average (A) from which the deviations were computed; likewise the coefficient for the standard deviation is

$$\frac{S.D.}{A} \dots\dots\dots\dots\dots (Formula\ 17).$$

More commonly the percentage ratio of the standard deviation to the mean, known as the *coefficient of variation,* is used as the measure of relative dispersion. The formula is

$$v(\text{coefficient of variation}) = \frac{S.D.}{A} \times 100 \dots\dots\dots (Formula\ 18).$$

The coefficient for the quartile deviation is found by dividing the quartile range by the sum of the quartiles, hence the formula is

$$\frac{Quartile\ 3 - Quartile\ 1}{Quartile\ 3 + Quartile\ 1} \dots\dots\dots\dots (Formula\ 19).$$

SKEWNESS

Skewness is a lack of symmetry, a deviation from the bell-shaped symmetrical curve shown in Charts 25 and 28. It may be due either to imperfections in the sampling, which cause the curve drawn from the sample to deviate from the symmetrical distribution which would appear if the entire universe were graphed; or it may be due to characteristics of the data which account for a deviation from the normal-frequency curve. Most distributions will show some variation from a perfect symmetrical curve, and in distributions of an economic character marked deviations are common. When the skewness in an adequate sample or in a complete universe is marked, it implies the existence of some predominant cause, as contrasted with the multiplicity of small causes which in the aggregate we call chance and which result in the normal-frequency form. A frequency curve of the price of bonds at a given date will often drop more sharply to the right than to the left of the mode, due to the fact that the redemption value of the bonds (usually 100 per cent) tends to fix 100 per cent as the upper limit. The "Age of Brides" curve in Chart 20 is pulled in the other direction; for while few women are married at an earlier age than fifteen, the majority marry before the age of thirty and yet the upper limit is fixed only by the maximum duration of life.

Most of the formulas used in statistical computations apply primarily to the normal-frequency, or symmetrical, curve, or to

CHART 29

SYMMETRICAL AND MODERATELY UNSYMMETRICAL FREQUENCY CURVES

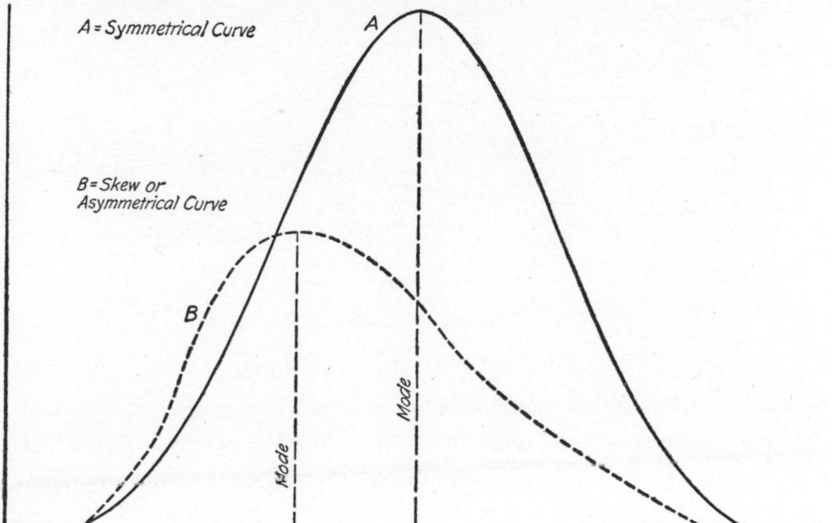

skew curves which exhibit only a moderate deviation from the symmetrical form. One type of the skew or asymmetrical curve is illustrated by curve B in Chart 29. The skew form is dominant in economic statistics; in fact, economic data frequently exhibit markedly skew forms. For example, a simple frequency curve of the distribution of wealth or income tends to a unilateral type, with the mode near one extreme. Other distributions are U-shaped, like the curve of death rates in Chart 30, with large

CHART 30

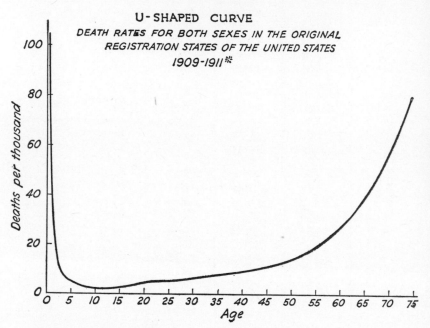

U-SHAPED CURVE

DEATH RATES FOR BOTH SEXES IN THE ORIGINAL REGISTRATION STATES OF THE UNITED STATES 1909-1911*

*Based on Table XXXIX.

frequencies near both ends of the distribution. A frequency curve for the age at which blind persons lost their vision would, likewise, tend to the U-type with two modes, one in infancy and the other in old age. Ordinarily the existence of a bimodal or multimodal grouping suggests the presence of two diverse elements in the data under consideration, each with a distinct mode.

In distributions of the moderately skew type, as in Chart 29, the relation between the mode and the mean gives an approximate measure of the skewness present. In a normal curve the mode, median, and mean coincide. In a curve positively skewed, —that is, with the longer tail to the right of the mode, the median

TABLE XXXIX

RATE OF MORTALITY PER THOUSAND IN THE ORIGINAL REGISTRATION
STATES OF THE UNITED STATES, 1910 [a]

Age in years	Annual rate	Age in years	Annual rate	Age in years	Annual rate
0– 1	114.62	25–26	5.54	50–51	14.37
1– 2	27.62	26–27	5.67	51–52	15.08
2– 3	12.34	27–28	5.85	52–53	16.01
3– 4	7.83	28–29	6.06	53–54	17.17
4– 5	5.65	29–30	6.28	54–55	18.49
5– 6	4.66	30–31	6.51	55–56	20.03
6– 7	3.91	31–32	6.78	56–57	21.72
7– 8	3.30	32–33	7.09	57–58	23.37
8– 9	2.82	33–34	7.40	58–59	24.97
9–10	2.47	34–35	7.72	59–60	26.73
10–11	2.27	35–36	8.04	60–61	28.58
11–12	2.19	36–37	8.33	61–62	30.62
12–13	2.22	37–38	8.59	62–63	32.96
13–14	2.36	38–39	8.84	63–64	35.55
14–15	2.57	39–40	9.11	64–65	38.25
15–16	2.84	40–41	9.39	65–66	41.06
16–17	3.16	41–42	9.72	66–67	44.08
17–18	3.52	42–43	10.09	67–68	47.41
18–19	3.89	43–44	10.52	68–69	51.12
19–20	4.28	44–45	10.99	69–70	55.14
20–21	4.68	45–46	11.52	70–71	59.52
21–22	5.00	46–47	12.08	71–72	64.29
22–23	5.19	47–48	12.63	72–73	69.38
23–24	5.29	48–49	13.18	73–74	74.82
24–25	5.42	49–50	13.77	74–75	80.78

[a] U. S. Bureau of the Census, *United States Life Tables,* prepared by James W. Glover, p. 54. These rates are for both sexes and are based on estimated population July 1, 1910, and the reported deaths in 1909, 1910, and 1911.

is moved somewhat to the right of the mode and the mean is moved still further to the right, due to the influence of the greater number of extreme items on that side. The difference between the mean and the mode is taken as a measure of skewness. To reduce this measure to a coefficient, we divide by the standard deviation. We may then write

$$\text{Skewness} = \frac{\text{Mean} - \text{Mode}}{\text{S.D.}} \quad \text{or} \quad s = \frac{A - Mo}{\text{S.D.}} \ldots . (\text{Formula } 20).$$

Other methods of measuring skewness are discussed in the various treatises on statistical method, but are not in extensive use in economic statistics.

REFERENCES

1. ALEXANDER, C., *School Statistics and Publicity,* chap. vi.
2. BOWLEY, A. L., *Elements of Statistics,* 4th ed., pp. 110-117.
3. DAVIES, G. R., *Introduction to Economic Statistics,* pp. 29-44.
4. KELLEY, T. L., *Statistical Method,* chap. iv, "Measures of Dispersion."
5. KING, W. I., *Elements of Statistical Method,* chaps. xiii, xiv.
6. MITCHELL, W. C., *Index Numbers of Wholesale Prices in the United States and Foreign Countries,* Bur. of Labor Statistics Bulletin No. 284, pp. 14-16 (1921).
7. RUGG, H. O., *Statistical Methods Applied to Education,* pp. 149-173, 178-180.
8. SECRIST, H., *An Introduction to Statistical Methods,* chap. xi.
9. THORNDIKE, E. L., *Mental and Social Measurements,* pp. 46-50 and chap. vi.
10. WEST, C. J., *Introduction to Mathematical Statistics,* chap. v, "The Form of the Distribution."
11. WHIPPLE, G. C., *Vital Statistics,* pp. 385-390.
12. YULE, G. U., *An Introduction to the Theory of Statistics,* pp. 90-105.
13. ZIZEK, FRANZ, *Statistical Averages,* part iii.

CHAPTER X

THE THEORY OF PROBABILITY AND ERROR

On several occasions we have made reference to the so-called normal-frequency or probability curve, and we should now be in a position to inquire more closely into the nature and theory of this important and interesting phenomenon. It is not the primary intent in this book to examine the underlying mathematical principles upon which much of statistical method rests, but it does appear probable that the meaning and significance of many of the terms used will become clearer if we turn aside to note the simpler features of the theory of probability.

Phrases such as "the probabilities are," "the probable result," etc., are in common use, yet it is doubtful whether many of us could indicate the precise meaning with which these terms are used. By the "probable result," do we mean the certain result, the most likely result, a result which is as likely to occur as some other result, or do we mean still something else?

As the term is used in statistical method, the probability of the occurrence of an event may be defined as the expected relative frequency of the event in an infinite number of observations or trials.[1] This expected ratio may be based upon a priori knowledge of the conditions determining the probability, as in simple games of chance, or, as is usual in social phenomena, upon empirical data. The probability ratio is a fraction between the limits zero (impossibility) and unity (certainty).

Within the limits of human knowledge and belief, the probability that the sun will rise in the west to-morrow is zero; the probability that any one of us will some time die is certainty or

[1] Cf. discussion of "A Priori and Empirical Probabilities," in Arne Fisher, *The Mathematical Theory of Probabilities,* chap. vii.

165

(1). But between these limits there are all possible degrees of probability.[1]

For example, the chance that a head will come up when a coin is tossed is, assuming a perfect coin and an haphazard toss, one out of two; that is, there is one chance that a head will turn up to one chance that a tail will appear. But what are the relative chances if five, six or seven coins are thrown? This question seems far afield from statistics, but we shall see presently that there is a close and interesting connection.

If two coins are tossed both may come heads, both tails, or one a head and the other a tail. Let us record the possible combinations as follows, using H for head, T for tail, and the letters (a) and (b) over the columns as key numbers to identify the respective coins.

Possible Combinations

(a)	(b)	(a)	(b)	(a)	(b)
H	H	H	T	T	T
		T	H		

There is only one **HH** (both heads), two **HT**'s, and one **TT**. This might be written

$$H^2 + 2\,HT + T^2$$

and we begin to recognize a resemblance to the result obtained in elementary algebra when we square any binomial.

Let us see what happens if we take more coins at each throw. If four coins (designated as a, b, c, and d) are thrown, the possible combinations are

All heads	3 heads	2 heads	1 head	No heads
(a)(b)(c)(d)	(a)(b)(c)(d)	(a)(b)(c)(d)	(a)(b)(c)(d)	(a)(b)(c)(d)
H H H H	H H H T	H H T T	H T T T	T T T T
	H H T H	T H H T	T H T T	
	H T H H	T T H H	T T H T	
	T H H H	H T T H	T T T H	
		H T H T		
		T H T H		

---

[1] In the terminology of probability, when an event is in question—that is, it may or may not happen—the chances of "success," the chances that it will happen, are designated by the symbol p, and the chances of failure, the chances that it will not happen, by q. The sum of p and q is always unity. If one of six names is drawn at random, the chance of success (p) for any one name is 1/6; the chance of failure (q) is 5/6.

If we think of four heads as "heads to the fourth power" (H^4), and so on, the above combinations may be written

$$H^4 + 4H^3\,T + 6H^2\,T^2 + 4H\,T^3 + T^4$$

The reader will note that there seems to be a regular law according to which the combination of a given number of heads and tails is determined. In fact the results obtained are the terms of the binomial expansion resulting from raising the binomial $(H + T)$ to the fourth power, if four coins are tossed at one time; to the tenth power, if ten coins are simultaneously tossed, and so on. Let us inquire into the expected results from tossing ten coins. We might use the same process of listing all possible combinations as was done above. A simpler method is to determine the coefficients, the number of times each combination appears, by use of the binomial triangle, which follows. This is one of those peculiar but distinctly useful empirical short cuts which the mathematician has devised for lessening his labors. It is constructed by setting down first as many ones in a column as the power to which the given factor is to be raised. Then beginning at the top, each coefficient in the successive rows is obtained by adding the pair of coefficients in the preceding row located just above and above and to the left, respectively, of the term to be obtained, and, lastly, at the end of each row of figures thus obtained, setting down a "1." For example, the coefficient of the second term in the tenth power is $(9 + 1)$ or 10; and the coefficient of the third term is $(36 + 9)$ or 45.

BINOMIAL TRIANGLE [a]

Power   *Scheme for Determining Coefficients of the Terms*
in the Expansion of a Binomial to
a Given Power

Power											
1st 1	1										
2d 1	2	1									
3d 1	3	3	1								
4th 1	4	6	4	1							
5th 1	5	10	10	5	1						
6th 1	6	15	20	15	6	1					
7th 1	7	21	35	35	21	7	1				
8th 1	8	28	56	70	56	28	8	1			
9th 1	9	36	84	126	126	84	36	9	1		
10th 1	10	45	120	210	252	210	120	45	10	1	

[a] Frequently designated as Pascal's Arithmetical Triangle.

The coefficients of the expansion of the binomial $(H + T)$ to the tenth power, which total 1,024, are given in the bottom row of the above table. That is, if ten coins are tossed, the chances are 1 out of 1,024 that all ten will be heads (H to the 10th power); 10 out of 1,024 that all but one will be heads and so on. All the separate probabilities added together give 1,024/1,024 or unity, which, as we have seen above, is the symbol for certainty. Let us compare these theoretical coefficients with the results obtained by actual experiment. Students in the classes in statistical method in the University of Wisconsin experimented with the tossing of ten coins, counting each time the number of heads which came up. The results, compared with the theoretical results, are given in the following frequency table:

TABLE XL

COMPARISON OF THE ACTUAL RESULTS FROM THE TOSSING OF TEN COINS 1,024 TIMES WITH THE THEORETICAL NUMBER ACCORDING TO THE BINOMIAL THEOREM

Number of heads up in a throw	Number of throws resulting in given number of heads	
	Actual number	Theoretical number
0	2	1
1	10	10
2	38	45
3	106	120
4	188	210
5	257	252
6	226	210
7	128	120
8	59	45
9	7	10
10	3	1

The data in the above table are plotted in Chart 31. The narrow vertical bars represent the actual frequency. The small circles represent the theoretical frequencies. By drawing a smoothed frequency curve [1] connecting these circles we have a

[1] The construction of a smoothed frequency curve from the binomial coefficients for the tenth power is not strictly accurate, as there are no intermediate values between the determined coefficients as is implied by a smoothed curve. However, when the power becomes large the coefficients, if plotted, approach

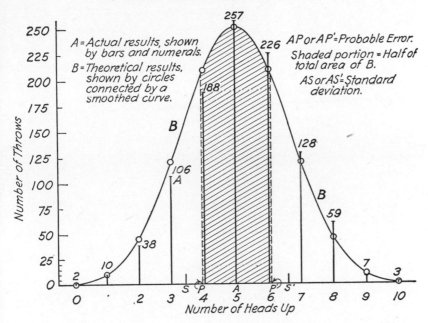

CHART 31

BINOMIAL CURVE

ACTUAL AND THEORETICAL RESULTS FROM TOSSING TEN COINS 1,024 TIMES

(Based on data in Tables XL and XLI)

rough approximation to the bell-shaped symmetrical curve designated variously as the probability curve, the curve of error, the
Gaussian curve, and the normal-frequency curve. It is known as
the probability curve because, as just illustrated, it represents the
theoretical probabilities of chance phenomena; as the curve of
error, because, if repeated observations are taken of the same
fact, such as the length of a line, each observation is apt to differ
from the true length, and these deviations if grouped and plotted
are found to approximate the probability curve. It is called
the Gaussian curve after Gauss, to whom much of the earlier

more and more closely to a smoothed curve approximating the normal or
probability curve, hence the smoothed curve in Chart 31 is suggestive of real
relationships between the binomial distribution and the probability curve. Cf.
G. U. Yule, *An Introduction to the Theory of Statistics,* 6th ed., chap. xv,
"The Binomial Distribution and the Normal Curve."

analysis of the curve and of the theory of probability is credited. Lastly it is known as the normal-frequency curve not only be-cause of the tendencies just stated, but also because it appears on examination that natural as well as chance phenomena tend to be grouped according to the probability curve. If the length of leaves on a tree, or the height of a large group of men, or the several values of any similar variable natural characteristic, are classified into a frequency table and a curve constructed there-from, the result is an approximation to a symmetrical curve similar to the smoothed curve in Chart 31. This tendency we shall call the *law of normal frequency,* which is that the *variate values of a natural phenomenon tend to be symmetrically distrib-uted about the mode in proportions determined by the law of chance distribution.*

The reason for this similarity is that the variations in natural phenomena are, like the results of coin tossing, due to chance.

Chance means the result of a multiplicity of causes, no one of which is dominant. A multitude of small factors determines whether a coin will fall head or tail—the twist of one's wrist, the air currents, the shape of the floor, etc., etc. Likewise, the height of a given individual is the result of many causes. An interesting suggestion is found in the thought that if we go back ten generations (to the tenth power) we have 1,024 ancestors, all presumably exercising some influence upon the stature of the given individual. Some authorities explain the form of chance distributions by reasoning that when reduced to the simplest natural factors, there must be for each element a "50-50 chance" —that is, an equal tendency to vary either in one direction or the other, and the theory of normal distribution has been stated in terms implying this dominance of the law of the "square deal" or equal chance, viz.: [1]

"In general, any statistical data can be analyzed into ele-

[1] C. J. West, *Introduction to Mathematical Statistics,* p. 59. The italics are added by the present writer.

The equation of the curve of chance distribution has been derived in several ways by different writers, the most notable of which are those of Hagen and Gauss. The latter bases his explanation upon the hypothesis that "the most probable value of a quantity which is observed several times, with equal care, is the arithmetical mean of the measurements." Cf. Mans-field Merriman, *A Text-book on the Method of Least Squares,* pp. 17-35.

mental components. Whenever these elemental values are relatively small in comparison with the resultant values and at the same time each element is *equally likely* to take any value within a small range, then the resultant data are said to be normally distributed."

When, however, some one or two of the many causes tend to be dominant, then there appears a skew curve. This happens to some extent in most social or economic phenomena, but often the skewness is not so great but that the principles of the probability curve can be applied with substantial accuracy. The existence, however, of a marked skew necessitates the use of care in the application of the various statistical formulas, as most of them are based upon the assumption of a symmetrical or only moderately skew curve. Furthermore, the existence of a marked skew is a challenge to the statistician to determine the direct cause of the skew, the specific forces which carry the distribution away from the influence of chance.

It should be noted, in passing, that a moderate deviation from the normal may, in a sample, be merely due to the inadequacies of the sample, just as in Chart 31 we see some slight differences between the actual and the theoretical distributions.

RELATION OF THE NORMAL FREQUENCY CURVE TO STATISTICAL METHOD

To understand readily the uses of the normal probability curve in statistical method, it will be necessary to examine more closely into its characteristics. We have noted its tendency to bell-shaped symmetry with relatively high concentration about the mean, and also the theory which accounts for this shape, but what use can we make of our knowledge of the curve?

One important *use* is the expression of the degree of precision of the various averages and coefficients calculated from samples. The method of measuring precision, in so far as it is conditioned by chance elements, is to give the amount of the "probable error." Simply stated, the *probable error* [1] of any dis-

---

[1] See also the discussion of the "probable error" in the preceding chapter. Analogous to the probable error is the "vie probable." This is "the number

tribution *is the median deviation from the mean.* There is an even chance that any one deviation picked at random will exceed the probable error. Let us see how this pertains to averages computed from samples.

Assume that a sample is picked at random from a large group of items and an average calculated, and that the process is repeated many times and for each sample an average computed. It will be found that, although the samples are from the same "universe" or aggregate, yet the averages differ somewhat from one another. And if these averages are grouped into a frequency table and plotted as a simple frequency curve, we have a curve approximating the normal frequency form. However, normal frequency curves vary in the degree of concentration about the mean. Some are relatively high and narrow; others are lower and flatter. If the averages calculated from the samples tend to vary but slightly from the true average, then the normal frequency curve of averages will be high and narrow, indicating a slight dispersion. How can this fact be numerically expressed?

It can be mathematically demonstrated that if we measure from the central ordinate in a normal frequency curve a distance to the right equal to the standard deviation of the series and also a similar distance to the left, and erect ordinates or perpendiculars at these points, the ordinates will cut the curve at the points of inflection; and, furthermore, within the space bounded by the two ordinates, the segment of the base line between them, and the curve above that segment, will be included approximately 68 per cent of the total area of the curve, representing 68 per cent of the total frequencies.

Expressed in other terms, this means that 68 per cent of the total number of deviations are within the range plus or minus the standard deviation from the central ordinate. Similar percentages for any fraction or multiple of the standard deviation can be determined. Within a range from the mean equal to

of years which a person (at a stated age) has an even chance of living." According to the American Experience Mortality Table, for persons who attain the age of 10, 54.5 is the "vie probable"; that is, of those who reach the age of 10, one half are alive at the age 64.5.—C. C. Whipple, *Vital Statistics,* p. 427.

about two-thirds of the standard deviation in both directions is included an even half of the total area, and hence of the total frequencies. This latter figure (two-thirds of the S. D., or, to be more exact, 0.6745 S. D.) is called the probable error; that is, it is the range, considered both to right and left of the mean, within which half of the items fall.

If the dispersion of the data is great, this probable error will be large; if the dispersion is small—that is, if the items are concentrated closely about the central item, the probable error will be small, and, remembering that we are speaking of a distribution in which each item is an average calculated from a sample, we may say that the precision of the average is great. If the probable error is large as compared with the mean, the precision of the average is small.

On page 169 the area determined by the probable error is shaded; and distances to right and left from the mode equal to

TABLE XLI

CALCULATION OF THE STANDARD DEVIATION OF THE THEORETICAL FREQUENCIES UPON WHICH CURVE B, CHART 31, IS BASED

(Numerical data in Table XL)

Class	Frequency	Deviation from mean	Deviation squared	Product
	f	d	d^2	fd^2
Total	1,024			2,560
0	1	− 5	25	25
1	10	− 4	16	160
2	45	− 3	9	405
3	120	− 2	4	480
4	210	− 1	1	210
5	252	0	0	0
6	210	+ 1	1	210
7	120	+ 2	4	480
8	45	+ 3	9	405
9	10	+ 4	16	160
10	1	+ 5	25	25

the standard deviation are identified by the letters S and S[1]. The value of the standard deviation is calculated by the usual process, as indicated in the preceding table. To avoid the limitations involved in the discrete nature of the coin series, let us use the same frequencies as determined for the tenth power by the binomial expansion, but consider these as the frequencies of variate values in some continuous series. It is not necessary to use the short-cut method, as the average is obviously five, a most convenient point from which to calculate deviations.

Inserting the amounts found in the above table in the formula for the standard deviation, we have

$$\text{S.D.} = \sqrt{\frac{2560}{1024}} = \sqrt{2.5} = 1.58$$

Inasmuch as the "probable error" is 0.6745 of the S.D., it is 0.6745 (1.58), or 1.07.

Then the chances are even that an item chosen at random from the series represented by the curve will fall within a range from the mean of $\pm$ 1.07. If the curve is considered as an error curve for averages from samples, we may say that the chances are even that one of the averages chosen at random lies within a range of plus or minus 1.07 from the true average. The shaded area in Chart 31 represents the proportion of the total frequencies (50 per cent) within the probable error range.

Probable-error formulas. There are probable-error formulas for each of the statistical averages and coefficients calculated from a sample. It may be convenient to list some of them here. In each case the expression is the measure, in the sense just discussed above, of the unreliability of the given average or statistical coefficient, in terms of the probable distribution about the true value of a large number of estimates computed from similar samples.

LIST OF PROBABLE ERROR FORMULAS [1]

(1) P.E. of any distribution = 0.6745 S.D. . . . . (Formula 21).

(2) P.E. of the mean   = $0.6745 \dfrac{\text{S.D.}}{\sqrt{n}}$ . . . . (Formula 22).

[1] For a more complete list of probable-error formulas see D. Caradog Jones, *A First Course in Statistics*, p. 163.

(3) P.E. of the S.D. $= 0.6745 \dfrac{\text{S.D.}}{\sqrt{2n}}$ ....(Formula 23).

(4) P.E. of the proportion
shown by a sample $= 0.6745 \sqrt{\dfrac{p'(1-p')}{n}}$. (Formula 24).

(5) P.E. of coefficient of
correlation (r) $= 0.6745 \dfrac{(1-r^2)}{\sqrt{n}}$ .....(Formula 25).

Equation (21) merely states the numerical relation between the probable error and the standard deviation; equation (22) indicates the unreliability of the mean calculated from a sample; and equation (23), the unreliability of the standard deviation itself. Equation (24) is more fully explained below. Equation (25) is of significance in connection with the problem of correlation (Chapter XV).

It will be noted that in all cases the degree of precision varies directly with the square root of the number of items in the sample—that is, the probable error decreases with an increase in n, and increases with an increase in the standard deviation.

Probable error of a sample.[1] Let us note more closely the meaning of Formula 24, for the probable error of a sample. If we let

N = the number of items in some universe,

n = the number of items in a sample from that universe,

p = the proportion of items in the universe having some specified characteristic,

p' = the proportion in the sample having the given characteristic,

it may be mathematically demonstrated that, unless p is very small, the *chances are even* that the actual proportion in the whole group, the universe, will differ from p' by an amount given by Formula 24; or, using 2/3 as an approximation for 0.6745.

$$\text{P.E.} = 2/3 \sqrt{\dfrac{p'(1-p')}{n}}$$

For example, if in a sample of sixteen students, eight, or 50 per cent, are found to be freshmen, then the chances are even,

[1] Cf. A. L. Bowley, *Elementary Manual of Statistics,* p. 61, and F. S. Chapin, *Field Work and Social Research,* pp. 118-121.

assuming random selection of the sample, that the proportion (p) of freshmen in the entire student body (N) does not vary from 50 per cent by more than 8.5 per cent. The 8.5 per cent is obtained by inserting the value of p' (½) and the value of n (16) in the above formula, thus:

$$\frac{2}{3}\sqrt{\frac{\frac{1}{2}\left(1-\frac{1}{2}\right)}{16}} = \frac{2}{3}\sqrt{\frac{1/4}{16}} \text{ or } \frac{1}{64} = \left(\frac{2}{3}\right)\frac{1}{8} = \frac{1}{12} \text{ or } 8.5\%$$

Hence the chances are even ("50-50") that the true proportion of freshmen lies between 41.5 and 58.5 per cent of the total.

The probability of a deviation greater than any given multiple of the standard deviation.[1] By the use of principles developed by integral calculus it is possible to determine the chances that the true value lies within a given range of the empirical value found by the sample; for example, the following table gives the chances that the true value of a calculated average lies within a given range from the estimate:

Range	Approximate chances
± 0.6745 S.D., or P.E.	1 to 1
± 1 S.D.	2 to 1
± 2 S.D.	21 to 1
± 3 S.D.	369 to 1
± 4 S.D.	15,772 to 1

It will be noted from the above that the chances of a deviation exceeding three times the standard deviation are very small, and consequently it is usually considered that when an item varies from the mean by more than three or four times the S. D., it is good ground for questioning whether the item really belongs to the same group as the other items.

The characteristics of the probability curve are useful in interpreting the significance of a variance between two experiments. If a number of hogs are fed two different rations and a difference in results noticed, the query arises, is this difference a significant difference or due merely to variances which might

---

[1] The probabilities are calculated from table II of Karl Pearson, *Tables for Statisticians and Biometricians.*

be expected in two samples from the same universe? If the variance does not exceed the probable error of the sample, it is merely an even chance that the variation is really significant. If the variance is greater than six times the probable error, the chances are more than 15,000 to 1 that the variance is really significant of a true difference in results from the two methods of feeding.

For a more detailed discussion of the principles of probability and the mathematical principles involved in the analysis of the normal probability curve, the student should refer to the works on probability or least squares.[1]

Fitting a Normal Curve to a Distribution [2]

The equation of the normal or probability curve is

$$y = \frac{n}{\sigma \sqrt{2\pi}}\, e^{-\frac{1}{2}\left(\frac{x}{\sigma}\right)^2} \quad \ldots (\text{Formula } 26).$$

However, if it is desired to compare a frequency chart with a normal curve fitted to the same data, it is not necessary for us to solve this formidable-looking equation directly for each of the ordinates of the curve. Tables have been computed by which it is possible to plot readily any desired normal curve, given the mean, the standard deviation, and the total frequency of the distribution to which the curve is to be fitted. Table XLII gives a condensed form of such a table, adapted, with modifications in terminology, from a more complete presentation in Karl Pearson, *Tables for Statisticians and Biometricians,* Table II.

The ordinates of the desired normal curve are found by the following equation,

$$y = \left(\frac{nz}{\sigma}\right) C \quad \ldots\ldots\ldots\ldots (\text{Formula } 27).$$

[1] *E.g.,* O. M. Leland, *Practical Least Squares;* David Brunt, *The Combination of Observations;* J. M. Keynes, *A Treatise on Probability;* West, *op. cit.* chap. vi; Bowley, 4th ed., *Elements of Statistics,* part ii, chap. ii, and G. U. Yule, *op. cit.,* xv. The student who is lacking a mathematical training will probably find more profit, however, in reading the references to Whipple and Rugg, given at the close of the chapter.

[2] The symmetrical curves in the preceding chapter were plotted with the aid of the data given in table XLII.

Where

> $y =$ the ordinate of the normal curve corresponding to a given deviation from the mean divided by the standard deviation of the distribution,
>
> $n =$ the total frequency,
>
> $\sigma =$ the standard deviation of the distribution,
>
> $z =$ the entry in column B of Table XLII, or in Pearson's Table II, corresponding to any given deviation $\left(\frac{x-\bar{x}}{\sigma}\right)$ from the mean.
>
> $C =$ the class interval of the distribution.

All the quantities needed to apply the above formula, except the values of z, can be computed from a frequency table. The class interval (C) is introduced into the equation to put the normal curve on the same scale as the chart of the original frequencies. The determination of the ordinates of the normal curve for the midpoints of the classes will ordinarily be sufficient to indicate its approximate contour.

In Table XLII, columns C to F illustrate the method of determining the normal-frequency ordinates for a distribution with S. D. $=$ 10 and total frequency 10,000; and columns C and G to I give similar data for a distribution with S. D. $=$ 5 and total frequency $=$ 5,000 (for resulting curves see Chart 25, p. 148).

Errors in Arithmetical Processes

Errors in an estimate may arise from mistakes made by the computer or from errors in the quantities. Suggestions for ascertaining and eliminating mistakes of the computer are given in Appendix C. The statistician often wishes to know, in addition, what are the possible errors arising in the various mathematical processes from errors in the quantities. For this purpose it is necessary to distinquish between absolute error and relative error, the latter being the ratio of error found by dividing the absolute error by the estimate. Thus, if the cost of constructing a building is estimated at $10,000, with a possible error in either direction of $500, the possible relative error is five per cent. With these distinctions in mind, we may formulate the following rules for the simpler mathematical processes: [1]

[1] The rules given are largely adapted with modifications in terminology from A. L. Bowley, *Elements of Statistics,* 4th ed., chap. viii, and W. I. King,

TABLE XLII.—ORDINATES OF PROBABILITY CURVES [a]

A	B	C	D	E	F	G	H	I
GENERALIZED CASE			SERIES WITH EQUAL MEANS BUT VARYING DISPERSION (C) Class interval = one unit					
Deviation from mean ÷ σ	Relative ordinate (when n = 1)	Deviation from mean (absolute) (units)	Series A n = 10,000 σ = 10			Series B n = 5,000 σ = 5		
			Column C ÷ 10	Relative ordinate	Ordinate [10,000 z] 1/10	Column C ÷ 5	Relative Ordinate	Ordinate [5,000 z] 1/5
$\dfrac{(x-\bar{x})}{\sigma}$	z	$(x-\bar{x})$	$\dfrac{(x-\bar{x})}{\sigma}$	z	$nz\,\dfrac{C}{\sigma}$	$\dfrac{(x-\bar{x})}{\sigma}$	z	$nz\,\dfrac{C}{\sigma}$
.0	.3989	0	.0	.3989	398.9	.0	.3989	398.9
.1	.3970	1	.1	.3970	397.0	.2	.3910	391.0
.2	.3910	2	.2	.3910	391.0	.4	.3683	368.3
.3	.3814	3	.3	.3814	381.4	.6	.3332	333.2
.4	.3683	4	.4	.3683	368.3	.8	.2897	289.7
.5	.3521	5	.5	.3521	352.1	1.0	.2420	242.0
.6	.3332	6	.6	.3332	333.2	1.2	.1942	194.2
.7	.3123	7	.7	.3123	312.3	1.4	.1497	149.7
.8	.2897	8	.8	.2897	289.7	1.6	.1109	110.9
.9	.2661	9	.9	.2661	266.1	1.8	.0790	79.0
1.0	.2420	10	1.0	.2420	242.0	2.0	.0540	54.0
1.1	.2179	11	1.1	.2179	217.9	2.2	.0355	35.5
1.2	.1942	12	1.2	.1942	194.2	2.4	.0224	22.4
1.3	.1714	13	1.3	.1714	171.4	2.6	.0136	13.6
1.4	.1497	14	1.4	.1497	149.7	2.8	.0079	7.9
1.5	.1295	15	1.5	.1295	129.5	3.0	.0044	4.4
1.6	.1109	16	1.6	.1109	110.9	3.2	.0024	2.4
1.7	.0940	17	1.7	.0940	94.0	3.4	.0012	1.2
1.8	.0790	18	1.8	.0790	79.0	3.6	.0006	0.6
1.9	.0656	19	1.9	.0656	65.6	3.8	.0003	0.3
2.0	.0540	20	2.0	.0540	54.0	4.0	.0001	0.1
2.1	.0440	21	2.1	.0440	44.0			
2.2	.0355	22	2.2	.0355	35.5			
2.3	.0283	23	2.3	.0283	28.3			
2.4	.0224	24	2.4	.0224	22.4			
2.5	.0175	25	2.5	.0175	17.5			
2.6	.0136	26	2.6	.0136	13.6			
2.7	.0104	27	2.7	.0104	10.4			
2.8	.0079	28	2.8	.0079	7.9			
2.9	.0060	29	2.9	.0060	6.0			
3.0	.0044	30	3.0	.0044	4.4			
3.5	.0009	35	3.5	.0009	0.9			
4.0	.0001	40	4.0	.0001	0.1			
4.5	.0000 [b]	45	4.5	.0000 [b]	0.0 [c]			

Equations for normal curve:

$$y = \frac{n}{\sigma\sqrt{2\pi}}\, e^{-\frac{1}{2}\left(\frac{x}{\sigma}\right)^2}$$

$$y = \frac{nz}{\sigma};$$

or, to make the vertical scale comparable with a given frequency chart,

$$y = \left(\frac{nz}{\sigma}\right) C,$$

where C = the class interval.

[a] Adapted, with modifications in terminology, from seven place tables in Karl Pearson, *Tables for Statisticians and Biometricians*, table II.
[b] Less than .00005.   [c] Less than .05.

Addition.   The *possible absolute error* in a sum is the sum of the possible errors in the parts when each error is given the same sign.

Example: In computing percentages to one decimal place, the possible error in each percentage is .05, and if there are ten parts in the total, the percentage distribution might conceivably total either 99.5 or 100.5.   In this case, the most probable total, however, is 100.0, as the negative errors tend to offset the positive errors.

A corollary of the above principle is that a total can have no greater absolute accuracy than the least accurate item composing it.

The *possible relative error* in an estimated sum is equal to the sum of the possible relative errors in the parts when each is multiplied by the ratio of the corresponding part to the sum.

Averaging.   The *possible absolute error* in an arithmetic average is the arithmetic average of the possible errors of the items in the series when each error is given the same sign.

Example: If the cost of one process in manufacturing a machine is estimated as ten dollars with a possible error of two dollars in either direction and the cost of a second process as twenty dollars with a possible error of one dollar, the possible absolute error of the average cost of the two processes is $1.50.

The *possible relative error* in the arithmetic average of several estimates is the sum of the possible relative errors of these estimates, when each is multiplied by the ratio of the corresponding estimate to that of the sum of the estimates.

The relative *"error in a weighted average,"* says Professor Bowley [1] "is the sum of (1) an error due to errors in the *quantities,* similar to the error of an unweighted average, and (2) an error due to errors in the *weights,* which becomes very small when the original quantities are nearly equal."

Multiplication.   The *possible relative error* in a product is approximately the sum of the possible relative errors of its factors, when both errors are small and of the same sign.

Example: If in estimating the labor expense of producing a given article there is a possible error in the amount of labor time required

Elements of Statistical Method, chap. viii.   These references also contain discussion of errors arising in other processes than those mentioned herein

[1] *Op. cit.,* p. 184.   The italics are in part the present author's.

of 2 per cent and a possible error in the rate of wages of 1 per cent, the approximate possible error in the product of time and wage is 3 per cent.

Division. The *possible relative error* in a quotient or ratio is approximately the sum of the possible relative errors in the divisor and dividend when they are small and are given the same sign.

Example: If a wage bill is estimated at $1,000 with a possible error of $20, or 2 per cent, and the number of men receiving this total wage as one hundred, with a possible error of two, the approximate possible error in the average wage received per man is 4 per cent.

It should be noted that in the above discussion we have been speaking of maximum possible errors and that the probable errors are much smaller than the possible errors.

Compensating and cumulating errors. Errors and mistakes are of two significantly different types. In the case of compensating errors, excesses tend to be balanced by deficits, errors in one direction by errors in the other. Chance errors are of this type, deviations greater than the true amount tending to balance those less than the true amount. Cumulating errors, on the other hand, are due to some constant factor always causing a deviation in the same direction, and hence do not neutralize each other. If persons making crop estimates have a natural tendency to overestimate the condition of the crop, the error is not eliminated by increasing the number of crop reporters.

While minor mistakes on the part of the computer may tend to neutralize one another, reliance should be placed upon elimination of such mistakes by careful checking rather than upon the uncertain chance of the mistakes being fully compensating.[1]

REFERENCES

1. BOWLEY, A. L., *Elements of Statistics,* 4th ed., pp. 259-286, "Algebraic Probability and the Normal Curve of Error"; 178-195, "Accuracy."
2. BRUNT, DAVID, *The Combination of Observations.*
3. KELLEY, T. L., *Statistical Method,* chap. v, "The Normal Probability Distribution."

[1] See suggestions in the laboratory instructions in Appendix C for methods of ascertaining and eliminating mistakes.

4. KEYNES, J. M., *A Treatise on Probability.*
5. KING, W. I., *Elements of Statistical Method,* chap. viii, "Approximation and Accuracy."
6. LELAND, O. M., *Practical Least Squares.*
7. MERRIMAN, M., *A Textbook on the Method of Least Squares.*
8. PEARL, RAYMOND, *Medical Biometry and Statistics,* chap. x, "The Probable Error Concept," chap. xi, "Elementary Theory of Probability."
9. PEARSON, KARL, *Tables for Statisticians and Biometricians,* tables II and III.
10. RUGG, H. O., *Statistical Methods Applied to Education,* pp. 191-232, and tables II-VI, in Appendix.
11. SECRIST, H., *An Introduction to Statistical Methods,* pp. 410-415, "The Probable Error," pp. 25-28, "Accuracy."
12. WEST, CARL J., *Introduction to Mathematical Statistics,* chap. vi, "The Normal Probability Curve."
13. WHIPPLE, G. C., *Vital Statistics,* chap. xii, "Probability."

CHAPTER XI

THE CONSTRUCTION OF INDEX NUMBERS

THE index number is one of the most promising of the statistical devices for measuring and expressing quantitatively the significance of changing phenomena. We have index numbers of production, of employment, of wages, of stock market prices, of commodity prices, and of many other economic series. Price-index numbers have been used by laborers as an argument for wage increases, and subsequently, as the price tide turned, by employers as arguments for wage cuts. In some instances changes in index numbers were accepted during the war period as the basis for a variable wage, to increase as the index number rose, to decrease as it fell. In Great Britain "three million laborers have their wages regulated annually by an index number of prices." [1] The future promises to see a still greater and more effective use of the index number device. Obviously it is essential for the person who would be well equipped to analyze the changes in industrial conditions, be he business man, economist, or sociologist, to know what an index number is, how it is compiled, and to what uses it commends itself, not only that he may understand and appraise the existing index numbers and their uses, but in order that he may, on occasion, compute special index numbers adapted to the peculiar problems to whose solution his attention is devoted. What, then, is an index number?

Concisely stated, an index number is a *series of numbers representing the changes in some other number or group of numbers*. It is a representative series. *A simple index number* represents the changes in a single variable; a *composite index number,* the aggregate or average change in a group of variables. Both forms are devices to facilitate the comparison of chrono-

---

[1] I. Fisher, *The Making of Index Numbers,* p. 368.

logical variations.[1] The subsequent discussion refers chiefly to composite index numbers. If five ships sail from New York to London and a number is published each hour announcing the average progress of the group, we have a composite index number. Likewise, the consecutive values of a chronological variable designed to show the average changes in the prices of a group of commodities is a composite index number.

METHODS OF COMPUTATION

Probably the reader will reach most readily an understanding of index numbers if we begin our analysis with a descriptive study of the more common *forms* rather than with the principles determining the choice of forms and methods.

TABLE XLIII.—SIMPLE INDEX NUMBER

Average Monthly Production of Crude
Petroleum in the United States [a]

Year	Thousands of bbls.	Index number relative to 1913
1913	20,704	100
1914	22,147	107
1915	23,425	113
1916	25,064	121
1917	27,943	135
1918	29,661	143
1919	31,531	152
1920	36,911	178
1921	39,137	189
1922	45,933	222

[a] *Survey of Current Business,* November, 1923, pp. 78-79.
The *Survey of Current Business* publishes many series of simple index numbers for a wide variety of economic data. The series of "relative" prices in columns (b), (d), and (f) of table XLVII are also simple index numbers.

[1] Occasionally index numbers are used for static comparisons. Thus Mr. John Hilton, in his study of comparative real wages in various countries in 1922, puts the real value of the remuneration received in selected occupations in the United Kingdom as 100, and uses the following "index numbers" to express the relative real value of wages in the other countries when measured by their power to purchase certain articles of food: Germany, 46; France, 57; Belgium, 50; and the United States, 206. See *The Manchester Guardian Commercial: Reconstruction in Europe,* October 26, 1922, p. 544.

Simple index numbers. Simple price index numbers are computed by percentaging—that is, by dividing the price for each period by the price of some one period taken as a base and expressing the result in percentages, which are referred to as relatives. The formula is

$$\text{Relative for given period} = \frac{\text{Price for given period}}{\text{Price for base period}} \times 100 \text{ (Formula 28)}.$$

The table on the opposite page illustrates the nature of a simple relative index number of quantity production.

Composite index numbers are computed either as aggregates of actual prices or as averages or sums of relatives. These two types may be designated, respectively, as *aggregative index numbers* [1] and *composite relative index numbers*. The meaning of these terms will be clearer on examination of Table XLIV (p. 186) and Table XLVII (p. 188).

Table XLIV represents the calculation of an aggregative index number based on the sum of weighted actual prices of potatoes, eggs, and milk. Let us illustrate the method of computation. The average price of potatoes for the year 1913 was $0.017 per pound. This price is multiplied by the weight, or numerical measure of the relative importance assigned to potatoes, which is 704. The 1913 prices of eggs and milk are likewise multiplied by their respective weights, and then the total cost of the three products added to give the index number in column (g). Index numbers for 1914 and the subsequent years are similarly calculated. Ninety dollars and ninety-four cents represents the cost in 1922 of the given bill of goods: 704 pounds of potatoes, 61 dozen eggs, and 337 quarts of milk. Dun's index number is computed by the aggregative method, the

---

[1] The term "aggregative" is coined by Professor Irving Fisher in his exhaustive treatise on "The Making of Index Numbers." He analyzes the various possible formulas for use in constructing index numbers, assigning to each a key number and testing it for conformity to the criteria of a good index number. The aggregative index number, weighted with base year quantities, is No. 53, and the formula is $\frac{\Sigma (p_1 q_0)}{\Sigma (p_0 q_0)}$, when $p_1 =$ the price in the given year; p_0, the price in the base year; and q_0, the quantity in the base year.

TABLE XLIV.—WEIGHTED AGGREGATIVE INDEX NUMBER [a]

	(a)	(b)	(c)	(d)	(e)	(f)	(g)
	Cost of quantity used per year by average workingman's family						Index number (Sum of the products of prices and quantities)
Year	Potatoes 704 lbs.		Eggs, strictly fresh, 61 dozen		Milk 337 quarts		
	Price per pound	Total cost	Price per dozen	Total cost	Price per quart	Total cost	(b)+(d)+(f)
1913	$.017	$11.97	$.345	$21.04	$.089	$29.99	$63.00
1914	.018	12.67	.353	21.53	.089	29.99	64.19
1915	.015	10.56	.341	20.80	.088	29.66	61.02
1916	.027	19.01	.375	22.88	.091	30.67	72.56
1917	.043	30.27	.481	29.34	.112	37.74	97.35
1918	.032	22.53	.569	34.71	.139	46.84	104.08
1919	.038	26.75	.628	38.31	.155	52.24	117.30
1920	.063	44.35	.681	41.54	.167	56.28	142.17
1921	.031	21.82	.509	31.05	.146	49.20	102.07
1922	.028	19.71	.444	27.08	.131	44.15	90.94

[a] The prices used in this table are taken from Bulletin 334 of the Bureau of Labor Statistics and represent average retail prices for the United States. The weights used are the quantities annually consumed by an average workingman's family as determined by the 1918 budget study of the Bureau of Labor.

figures which are given representing the wholesale cost in dollars of a list or bill of goods.[1]

To make comparisons somewhat easier, the compilers of index numbers sometimes reduce the aggregates of **actual** prices (as in column "g," Table XLIV) to a series of percentages, obtained by dividing each aggregate by the aggregate of some one year taken as the base year. Thus if 1913 is selected as the base year, $63.00 is taken as 100 and the aggregates for the other years expressed as percentages of $63.00, as in Table XLV following. The formula used is:

$$\text{Index number of the given year} = \frac{\text{Sum of weighted prices in given year}}{\text{Sum of weighted prices in base year}} \times 100$$

(Formula 29).

[1] See discussion of this index number in Chapter XII, *infra*.

TABLE XLV

INDEX NUMBER COMPUTED IN TABLE XLIV REDUCED TO RELATIVES
WITH 1913 AS THE BASE YEAR

Year	Aggregative index number (Table XLIV, "g")	Relative to 1913
1913	$63.00	100
1914	64.19	102
1915	61.02	97
1916	72.56	115
1917	97.35	155
1918	104.08	165
1919	117.30	186
1920	142.17	226
1921	102.07	162
1922	90.94	144

Both the wholesale and retail price index numbers of the Bureau of Labor Statistics are now computed as aggregates of weighted actual prices as in Table XLIV, and expressed as percentages of the 1913 aggregate. This method of reducing the sums of prices to percentages in the last stage is essentially different in process from the method of computing an index number by the average-of-relatives method. In the latter method, each individual price series is first reduced to relatives—that is, to a series of percentages or simple index numbers representing the ratio between the price in the base year and each subsequent price. However, though involving different procedure, these two methods are identical in results when a common base year is used and the relatives are weighted according to total values in the base year. With any other weights the results will differ, the degree of difference depending upon the extent to which the weights differ.

The simple aggregative index number (Fisher's formula No. 51). An unweighted average index number could be calculated from the price data in Table XLIV by adding the unit prices of the three commodities for each respective year. Thus for 1913 and 1914 the process would be as follows:

TABLE XLVI

Commodity	1913 Price	1914 Price
Potatoes	$.017	$.018
Eggs	.345	.353
Milk	.089	.089
Index number..............	$.451	$.460

This method is objectionable because it gives disproportionate influence to the relatively high-priced commodities, like eggs, of which a smaller number of units is used.

The **average-of-relatives method** is illustrated in Table XLVII. The 1914 relative price for potatoes, for example, is obtained by dividing $.018 by $.017 and multiplying by 100; and the index number for 1914 is obtained by taking an average of the 1914 items in columns (b), (d), (f)—that is, an average of the 1914 relative prices of the three commodities. In Table XLVII the simple arithmetic average was used. A weighted mean, the median, the mode, or some other average, might have

TABLE XLVII [a]

UNWEIGHTED INDEX NUMBER COMPUTED BY THE AVERAGE-OF-RELATIVES METHOD

Base: 1913 price = 100

Year	Potatoes		Eggs, strictly fresh		Milk		Index number (Arithmetic average of relatives)
	Price per pound	Relative price	Price per dozen	Relative price	Price per quart	Relative price	
	(a)	(b)	(c)	(d)	(e)	(f)	(g)
1913	$.017	100	$.345	100	$.089	100	100
1914	.018	106	.353	102	.089	100	103
1915	.015	88	.341	99	.088	99	95
1916	.027	159	.375	109	.091	102	123
1917	.043	253	.481	139	.112	126	173
1918	.032	188	.569	165	.139	156	170
1919	.038	224	.628	182	.155	174	193
1920	.063	371	.681	197	.167	188	252
1921	.031	182	.509	148	.146	164	165
1922	.028	165	.444	129	.131	147	147

[a] For original sources of data see table XLIV, footnote.

been used.   The considerations determining which average is preferable are discussed in a subsequent portion of this chapter.

Link and chain index numbers.   When it is desired to compare readily prices in each year with those of the *immediately preceding* year, a link relative index number may be used.   In a link index number, each year is taken as the base from which to calculate the relative for the succeeding year, which is expressed in terms of percentage increase or decrease.   Thus the aggregate of prices in Table XLIV, column (g) may be translated into a link index by subtracting the aggregate for each year from that of the immediately following year, dividing the result by the aggregate for the first of the two years, and multiplying the quotient by 100.   The result appears in Table XLVIII.

TABLE XLVIII[a]

LINK INDEX NUMBER OF THE PRICES OF POTATOES, EGGS, AND MILK

Year	Increase (+) or decrease (—) from preceding year		Year	Increase (+) or decrease (—) from preceding year	
	Dollars	Per cent		Dollars	Per cent
1913	....	....	1918	$+ 6.73	+ 6.9
1914	$+ 1.19	+ 1.9	1919	+ 13.22	+ 12.7
1915	— 3.17	— 4.9	1920	+ 24.87	+ 21.2
1916	+ 11.54	+ 18.9	1921	— 40.10	— 28.2
1917	+ 24.79	+ 34.2	1922	— 11.13	— 10.9

[a] Computed from table XLIV, column (g).

A *chain* index number may be obtained from this link index number by welding the links together—that is, by multiplying the link index numbers together serially.   To illustrate, the 1914 index number would be represented as 101.9 per cent.   To get the 1915 chain index number multiply this figure by .951 (1.00-.049) ; then to get the 1916 chain index number multiply the 1915 chain index number by 1.189 (1.00 + .189).

CRITERIA OF A GOOD INDEX NUMBER

With the foregoing description of the forms of index numbers in mind, let us note the characteristics which a good index number must possess.   It will conform to the criteria of (1) fair sampling, (2) practicability, and (3) mathematical accuracy. That is to say, a good index number will be constructed from sample data which are appropriate and adequate for the purpose in mind; the methods of construction will not involve a prohibitive amount of labor or expense; the results will be expressed in a form adapted to ready interpretation and comparison; and the processes of computation to which the data are subjected will be designed to bring results which are mathematically logical and consistent with the purpose of the index number.

Mathematical accuracy. In his recent valuable treatise on *The Making of Index Numbers*,[1] Professor Irving Fisher has analyzed in detail the various possible methods of constructing index numbers. He points out that to be mathematically consistent an index number should not be freakish and should conform to (1) the *time-reversal* and (2) the *factor-reversal* test. An index number which conforms to the time-reversal test is so constructed that a shift in the base year does not change the relative size of the index figures for the respective years. If 1913 is taken as the base and the index number for 1923 is 200, then if the base is shifted to 1923, the index number for 1913 should be 50. One of the primary objections to an index number based upon a simple average of relatives is that it does not conform to the time-reversal test.[2] For example, if an index number of prices is constructed for the years 1880 to 1920, using a simple arithmetic average of relatives, the apparent increase will be greater if 1880 is used as a base than it will be if 1920 is taken as the base period. This variance may be expressed by saying that, with 1880 as a base, the index number shows an upward bias, but with 1920 as a base it shows a downward bias. The "ideal formula" discussed later in this chapter is designed to eliminate this bias.

The factor reversal test rests on the proposition that inasmuch

[1] Irving Fisher, *The Making of Index Numbers; a Study of Their Varieties, Tests and Reliability*, 1922, pp. 64-82.
[2] See the interesting controversy between Professor Irving Fisher and others in the 1923 columns of the *Statist* concerning the amount of upward bias evidenced by the *Statist* index number, which is a simple average of relatives with 1867-77 as the base.—*E.g. Statist*, April 7, 1923, p. 547.

as total value is the product of quantity and price, a consistent method of making index numbers, applied to the construction of separate index numbers of the quantities marketed and of prices, produces results which, when multiplied together, will give the correct index of total value. For example, if the index of the quantity of foodstuffs marketed is 200 and the price index 300, then, if the method of construction conforms to the factor reversal test, the index of total value of foodstuffs marketed is 600.

An index number may exhibit no definite bias and yet be freakish.[1] A freakish index number is highly erratic, either because it is "insensitive to many of the factors of which an index number is expected to be a sensitive barometer," or because it is influenced by factors to which it ought not to be sensitive. The mode is freakish because changes in several items in the group may leave it unchanged; the simple arithmetic average of prices is freakish because a mere change in the unit of quotation may materially change the index number.

Steps and Problems in the Computation of an Index Number

We have noted some of the forms of index numbers in common use and the standards to which an index number should conform. Let us now consider the problems which confront the statistician at each step in the computation of an index number of prices. The steps and decisions necessary are as follows:[2]

1. Definition of the *purpose* for which the index number is to be used.
2. Choice of the *kinds* of commodities and quotations to be used.
3. Determination of the size of the sample—the *number* of commodities and quotations.
4. Selection of the *sources of information* on prices and weights and of the *method of collecting* the desired data.

---

[1] Fisher, *The Making of Index Numbers*, pp. 112-116.
[2] Adapted in part from W. C. Mitchell, *Index Numbers of Wholesale Prices in the United States,* 1921 edition, pp. 23 ff.

5. Choice of the *methods of averaging* to be applied to the *original quotations*.
6. Determining what *weights,* if any, are to be used.
7. Choice between the use of sums or averages of *actual prices* and sums or averages of *relatives*.
8. Choice of the *base* period.
9. Settling the form of *average* to be used in combining relatives of the several commodities.
10. Selection of the method of handling *changes* in the commodities included.
11. Determining the *final form* in which the index number shall be expressed and published.

The steps in the computation of other than price index numbers are essentially the same as those enumerated above. In a brief discussion, it is impossible to suggest all the problems which will arise, or to attempt to suggest rules adequate to guide the compiler in all phases of any one problem. We can, however, take note of the more common problems and the methods used in their solution. Let us consider these somewhat in the order in which they arise when a price index is to be computed.

(1) **The purpose of an index number.**[1] Historically, index numbers have been largely so-called *general-purpose price index numbers,* with no clearly defined specific purpose other than the measurement of the general change in the price level; but in recent years a more careful analysis of index numbers, combined with attempts to make them serve effectively in the interpretation of business conditions, has made obvious the desirability of *special* index numbers, constructed with a specific use in mind. A clear understanding of the purpose for which an index is intended affords the necessary clew to guide the compiler through the labyrinth of subsequent choices of content and method. If his purpose is to show changes in the cost of food of workingmen, the prices used should be retail prices of the grades of foods used by workingmen in the given country or community. If a cost-of-living index number is desired, the prices of the other items in

[1] Cf. W. C. Mitchell, *Index Numbers,* 1921 edition, p. 24.

the family budget besides foods should, if possible, be included. If the prices of raw materials are to be compared with the prices received by the manufacturers for their products, it is logical to use wholesale prices. No comprehensive rule can be formulated, except that, if possible, the purpose of the index number should be clearly determined in advance of its compilation, and methods chosen which are appropriate to that purpose.

(2) **The assortment of commodities and quotations.** The formulation of the purpose of an index number largely determines the kinds of commodities for which it will be appropriate to include quotations, and gives a clew to many of the other decisions which must be reached. If the index number is designed to show changes in the cost of living, it should be constructed from retail prices; if it is designed to show changes in the costs of producing manufactured goods, the prices of raw materials, wage rates, and probably interest rates should be used.

The accuracy and usefulness of an index number rests primarily on the character of the price quotations on which it is based. If these are unreliable or not representative, no amount of care in the subsequent steps in the compilation will produce a satisfactory index number. Good workmanship does not make an all-wool coat out of shoddy. Space does not permit a full discussion here of the many problems to be solved in selecting the original quotations, but too much emphasis cannot be placed on the importance of care in that respect.

To make it possible for the user of an index number to judge the methods employed in its compilation and to recombine the quotations in other ways if he so wishes, it is highly desirable that, when practicable, publishers of index numbers give in full the original quotations and the weights, if any, used in the computation.

(3) **Number of commodities and quotations.**[1] How many commodities and quotations thereon are desirable? Is a small number adequate or must the number be large? The New York *Annalist* index number of foods is based on the prices of only

[1] Cf. W. C. Mitchell, *Index Numbers,* 1921 ed., pp. 34 ff., for superiority of large index numbers.

twenty-five commodities; the Bureau of Labor Statistics wholesale number for 1921 and 1922 was based on 404 quotations or series. If the quotations are available and the expense is not prohibitive, the longer list is preferable. At best the prices used are a sample, and we have seen that the probability of the accuracy of a sample increases with the size of the sample.[1] It should be noted, however, that if a small list of quotations includes those for the more important commodities, a quadrupling, for example, of the number of quotations will probably not bring a doubling in the precision of the sample as suggested by the laws of sampling. Professor Irving Fisher suggests that, "After 50, the improvement obtained from increasing the number of commodities is gradual, and it is doubtful if the gain from increasing the number beyond 200 is ordinarily worth the extra trouble and expense." Particularly when weights are used, additions to the list after the great staples are included have but slight effect on the index number.

(4) **Sources of information.** From what sources may the price quotations be obtained?

The sources availed of in practice may be illustrated by the Bureau of Labor Statistics wholesale-price index number. The price quotations given for 1921 and 1922 were drawn from the following sources:[2]

Source	Number of Quotations
Standard trade journals	257
Manufacturers or sales agents	160
Boards of trade, etc	31
Federal or state bureaus	6
Total	454

Of these 454 quotations, however, only 404 were used in the computation of the index number.

(5) **Averaging the original quotations.** If more than one quotation is obtained for a given commodity, shall each quotation be used separately or shall they be averaged?

[1] Cf. Chapter II, supra, and Fisher, *The Making of Index Numbers,* pp. 336-340.

[2] U. S. Bureau of Labor Statistics, Bulletin no. 335, "Wholesale Prices," 1890-1922, p. 5.

In fact, in many instances the prices which enter into the computation of an index number are themselves averages of several quotations. Of the 404 series of quotations which appear in the above-mentioned price bulletin of the Bureau of Labor Statistics, 119 are monthly averages. Sometimes, instead of averaging the several quotations for the same commodity, the two or more original series are used separately. This duplication of quotations for certain commodities acts as a sort of rough weighting system. Because of their simplicity and amenability to combination, simple arithmetic means should be used for the averaging of original quotations.

(6) **Weighting.**[1] Shall each commodity be given an equal importance or shall a system of weights be used, and if so, what system? Is the system of weights which is appropriate for the aggregative method also appropriate for the average-of-relatives method? Should the same weights be used each year or should they be varied as conditions change?

Weighting means counting certain items more than once in computing an average or sum, the object being to give each quotation an influence on the average proportionate to the actual importance of the group represented by the quotation.

Ordinarily a logical system of weighting is merely a device intended to make a sample as nearly representative as possible by counting each item enough times so that its relative number in the sample will approximate its proportionate share in the total. In Table XLIV, the price per pound of potatoes is multiplied by 704, and the price of eggs per dozen by 61, because it is estimated that the average workingman's family consumes in a year about 704 pounds of potatoes and 61 dozen eggs. This method of multiplying the price per unit by the estimated number of units may be designated as the *physical-quantity method of weighting*. It is applicable when the index number is a sum of actual prices.

On the other hand, when the index number is based on an

---

[1] For an illuminating discussion of weighting see W. C. Mitchell, *Index Numbers,* 1921 ed., pp. 59-68; also H. Secrist, *Statistical Methods,* 323-327; and, particularly, Irving Fisher, *The Making of Index Numbers,* chap. iii and appendix ii.

average of relatives, it is illogical to use the physical-quantity method of weighting. If in Table XLVII we were to multiply the relative price of potatoes by 704 and that of eggs by 61, the result would be that a 5-per-cent change in the price of potatoes would have more than ten times as much influence on the index number as a 5-per-cent change in the price of eggs. To be logical, the method used must make allowance, not only for the larger quantity of potatoes entering into the budget, but also for the fact that eggs cost more per dozen than potatoes per pound. This object is gained by the use of the *aggregate-value* or of the *proportion-of-total-value* methods of weighting. In the latter method, as applied to a cost-of-living index number, the weight used is the proportion of the total annual budget which is expended for each of the items used in compiling the index number.

The proportion-of-total-value method may be illustrated by the data used in the cost-of-living index number compiled by the National Industrial Conference Board for the period July 1, 1914, to July, 1922. In Table XLIX, the first column of figures (B), gives the estimated per cent of the family budget expended for food, shelter, and the other items. The second column gives the percentage ratio of the cost of each item in July, 1922, to its cost in July, 1914. The cost of food is shown as 142, or a 42-per-cent increase over 1914; the cost of fuel, as 184. Then to allow each item to have a weight proportionate to its importance in the total budget the separate relatives in column (C) are multiplied by the percentages representing their respective shares of the total, and the resulting aggregate divided by the sum total of the weights, 100, to give the index number for July, 1922, or 155.6. In a similar way the values of the index number could be computed for each date for which prices are available.

The process of computing a composite price index number weighted in accordance with the respective proportions of total expenditure, may be summarized as follows: (1) divide the price of each commodity by its base-period price and express the result as a percentage or relative; (2) multiply these relatives by the respective percentage proportions of expenditure in the base year; (3) add the resulting products and (4) divide by 100.

TABLE XLIX

Based on the Cost of Living in Average American
Communities as Computed by the National
Industrial Conference Board [a]

1914 = Base (100)

A	B	C	D
Budget items	Relative importance in family budget (Per cent of total)	Ratio of cost in July, 1922, to cost in July, 1914 (Per cent)	Product B × C
All items	100.0		15,557.6
Food	43.1	142	6,120.2
Shelter	17.7	165	2,920.5
Clothing	13.2	154	2,032.8
Fuel	3.7	184	680.8
Light	1.9	155	294.5
Sundries	20.4	172	3,508.8

$$\text{Index number} = \frac{\text{Total products}}{\text{Total weights}} \text{ or } \frac{(D)}{(B)} = \frac{15,557.6}{100.0} = 155.6$$

[a] Adapted from the National Industrial Conference Board *Research Report Number 54*, "Changes in the Cost of Living, July, 1914, to July, 1922," p. 30. The method of computing the composite index number in table XLIX differs slightly from that used by the National Industrial Conference Board. Their data appear as percentage increases in cost between July, 1914, and July, 1922, hence the complete budget index is 55.6 per cent *increase* rather than the ratio of 155.6 per cent found in table XLIX.

Similar results may be obtained by multiplying the price relatives, not by the percentages of total expenditure, but by the respective aggregate values in the base year.

The proportion-of-total-value method is appropriate whenever the separate items are expressed as relatives. The term "total value" may mean the value of goods produced, consumed, or marketed, or, as above, the total of the family budget.

The physical-quantity and the proportion-of-total-value methods of weighting, if consistently applied to the same basic data and with a common base year, will give identical results, provided the results of the physical-quantity method are reduced to relatives in the last stage of the process.

A logical but somewhat crude method of weighting is found in some index numbers which are nominally simple arithmetic averages, in that two or more quotations for some of the more important commodities are included. This may be designated as the *multiple-quotation system of weighting.* Bradstreet's index number of wholesale prices is weighted, in part, by the use of the multiple quotation system.

Bradstreet's index number is also weighted, in a sense, by reducing each quotation to the price per pound basis. This *price-per-pound* basis is illogical in that it gives disproportionate influence to the high-priced commodities.

Should the weights used be constant throughout the entire period? This problem is clearly brought out in the attempts to formulate a cost-of-living index. If we base our computation on the articles of food which entered the budget of the average workingman's family as determined by the 1901 study of the Bureau of Labor Statistics, then our cost-of-living index number will, for the war period, show the cost of procuring the commodities used in 1901. But were these same commodities used in 1917 and 1918? Under the pressure of high prices and patriotic appeals, many substitutions were made. Even in normal times, consumption habits change somewhat.[1] Movie tickets and gasoline replace items in the older budgets and the proportions shift. Would it, then, be better to change the weights each year?

If a link index is used, the weights may be frequently changed, as only two successive years are compared, but it is the practice, where the base is fixed, to retain also a fixed system of weights. In the first place, the necessary information is not readily obtainable for a frequent change in the system of weights; and, if the weights are changed, the index number becomes a complex result of two variables, changing prices and changing weights, and comparison with previous years becomes next to impossible. It would

[1] The extent to which the relative importance of commodities entering into exchange varies will be seen on examination of Appendix B, *Bulletin* 269, U. S. Bureau of Labor Statistics, giving "The relative importance of commodities as measured by their wholesale values in 1909 and 1919."

be more significant to indicate that it would cost a workman $1,000 to buy in 1930 the same bill of goods which he purchased for $1,200 in 1920, than it would to show that it would cost $1,200 to buy in 1930 a changed bill of goods consisting, let us say, of a higher grade of clothing and more nourishing and palatable foods. Despite its defects, the fixed-weights system is ordinarily desirable for the sake of comparability.

The "ideal formula." [1] It has been suggested that in order to avoid the errors involved in the computation of a weighted index number using either the quantities in the base year or in the current year as weights we compute instead two aggregative index numbers, using the weights of the base year for one, and the weights of the current year for the other, and then take the geometric mean of the two indexes. The formula for this "ideal" index number is as follows (Fisher's formula No. 353):

$$P_1 = \sqrt{\left(\frac{\Sigma\, p_1\, q_1}{\Sigma\, p_0\, q_1}\right) \times \left(\frac{\Sigma\, p_1\, q_0}{\Sigma\, p_0\, q_0}\right)} \dots\dots\dots\dots\text{(Formula 30)}.$$

when P_1 = the index number for the given year or month,
Σ = the sum of terms like the one following,
p_1 = the price of any commodity in a given year (or other period),
q_1 = the quantity of that commodity in the given year,
p_0 = the price of that commodity in the base year,
q_0 = the quantity of that commodity in the base year.

This "ideal formula" meets both the time-reversal and the factor-reversal tests, but for practical use a modification designated by Professor Fisher as Formula 2,153 is recommended, because the time required for its calculation is materially less than the time required for the "ideal formula." [2] Formula 2,153, which also meets both the time-reversal and the factor-reversal tests, is

$$\frac{\Sigma\, (q_0 + q_1)\, p_1}{\Sigma\, (q_0 + q_1)\, p_0} \dots\dots\dots\dots\dots\dots\dots\dots\text{(Formula 31)}.$$

[1] Irving Fisher, *The Making of Index Numbers;* also W. C. Mitchell, *Index Numbers,* 1921 ed., pp. 91-93, with references to the original sources.
[2] See W. M. Persons, "Fisher's Formula for Index Numbers," *Review of Economic Statistics,* vol. iii, pp. 103-113, for discussion of some limitations on the superiority of the "ideal index number."

In this formula, it will be noted, the weights are averages of quantities in the base and given years. When weights are available only for the base year, the ordinary weighted aggregative formula, designated as No. 53, gives relatively accurate results. It is

$$\frac{\Sigma \ p_1 \ q_0}{\Sigma \ p_0 \ q_0} \dots\dots\dots\dots\dots\dots\dots\dots\dots\dots\dots\dots\dots\dots \text{(Formula 32)}.$$

It should be noted that the necessity for the use of weights decreases somewhat as the number of commodities used increases, inasmuch as the results from any logical system of weighting and the results from using the simple arithmetic average of a *large* number of relatives are not materially different. However, this does not mean that there is no gain from the use of weights. In one sense, nearly every index is weighted; for a nominally unweighted index number gives weight according to the price *unit* if based on actual prices; and if an unweighted average of *relatives* is used, while the real weighting ceases to be dependent merely on the unit in which prices are expressed, it may be said to rest upon the assumption that each commodity is equally important. Rarely is this true, and when the time and expense involved are not prohibitive, the use of a logical system of weights increases the probable accuracy of the index number.

(7) **Actual prices or relatives.**[1] Shall the index number be constructed by summating the actual prices or price averages, or shall the average-of-relatives method be used?

The extensive use of relatives has arisen largely from the desire to escape the crudities of a *simple* average of actual prices. With the development of more satisfactory systems of weighting there has been a reaction toward the use of actual prices, multiplied by the quantities used in a base period, though the final results may be turned into relatives in the last stage (see Table XLV). Both the wholesale and retail numbers of the Bureau of Labor Statistics illustrate the recent tendency to use aggregates of weighted actual prices, translated finally into a percentage series.

[1] Cf. Sir George H. Knibbs, "The Nature of an Unequivocal Price Index and Quantity Index," *Journal of the American Statistical Association,* March, 1924, pp. 42-60.

The method of using sums of actual prices, rather than averages of relatives, has the advantages that it is easier to combine two or more index numbers calculated on the former basis, and that such index numbers can be readily shifted from one base to another without introducing mathematical errors.

(8) The **base period.**[1] Shall a fixed base, or a progressive base giving a link relative, be adopted?

In a fixed base, should the base be the last year, the first year, or an average of the entire period or of a fixed period less than the total?

When the relatives system is used, the prices of some given date or period are selected as a base. The prices of all other periods are then expressed as percentages of the base-period prices. The base period may be fixed, or, as in the link index number, shifting, with the price of each year expressed as a percentage change from the price of the preceding year. A fixed-base period may be a day, a month, a year, or an average of years. A broadened base period has the merit that an average for several years is more likely to represent normal conditions than the price of a given year, or, particularly, of a single date. The period 1890-99 has been frequently taken as a base period. In recent years the use of 1913 as a base has become common, for the reason that users of index numbers have been particularly interested in a comparison of current prices with those of the immediately pre-war period. Professor Fisher concludes that ordinarily little is gained by broadening the base.[2]

A near base makes the index number more truly representative.[3] A careful study of price fluctuations indicates that an average is more representative of the whole array when a near rather than a distant base is taken. The fluctuations of individual prices from the preceding year are distributed in an approximately normal curve form and are well represented by an average; but the fluctuations as compared with a distant period are widely

[1] Cf. W. C. Mitchell, *op. cit.,* 1921 ed., pp. 81-91; H. Secrist, *Statistical Methods,* pp. 316-319.

[2] The *Making of Index Numbers,* pp. 312-317.

[3] Cf. W. C. Mitchell, 1921 ed., pp. 11-23; or H. Secrist, *op. cit.,* 308-316.

divergent and not distributed in a near approximation to a normal frequency distribution, hence an average is not so truly representative of the group.

As compared with the link index, any fixed base has the disadvantage that as the base becomes distant, the dispersion of individual variances from the base price increases and commodities which have much advanced in price exercise a disproportionate influence.[1] The link index facilitates comparison with the immediately preceding year and has the additional advantage of making easy the increase or decrease of the number of commodities included in the index. All that is necessary is that the commodities added be also added in the preceding year in computing the base amount.

On the other hand, the link index does not furnish a ready means of comparing current prices with years other than the immediately preceding year. The purpose of the index number will largely determine which is to be preferred. A commendable practice is the publication of an index number in both forms.

Shifting the base.[2] If a change in the base period becomes desirable, how may it be accomplished?

Professor Wesley C. Mitchell has shown that the more accurate method of shifting the base is a *complete recalculation* of the index series. A complete recalculation, however, is not always practicable, and a *short-cut* method is frequently used. Each number in the old series is divided by the index number of the new base period, computed on the old base, and the results multiplied by 100.

Thus, if we wish to change the base of the index number in Table XLV from 1913 to 1922 by the short-cut method, we divide the index number for each year by 144, the index number for 1922, and thus obtain a new series, as shown in Table L.

The short-cut method of shifting the base, when applied to an arithmetic average of relatives gives results which differ somewhat from the results obtained by a complete recalculation of the

[1] See W. C. Mitchell, *op. cit.,* 1915 ed., pp. 10-24, 37.
[2] W. C. Mitchell, *Index Numbers,* 1921 ed., pp. 84 ff.

TABLE L

SHORT-CUT METHOD OF CHANGING BASE FROM 1913 TO 1922

Based on Table XLV

Year	Index number on 1913 base	Divisor: 1922 index number	New index number, 1922 base
1913	100	144	69
1914	102	144	71
1915	97	144	67
1916	115	144	80
1917	155	144	108
1918	165	144	115
1919	186	144	129
1920	226	144	157
1921	162	144	112
1922	144	144	100

series, but the simplicity of the process makes it useful when close accuracy is not an essential.

When the geometric means of relatives are used as an index number, the base can be changed by the short-cut method without introducing mathematical errors.[1]

(9) **Choice of average.**[2] When relatives are used, how shall the separate series be averaged to find the composite index number? Shall we use the arithmetic mean, median, mode, geometric mean, or some other average?

Champions of the use of each of the several averages have appeared, but on first analysis none of the methods of averaging seems well adapted to index-number purposes. The mode, and to a less extent the median, are freakish. The arithmetic mean is most frequently used. It is familiar, easy to compute, and adapted to algebraic combination and manipulation. On the other hand, unweighted arithmetic means are liable to distortion from the occurrence of a few extremely high relative prices; furthermore,

[1] W. C. Mitchell, *Index Numbers,* 1915 ed., p. 82.
[2] Cf. I. Fisher, *The Making of Index Numbers,* chap. v; W. C. Mitchell, *Index Numbers,* 1921 ed., pp. 68-81; and H. Secrist, *Statistical Methods,* pp. 319-323.

the arithmetic means of relative prices cannot consistently be shifted from one base to another without recomputation in full.[1] Neither arithmetic nor harmonic means conform to the time-reversal test, arithmetic means having an upward bias and harmonic means a downward bias.[2] Geometric means have no definite bias, except as it may be introduced by a weighting system, but they are unfamiliar and somewhat laborious to compute.

Thus, it would appear that none of the averages is entirely satisfactory for index number purposes; but, as Professor Fisher has demonstrated,[3] any form of average which is not freakish can be utilized if its bias is rectified by combination with averages or with weights which have an opposite bias. The "ideal index number" is based upon this principle, and we have noted that a weighted aggregative is a good working substitute for the "ideal formula" if a moderate degree of accuracy is sufficient.

(10) **Changes in the commodities included.**[4] How may commodities be added without impairing the continuity of an index number?

As consumption or production habits change, new commodities appear and old ones cease to be used, or at least cease to be important. How may the compiler adjust his index number to the changed conditions and still make possible accurate comparisons with the earlier periods?

If satisfactory quotations are available for the new commodities for the entire period, it would be possible, and most accurate, to recalculate the index number from the beginning. Frequently, however, it is desired to include new commodities for which quotations are not available for the earlier years. Within a reasonable degree of accuracy this may be accomplished by the *"ratio method."*

Let us assume that in 1918 it became desirable to add butter to the commodities in Table XLVII, page 188, but that satisfactory quotations for butter were not obtainable prior to 1917. The

[1] W. C. Mitchell, *Index Numbers*, 1921 ed., p. 73.
[2] I. Fisher, *The Making of Index Numbers*, pp. 86-90.
[3] *Ibid.*, pp. 136 ff.
[4] For discussion of methods of "splicing" when new commodities are added see Irving Fisher, *The Making of Index Numbers*, pp. 310-311 and 427-428.

average retail price of butter was $.487 per pound in 1917; $.577 in 1918; $.678 in 1919.[1]

If we are to include these butter prices in the index number, it is necessary in some way to calculate relatives for them with 1913 as the base, to make them comparable with the relatives for the other three commodities. Inasmuch as, by assumption, the 1913 prices for butter are not available, the next best thing to do is to assume that the same relation holds between 1917 and 1913 butter prices as holds between the 1917 index for the group and the 1913 base; that is to say, butter prices in 1917 are 173 per cent of the butter prices in 1913. This assumption gives $.282 per pound as the estimated price of butter in 1913 ($.487 divided by 1.73 = $.282).

Using this estimated 1913 price, $.282, as the base, we get butter relatives of 173 for 1917, 205 for 1918, and 240 for 1919. These relatives can then be included with those for potatoes, eggs, and milk to get new composite index number for 1918 and 1919.

The degree of accuracy of this method rests, of course, upon the validity of the assumption that the change in the price of the added commodity from 1913 to 1917 is the same as the change in the index number for the group during that period.

(11) **Arithmetical form of publication.** Index numbers which are constructed from relatives are presented to the reader as sums or averages of percentages. The average form is preferable as it enables the reader more readily to determine the percentage change from the base period. The index number of the London *Economist* for the end of December, 1923, is 4580,[2] this being a sum of relatives. The significance of this becomes more obvious if it is reduced to an average of relatives, which would be 208.2, or an increase of 108.2 per cent over the base period (1901-1905).

Likewise index numbers which are constructed as sums of actual prices, for purposes of presentation and comparison can advantageously be reduced to percentages in the last stage of the computation process. Thus the Bureau of Labor Statistics index

---

[1] Bureau of Labor Statistics, *Bulletin* No. 270, "Retail Prices."
[2] The *Economist*, February 2, 1924, p. 191.

numbers of retaii and wholesale prices, though computed as aggregates of actual prices, are published as percentages.

This chapter has been devoted primarily to a treatment of the
problems involved in the computation of index numbers. The
analysis of the principal current index numbers and of the uses
to which index numbers are being put is reserved for discussion
in the next chapter.

REFERENCES

1. DAVIES, G. R., *Introduction to Economic Statistics,* chap. iii.
2. FISHER, IRVING, *The Making of Index Numbers.*
3. KING, W. I., *Elements of Statistical Method,* pp. 178-185.
4. KNIBBS, SIR GEORGE H., "The Nature of an Unequivocal Price Index
    and Quantity Index," *Journal of the American Statistical Associa-
    tion,* March, 1924, pp. 42-60.
5. MITCHELL, W. C., *Index Numbers of Wholesale Prices in the United
    States and Foreign Countries,* United States Bureau of Labor
    Statistics. *Bulletin* 173 (1915).
6. ——— *Bulletin* 284 (1921), revised edition.
7. SECRIST, H., *An Introduction to Statistical Methods,* chap. ix. "Prin-
    ciples of Index Number Making and Using," see also the bibli-
    ography following chap. ix.

CHAPTER XII

AMERICAN INDEX NUMBERS

In the previous chapter we were concerned with the general methods used in the construction of index numbers. In this chapter we shall study how those methods have been applied in the construction of the principal index numbers published in the United States. Particular attention will be given to those features which the reader must know in order to be able readily to find and interpret the published indexes, but some attention will also be given to the problems involved in the construction of special types of index numbers.

Price Index Numbers

Index numbers may be classified as *price* index numbers, *value* index numbers, or *quantity* index numbers. Of these, the first type has been most extensively used, though there has recently been a rapid development of non-price numbers. Most of the price index numbers are based on wholesale prices, but a few are retail numbers or represent special price series, such as index numbers of wages or of stock and bond prices. Among the wholesale-price index numbers, the student should at the least be able to interpret those published by *Dun's, Bradstreet's,* the New York *Annalist,* and the United States Bureau of Labor Statistics, as these are the indexes which are most frequently used in the many applications being made of index numbers in the analysis of economic conditions.[1]

Bradstreet's Index Number.[2]   *Bradstreet's,* a weekly

---

[1] These index numbers, and also Gibson's and the War Industries Board index numbers, are analyzed by Prof. W. C. Mitchell, in *Bulletin* 284 of the U. S. Bureau of Labor Statistics, *Index Numbers of Wholesale Prices in the United States and Foreign Countries,* 1921 ed.

[2] *Ibid.,* pp. 161-168.

"Journal of Trade, Finance and Public Economy," published in New York, gives a monthly index number of *wholesale* prices, based on ninety-six commodities. The commodities used are grouped into thirteen classes and an index number calculated for each class. The "all commodity" index is the sum of these thirteen indexes, each of which is constructed by adding together the *prices per pound* for each commodity included. Below is given the quotation of the total index number, verbatim as it appeared in the February 16, 1924, issue, p. 115, together with the separate index of food prices, calculated on the weekly basis.

BRADSTREET'S PRICE INDEX NUMBERS
Monthly

Feb. 1, 1924	Jan. 1, 1924	Dec. 1, 1923	Nov. 1, 1923	Feb. 1, 1923
$13.1966	$13.2710	$13.4358	$13.1378	$13.7236

Weekly

Feb. 14, 1924	Feb. 7, 1924		Feb. 15, 1923	June 1, 1916
$3.35	$3.38		$3.40	$2.65

Monthly index numbers from January, 1914, and annual index numbers, 1892-1923, are given in *Bradstreet's,* April 7, 1923.

As this index number is merely a sum of prices, on the per pound basis, there is *no base period,* but the significance of any given issue of the number can be determined by comparison with some previous number—that is, by at least a mental reduction to a relative index number with some chosen date as 100.

The reduction of each price series to a per pound basis virtually results in a system of weighting in which the emphasis is given to the high priced articles. Some articles, like opium and silk, cost several hundred times as much per pound as coal and coke. This illogical element in the weighting system is somewhat neutralized by the introduction of a logical element, in that more than one quotation is used for some of the more important commodities like pig iron, coal, lumber, and hog products, and only one for less important articles like currants, tea, and mackerel.

Bradstreet's also publishes monthly a list of wholesale prices of 106 commodities, including those from which their index number is computed.

Dun's Index Number.[1] *Dun's Review,* published by the mercantile agency of R. G. Dun & Co., New York City, contains a monthly index number, which appears about the middle of the month. It is based on wholesale prices of some 300 commodities, weighted in accordance with estimated annual per-capita consumption. The number appears in the following form: [2]

	Bread stuffs	Meat	Dairy & Garden	Other Food	Cloth- ing	Metals	Miscel- laneous	Total
	$	$	$	$	$	$	$	$
1921, Jan. 1...	32.697	15.240	25.176	20.690	34.108	28.149	42.540	198.600
1922, Jan. 1...	23.531	13.850	22.914	17.954	31.591	21.312	33.292	164.444
1923, Jan. 1...	29.516	17.276	22.564	19.014	38.154	22.987	36.126	185.637
1924, Jan. 1...	29.229	15.868	23.424	20.398	40.755	23.251	37.005	189.930
Feb. 1...	30.894	15.880	22.737	20.276	40.563	23.307	37.438	191.095

The "Annalist" Index number.[3] The New York *Annalist,* a weekly financial journal, publishes a weekly index number, with yearly averages, based on wholesale prices of twenty-five food commodities "selected and arranged to represent a theoretical family's food budget." This is a relative series, with the years 1890-99 as the base period. It is obtained by computing the simple arithmetic average of the relative prices of each of the twenty-five commodities, and hence is unweighted, except for the fact that some of the more important commodities are represented by more than one quotation. Thus there are quotations for steers, fresh beef, and salt beef. The index appears as follows, accompanied by an illustrative graph and by prices for the items composing the index: [4]

[1] Cf. W. C. Mitchell, *op. cit.,* 1921 ed., pp. 168-171.

[2] *Dun's Review,* February 9, 1924, p. 8. Publication of this index number began in January, 1901, and the September 7, 1901, issue, pp. 8-9, contains an explanation of the method of computation and gives monthly data for the period beginning January, 1898. The annual index begins in 1860.

[3] Cf. W. C. Mitchell, *op. cit.,* Bulletin 284, pp. 159-161.

[4] *The Annalist,* February 11, 1924, p. 219.

THE "ANNALIST" INDEX OF WHOLESALE FOOD PRICES
(Base — Averages 1890-99 = 100 Per Cent)

WEEKLY AVERAGES

Feb. 9, 1924...... 183.002	Feb. 10, 1923...... 180.856
Feb. 2, 1924...... 179.206	Feb. 11, 1922...... 168.441
Year to date..................... 178.079	

YEARLY AVERAGES

1923..............178.000	1918.............. 287.080
1922..............186.290	1917.............. 261.796
1921..............174.308	1916.............. 175.720
1920.............282.757	1913.............. 139.980
1919..............295.607	1896.............. 80.096

Bureau of Labor Statistics wholesale price index.[1]   The Bureau of Labor Statistics publishes in the *Monthly Labor Review* index numbers for nine classes of commodities [2] and also for the entire list of over three hundred wholesale commodities, raw and manufactured.   The quotations are obtained from trade journals, reports of boards of trade, chambers of commerce, produce exchanges, and from leading manufacturers and their selling agents.[3]   The index number appears as a relative index, or series of percentages, constructed as an aggregate of weighted prices and then reduced to relatives with 1913 as the base.   For many years the weighting was in accordance with the amount of goods placed upon the market in 1909, but now weights based on the 1919 census have been substituted.

Federal Reserve Board wholesale price indexes.[4]   In addition to giving the quotations of the actual prices of many commodities, the monthly *Federal Reserve Bulletin* publishes a large number of wholesale price index numbers, being in part reprints of other published numbers and in part series compiled

[1] See fuller discussion in W. C. Mitchell, *op. cit.,* no. 284, pp. 115-133.   This index number is also published in occasional special wholesale price bulletins —*e.g.,* whole no. 335 (1890-1922).

[2] The classes are: farm products, food, cloths and clothing, fuel and lighting, metals and metal products, building materials, chemicals and drugs, housefurnishing goods, and miscellaneous.

[3] See previous chapter for sources of quotations used in 1921 and 1922.

[4] See Federal Reserve *Bulletin* for May, 1920, p. 500, for method of preparation; also Mitchell, *op. cit., Bulletin* 284, pp. 133-137.

by the Federal Reserve Board. One group consists of wholesale price indexes compiled by the Board for purposes of international comparison, the plan being to construct for the principal countries index numbers on a similar plan and from commodities so selected and classified as to facilitate logical comparisons.

The Board is now (February, 1924) publishing such special index numbers for the United States, England, France, Canada, and Japan, covering six classes of commodities: goods produced, goods imported, goods exported, raw materials, producers' goods, and consumers' goods.

The Board publishes an "all commodities" index number in the *Federal Reserve Bulletin* which is based on the data gathered by the Bureau of Labor Statistics, with the indexes for separate groups arranged along lines appropriate for use in the study of business conditions. The groups are: raw materials, divided into agricultural products, animal products, forest products, and mineral products; producers' goods; and consumers' goods.

Fisher's weekly index number. A weekly index number of wholesale prices, compiled by Professor Irving Fisher, is published in the press each Monday for the week ending the previous Friday noon. This series is a weighted aggregative, based on the price quotations given in *Dun's Review*.[1]

Bureau of Labor Statistics retail price index, foods.[2] The U. S. Government publishes in the *Monthly Labor Review* an index number of retail food prices, based on forty-three foodstuffs,[3] from about fifty industrial cities. The list includes such articles as sirloin steak, butter, milk, bread, potatoes, and is re-

[1] Irving Fisher, "A Weekly Index Number of Wholesale Prices," *Journal of the American Statistical Association*, September, 1923, pp. 835-840.

[2] See Bur. of Lab. Statistics Bul. No. 334 for full statement of retail prices. The monthly index numbers for 1913 to 1920, inclusive, for each of twenty-two commodities and the total, appear in the *Monthly Labor Review*, February, 1921, pp. 19-21, for 1913 to 1920; in February, 1923, p. 69, for 1921 and 1922; and in February, 1924, p. 37, for 1922 and 1923.

[3] Prior to 1921 a smaller number of commodities was used. The method of making the transition is described in the *Monthly Labor Review*, March '21, page 25. "The change in the cost of 43 articles between December, 1920, and January, 1921, has been found, and this percentage of change has been applied to the index number for December, 1920, as based on 22 articles. This preserves the continuity of the index number. . . ."

stricted to commodities for which the Bureau has been able to obtain satisfactory weights.

Method of calculation. The several quotations for the given month for a commodity are averaged and then multiplied by a "physical quantity" weight based on an investigation conducted by the Bureau of Labor Statistics on the cost of living of workingmen's families. The resulting aggregates are reduced to relatives with 1913 as the base. In other words, the index number is a percentage obtained from an aggregate of actual prices weighted by physical quantities determined on the family budget system, and gives what we may call the cost of the family "food market basket."

Cost-of-living index numbers. It is not unusual to find the Bureau of Labor Statistics index of food prices, the *Annalist* index of wholesale food prices, or the several general wholesale price numbers, referred to as "cost-of-living" index numbers. Such use is apt to be misleading, for it can scarcely be assumed that an index number of wholesale prices is a measure of changes in the cost of living. The prices paid by the consumer are retail prices. Nor is a food index alone adequate. Food prices are apt to fluctuate more violently than an index which is representative of all the main lines of expenditure for consumption.

There are, however, now being published for the United States two series which are designed to portray changes in the total cost of living, in that they include, not only foods, but also the retail prices of other important elements in the typical family budget, such as rent, fuel, and clothing.

Bureau of Labor Statistics: Monthly Labor Review. During the war the Bureau of Labor Statistics, at the request of the Shipbuilding Labor Adjustment Board, inaugurated an index number of the cost of living.[1] It appears in the *Monthly Labor Review* at intervals of about six months, and at the present time (February, 1924) is compiled from data from thirty-two cities. The weighting is based upon "figures obtained from over 12,000

[1] Barnett, G. E., "Index Numbers of the Total Cost of Living," *Q. J. Econ.,* February, 1921, p. 242.

families in 92 localities in a careful survey of the cost of living" by the Bureau in 1918.[1]

The following table gives the index numbers for each of the major budget divisions and also for the total, expressed in terms of percentage change from the 1913 costs. The group weights are given in the captions, in percentage terms.

TABLE LI

Cost of Living Index

Changes in the cost of living in the United States

December, 1914, to December, 1923 [a]

Weight =	100	38.2	16.6	13.4	5.3	5.1	21.3
	Per cent increase over 1913 average cost						
Date	Total budget	Food	Cloth-ing	Hous-ing	Fuel and light	Furniture and furn-ishings	Miscel-laneous
Dec., 1914	3.0	5.0	1.0	(b)	1.0	4.0	3.0
Dec., 1915	5.1	5.0	4.7	1.5	1.0	10.6	7.4
Dec., 1916	18.3	26.0	20.0	2.3	8.4	27.8	13.3
Dec., 1917	42.4	57.0	49.1	0.1	24.1	50.6	40.5
Dec., 1918	74.4	87.0	105.3	9.2	47.9	113.6	65.8
Dec., 1919	99.3	97.0	168.7	25.3	56.8	163.5	90.2
Dec., 1920	100.4	78.0	158.5	51.1	94.9	185.4	108.2
Dec., 1921	74.3	49.9	84.4	61.4	81.1	118.0	106.8
Dec., 1922	69.5	46.6	71.5	61.9	86.4	108.2	100.5
Dec., 1923	73.2	50.3	76.3	66.5	84.0	122.1	101.7

[a] From *Monthly Labor Review*, February, 1924, p. 94.   [b] No change.

National Industrial Conference Board: [2] In its "Research Reports" the National Industrial Conference Board has published a series of studies in the monthly changes in the cost of living since July 1, 1914. Changes are expressed in terms of percentage increase or decrease from July 1, 1914. Separate indexes are

[1] See *M. L. Rev.*, vol. 8, p. 1373, May, 1919; also June, 1919, 1651-1666; July 19, vol. 9, pp. 75-114; August, p. 117 (summary for 12,096 white families and 741 colored).

[2] For example, see Research Report no. 63, *Changes in the Cost of Living, July, 1914-July, 1923.*

given for shelter, clothing, food, light and heat, and sundries. (See Table XLIX in preceding chapter.)

Wage indexes. A wage index number may show the movement (1) in *wage rates* per hour or for longer periods, (2) in *total payroll,* (3) in *average per-capita earnings,* (4) in *full-time weekly earnings,* or (5) in estimated *real wages.* The first type of index shows changes in the nominal remuneration and its significance is affected by changes in the length of the working day or in the amount of unemployment. However, wage rates are useful when it is desired to show changes in the prices of labor in the way that changes in the prices of commodities are shown. For the purpose of indicating changes in the relative well-being of workers, actual average earnings are preferable to wage rates, and an index of real wages is more significant than an index of money wages. An index of real wages is usually obtained by the following formula: [1]

$$\text{Real wage index number} = \frac{\text{Money wage index number} \times 100}{\text{Cost-of-living index number}}$$

(Formula 33).

In other words, if the money wage index shows an increase of 50 per cent and the cost of living also shows an increase of 50 per cent, the real wage index remains unchanged.

In interpreting the significance of changes in *average earnings,* it is necessary to keep in mind the fact that in periods of slack work average earnings may show an increase because the older and more capable men only are retained.

Full-time weekly earnings may be computed by calculating average hourly earnings from payroll data and then converting these to a weekly basis by multiplying by the standard hours per week.

An *hour-rate* index is published by the Bureau of Labor Sta-

---

[1] *Curve division.* The novice in statistical practice is often puzzled by the expression "dividing one curve by another" or "one series by another." Thus wages are reduced to purchasing power by dividing the index of money wages by the best available index of change in the prices of things the laborer buys. This is accomplished by dividing the wage index for a given date or period by the price index for the same date or period, and so on for all periods in the series. Dividing one curve by another is the same process.

tistics,[1] and has been carried back to 1840. The Federal Reserve Bank of New York compiles quarterly an index number for the rates of pay for common labor, as determined from "returns submitted by representative employers of labor."[2] Average weekly earnings and total payroll in New York State factories are reported in the *Industrial Bulletin*[3] with an accompanying graph comparing the trend of wages with that of retail prices and the cost of living. Index numbers representing these data are published in the *Survey of Current Business*.

Likewise the Wisconsin Industrial Commission publishes in its monthly bulletin, the *Wisconsin Labor Market,* a chain index of average *weekly earnings,* by industries. The average weekly earnings are obtained by dividing the total weekly payroll by the number of names on the payroll, hence they do not represent full-time weekly earnings, as there are doubtless some workers on the payroll who have not worked the entire week. Similar data, in the form of index numbers, appear in *The Labour Bulletin,* issued by the Illinois Department of Labor. The National Industrial Conference Board has compiled indexes of weekly and hourly earnings.[4]

Index numbers of security prices. The movement of security prices is considered to have high barometric value for the interpretation of future business conditions;[5] hence the problem of constructing an index number of such changes is of special interest. The New York *Annalist* publishes each week, on the front page, a graph showing the average and the high and low prices of fifty stocks, one half industrials and one half railroads.

[1] *Wages and Hours of Labor Series—e.g.,* no. 274, *Union Scale of Wages and Hours of Labor,* May 15, 1919, p. 22.

[2] Cf. W. R. Burgess, "Index Numbers for the Wages of Common Labor," *Jour. Amer Stat. Assoc.,* March, 1922, pp. 101-103.

[3] The Industrial Commissioner of New York State, *The Industrial Bulletin* (monthly).

[4] Research Report no. 62, *"Wage Changes in Industry, July, 1914-July, 1923,"* and no. 69, *"Wages, Hours, and Employment in American Manufacturing Industries, July, 1914-January, 1924."*

[5] D. F. Jordan, *Business Forecasting,* p. 168. See also W. M. Persons, "An Index Chart Based on Prices and Money Rates," *Rev. of Econ. Statistics,* January, 1922, pp. 7-11.

Similar averages are published in several of the commercial weeklies and in the financial columns of the daily papers.[1]

The problems involved in the construction of stock index numbers are exhaustively discussed by Professor W. C. Mitchell in an article appearing in *The Journal of Political Economy*.[2] He suggests, for example, that there are "three different criteria of the importance of a given stock, criteria upon which may be based three sets of weights, each of which is appropriate for special ends. If the aim is to show the average changes in the prices of securities held by the public, the amount of stock outstanding yields the logical set of weights. If the aim is to throw light on the changes in the prices of business enterprises as such, then gross earnings, the best available gauge of volume of business transacted, may be used as weights. If the aim is to find average changes in the prices of stocks that are traded in, then the number of shares sold should be used. Other aims might make still other systems of weights desirable. . . ."[3]

Index of foreign exchange rates. The Federal Reserve Board is publishing in its Bulletin an index of foreign-exchange rates, designed to express the degree of appreciation or of depreciation of foreign exchange in terms of the currencies of eighteen leading countries. Table LII shows these index numbers for the period January to December, 1920, inclusive, the first column expressing the relative cost of exchange on foreign countries in terms of dollars, the second column representing the relative exchange purchasing power of a dollar in terms of foreign currencies. It will be noted that the second column is obtained by dividing 100 by the figures in the first column and multiplying by 100.

[1] Cf. quotations in *Bradstreet's;* Babson's desk chart; New York *Times;* the Standard Statistics Corporation's publications; and the *Wall Street Journal.*

[2] W. C. Mitchell, "A Critique of Index Numbers of the Prices of Stocks, *Jour. Pol. Econ.,* July, 1916, vol. xxiv, pp. 625-693. Incorporated in part in Secrist, *Readings,* pp. 354-366.

[3] Cf. the discussion of the methods employed in constructing an index of industrial security prices as a measure in studying the relation of such prices to the business cycle.—Edwin Frickey, in "An Index of Industrial Stock Prices," *Rev. of Econ. Statistics,* 1921, pp. 264-278.

TABLE LII

INDEX OF AVERAGE FOREIGN EXCHANGE RATES: 1920 [a]

Month	Dollar cost of exchange on foreign countries (Per cent of par)	Average exchange purchasing power of a dollar
Jan.	78	128
Feb.	70	143
Mar.	72	139
Apr.	73	137
May	72	139
June	74	135
July	74	135
Aug.	66	152
Sept.	67	149
Oct.	61	164
Nov.	58	172
Dec.	55	182

[a] The description of the method used in formulating the index of foreign-exchange rates is found in the *Federal Reserve Bulletin* for July, 1921, pp. 794-799, and includes a discussion of similar index numbers computed in England, Sweden, Norway, and Germany. The September, 1921, issue contains the numbers from Nov., 1918, to that date.

These index numbers are based on monthly averages of "noon buying rates for cable transfers in New York, as published daily by the Treasury in accordance with the Act of May 27, 1921," each reduced to percentages of par. They are weighted geometric means.

The *method of weighting* is of special interest. The rate of each country, expressed as a percentage of par, is weighted "by the total volume of merchandise and gold and silver imports and exports from and to each respective country for the *preceding month*." The usual practice of using a constant set of weights is here abandoned in favor of a changing system, which "has the advantage of giving each country the relative importance it possessed on the most recent available date." If trade with Germany increases, the low rate on the German mark increases in significance and the weight appropriately increases. Beginning with the November, 1921, issue, the weights of the several countries are expressed as parts of 1,000. Thus the weight for England for that month was 249, for Germany 75 and for China 44.

INDEXES OF TOTAL VALUE

The index numbers so far considered all refer to the movements of prices, either of ordinary commodity prices or of the prices of some special commodities as stocks and bonds or labor. Value index numbers, on the other hand, portray the movement of economic conditions expressed in terms of aggregate value. Many such series are published in the *Survey of Current Business,* a few of which are quoted below as illustrative of the type and variety of this sort of index number:

TABLE LIII.—VALUE INDEX NUMBERS [1]
For the month of Dec., 1923

	Numerical Data In thousands of dollars	Index Numbers (1913 = 100)
Mail order houses, total sales.......	35,860	318
F. W. Woolworth Co. ten-cent stores, total sales	32,626	591
Imports	288,067	193
Customs receipts.................	40,946	154

Such index numbers are, of course, really compound, in that they are the joint results of changes in prices and in physical quantities. Mail-order sales may increase, either because prices are higher or because more goods are sold. In the effort to distinguish the influence of these two forces, there is developing a series of index numbers designed to represent, not changes in prices or in total value, but in the physical quantities of things produced, on hand, sold, etc.

QUANTITY INDEX NUMBERS

Index numbers of quantities, into which the price element does not enter, are of a wide and increasing variety. Of this group those which attempt to measure the fluctuations of production and of employment and unemployment are of special interest.

[1] *Survey of Current Business,* February, 1924, pp. 52-55.

Indexes of employment and unemployment.[1] Our available information as to the conditions of employment consists chiefly in the evidence as to varying numbers on the payrolls of manufacturing industries, the unemployment reported by trade unions and the activities of the public employment offices. The Bureau of Labor Statistics and the Industrial Commissions of Illinois, New York, Wisconsin, and several other states, are now publishing index numbers which show the fluctuations in employment in representative plants of the important industries. These index numbers do not purport to show the total employment, but they represent a sample sufficiently large to give significant information as to the trend.

Many of these indexes are published in the *Survey of Current Business;* also composite index numbers appear in the *Annalist,* the *Federal Reserve Bulletin,* and the *Review of Economic Statistics.* Of these, the most comprehensive is the recently inaugurated index compiled under the direction of Professor William A. Berridge and published in the *Federal Reserve Bulletin.*

It is highly desirable that information of this kind be extended. The conditions of employment tell us much concerning the general business conditions, and the probable purchasing power of the workmen, and, because of the influence of unemployment upon economic prosperity, the fluctuations in employment have a close relation to the social problems of suicide, crime, marriage, etc.

Indexes of physical production. An index of physical production is of special interest as affording a clew to real changes

---

[1] Several studies by Professor William A. Berridge have contributed materially to the perfection of the methods of analyzing employment and unemployment statistics. See W. A. Berridge, *Cycles of Unemployment in the United States, 1903-1922;* also the *Review of Economic Statistics,* January, 1922; *Journal of Amer. Stat. Assoc.,* xviii, March, 1922, pp. 42-55, and June, 1922, pp. 227-240; and *Federal Reserve Bulletin,* December, 1923, pp. 1272-1279, and February, 1924, pp. 83-87.

See also, two volumes issued by the National Bureau of Economic Research, entitled *Business Cycles and Unemployment,* with results of an investigation conducted for a committee of the President's Conference on unemployment; and *Employment, Hours, and Earnings in Prosperity and Depression,* 1920-1922, by W. I. King. Likewise *Bulletin* 310 of the U. S. Bureau of Labor Statistics, by E. S. Bradford, is devoted to statistics of employment and unemployment and their analysis.

in economic conditions. Is the production of the things we use keeping pace with population? What is the real waste through decrease in goods produced in a business depression? How much of the increase in prices in the war period may be attributed to decrease in the physical quantities of goods produced? These and similar questions suggest the large importance of having a measure of production which is divorced from the price element. The value index of production may increase greatly, but the increase may lie solely in the price factor and not be a real indication of an increasing abundance of economic goods.

It is a relatively simple matter to construct an index number showing the changes in the quantities produced in a single industry. Indexes of this kind for coal, in thousands of tons; for petroleum, in thousands of barrels; for tires, in thousands. etc. —are published in the *Survey of Current Business,* but a much more complicated problem arises when we attempt to obtain a composite index showing the trend in total production, or some major phase thereof, as manufacturing.

Composite indexes of physical production. How can we add together tons of coal, yards of cloth, bushels of wheat, and so on, to get a significant total, and without introducing the price element in such a way as to make the result indicate, not physical quantities, but value?

There are three possible ways of accomplishing this combination of unlike things, all of which rest on the comparative value of the product of the several industries in some year or years taken as a base. We may designate the three methods as the *proportion of total value* method, the *standard price,* and the *standard quantity method.* Let us illustrate the first by means of the computations in Table LIV.

It will be noted that the index found for the current year is independent of the price or total value in that year, neither one of which is given.

The *standard price* [1] method consists in multiplying the quan-

---

[1] The standard price method was used by Prof. W. C. Mitchell in the compilation of the War Industries Board Index number of the production of raw materials for the years 1913-1918. See *Rev. of Econ. Statistics,* 1920, p. 246.

TABLE LIV

COMPUTATION OF AN INDEX OF PHYSICAL PRODUCTION BY THE PROPORTION
OF TOTAL VALUE METHOD, APPLIED TO HYPOTHETICAL DATA

A	B	C	D	E	F	G	H
	BASE YEAR				CURRENT YEAR		
Arti-cle	Physical quantity	Unit price	Total value	Fraction of total value (Weights)	Quan-tity in current year	Relatives (F÷B)×100	Product of relatives by weights (G×E)
(a)	100 lbs.	$.10	$10.00	.10	200	200	20
(b)	20 tons	2.00	40.00	.40	30	150	60
(c)	50 yds.	1.00	50.00	.50	40	80	40
Total.......			$100.00	1.00	Index number for current year........... 120		

tities in the current year by the price in the base period, summating the results, and dividing by the aggregate value in the base year.

The *standard quantity* method consists in dividing the quantities in each year by the number of units purchasable for a dollar in the base period, and then reducing the resulting aggregates to relatives by dividing each one by the aggregate in the base year. By applying the standard price and the standard quantity methods to the above data, the student will see that the results are identical with those found by the proportion of total expenditure method, all being merely different ways of expressing the same relationships.

Within recent years several economists have computed indexes of physical production, which differ in details but are sufficiently similar in the results shown to indicate the probability that they are substantially accurate.[1] Dr. W. I. King has compiled a per-capita index of physical production for the years 1880 to 1919 and a monthly index for the period January, 1914, to May, 1920; Mr. W. W. Stewart has computed an index for the years 1890-1919, based on materials, manufactures, and transportation; Pro-

[1] See list of references at close of chapter.

fessor G. R. Davies, an index for the years 1870-1920, for crops and minerals; and Professor E. E. Day, one for the period beginning with 1879, with separate series for agriculture, mining, and manufacturing.

Several indexes of quantity production are now (1924) currently published.[1] Among these are separate series for the marketing of agricultural products, the extraction of minerals, the production of basic commodities, the production of manufactured goods, and of various groups of manufactured articles, such as consumption goods.

For a fuller statement of the methods used and results obtained in constructing the several index numbers mentioned, the reader will find it profitable to consult the accompanying references.

It should be noted that an approximation to the trend of physical production can be obtained by a comparison between the price movement and some one of the single series which are good indicators of the general movement of business. Thus Dr. W. I. King compares with his index of physical production a curve obtained by dividing bank clearings outside of New York by the price curve and comes to the conclusion that "apparently the best single indicator of the extent of physical business in the United States is the volume of bank clearings outside of New York City."[2] Professor E. E. Day suggests that freight tonnage is an even better "single-series barometer of the physical volume of agriculture, mining, and manufactures combined."[3]

Indexes of the volume of trade.[4] The measurement of the total volume of trade, or the aggregate exchange of goods

[1] See current numbers of the *Federal Reserve Bulletin,* the *Review of Economic Statistics,* the Standard Statistics Co. *Daily Trade Service,* and the *Survey of Current Business;* and, for methods of construction, see the references at the close of this chapter.

[2] In, "Is Production Keeping Pace with Population," *Bankers Statistics Corporation,* August 24, 1920.

[3] *Review of Economic Statistics,* 1921, p. 21.

[4] For discussion of methods of estimating the volume of trade, see E. W. Kemmerer, *Money and Prices,* 1909, p. 127; Irving Fisher, the *Purchasing Power of Money,* 1911, p. 478; Warren M. Persons, "An Index of Trade for the United States," *Review of Economic Statistics,* vol. v (1923), p. 71; and Carl Snyder, "A New Index of the Volume of Trade," *Journal of the American Statistical Association,* December, 1923.

and services, is even more complicated than the measurement of quantity production, but the problems involved are essentially similar, in that methods must be devised for the combination of diverse elements, such as wholesale trade, building construction, and factory employment, in such a way that the distorting influence of price changes will be avoided and that each series exercises an appropriate influence on the composite.

For some purposes it is highly desirable to adjust indexes of production or of the volume of trade for typical seasonal variations and for the growth element. Methods of accomplishing such corrections are set forth in the following chapter.

REFERENCES

1. BARNETT, GEO. E., "Index Numbers of the Total Cost of Living," *Q. J. Econ.*, February, 1921, pp. 240-263.

2. BURGESS, W. H., "Index Numbers for the Wages of Common Labor," *Jour. Am. St. Assoc.*, March, 1922, pp. 101-103.

3. DAVIES, G. R., *Introduction to Economic Statistics*, chap. iii (part), "Indexes of Wages and Prices." Chap. iv, "Quantity Indexes and their Uses."

4. DAY, E. E., "An Index of the Physical Volume of Production," in *Rev. of Economic Statistics*, September, 1920-January, 1921: vol. ii, pp. 247-259, 287-299, 309-337, 361-367; vol. iii, 19-23.

5. ———— "The Volume of Production of Basic Materials in the United States, 1909-1921," *Rev. of Economics Statistics*, July, 1922, pp. 215-230.

6. FISHER, I., *Purchasing Power of Money*, pp. 290-292 (calculation of volume of trade) and appendix no. 9 to chap. xii, pp. 478-486.

7. KING, W. I., "Is Production Keeping Pace with Population?" *Bankers Statistics Corporation*, New York, August 24, 1920.

8. MITCHELL, W. C., *Index Numbers*, U. S. Bureau of Labor Statistics Bulletin, no. 284, especially pp. 94-114; 115-175; and no. 173, pp. 93-114, 115-116.

9 ———— "A Critique of Index Numbers of Prices of Stocks," *Jour. Pol. Econ.*, July, 1916, pp. 625-693, incorporated in part in Secrist, *Readings, op. cit.*, pp. 360-366.

10. SECRIST, H., *Introduction to Statistical Methods*, chap. x, "American Price Index Numbers Described and Compared."

11. STEWART, W. W., "An Index Number of Production" (and discussion), *Amer. Econ. Rev.*, March, 1921, pp. 57-81.

12. War Industries Board, *History of Prices During the War*, Wesley C. Mitchell, editor in chief.

CHAPTER XIII

SEASONAL AND LONG-TIME TRENDS

Elements of a time series. The methods of statistical analysis which are used in the interpretation of economic statistics are in many respects identical with those used in the physical, biological, and mental sciences. In fact, a considerable part of the calculus of mass phenomena has been evolved by scientists in these other fields. When, however, we approach the analysis of historical series we come to a problem which is especially characteristic of economic and social facts. The time element enters into a very large proportion of economic data; the statistics of social phenomena are prevailingly statistics of historical movements. In previous chapters we have noted the use of index numbers as one method of analyzing historical series. In this chapter we shall turn our attention to the problem of separating a time series, presumably the result of several forces, into its chief constituent elements.

To illustrate, the number of freight-car loadings per week on the railroads of the United States is determined by several factors, the chief of which are: (1) the long-time or secular [1] trend; (2) the seasonal variation; (3) the cyclical movement, and (4) various residual or irregular forces less capable of reduction to uniform principles. The number of car loadings in October, 1922 (941,792) was larger than in April, 1921 (698,156), partly because of the general growth in business from year to year; partly because of a tendency for shipments to be more active in certain months of the year; and partly because April, 1921, was in the trough of the business cycle and October, 1922, in the expansion phase. A difference in car loadings between two periods may also be due to a great strike or some other unusual incident which materially affects railroad shipments. If we are

[1] Secular: relating to long intervals of time; from sæculum, age.

to make comparisons of two or more historical series or the curves which represent them, we must, if our comparisons are to be significant, take these several factors into consideration. If we are interested in the relatively long-time movements we must isolate those elements in each curve. If we wish to determine the influence of the business cycle upon a given phenomenon, such as factory employment, we must eliminate the long-time trend, and if monthly figures are used, also the seasonal variations.

SECULAR TRENDS

Let us turn our attention first to the methods of determining the long-time, or, as it is frequently designated, the secular trend, or merely *trend*. A computed trend is our best estimate of the general course of a time series, either expressed in numerical terms or represented by a graph. Strictly speaking, a secular trend, as distinguished from cyclical movements, is determinable only from data over a period of time long enough to enable the influence of fundamental tendencies to become evident. Consequently, in the following illustration of computing a trend based on data for only three years, the general movement evidenced is a trend only in comparison to the still shorter monthly fluctuations.

The moving average. A common process of obtaining an approximation of a trend is the moving average method.

To illustrate the process involved, let us take the monthly average price of fresh eggs in the United States for the years 1917 to 1919, as given in column B of Table LV and graphically represented by the wavelike curve A in Chart 32. An examination of this curve suggests the presence of two distinct movements. The first is the familiar seasonal movement in egg prices, with a peak in December or January, followed by a sharp fall in the next two or three months. The second movement is a general rise through the three years. Let us proceed to calculate the degree of this latter movement by the moving average method trying first a *three-month average* centered on the middle month. The prices for the first three months (55, 51, and 35 cents) are averaged, giving 47 cents, which figure is placed opposite the

TABLE LV.—MOVING AVERAGES

AVERAGE PRICE PER DOZEN OF STRICTLY FRESH EGGS IN THE UNITED STATES: 1917-1919 [a]

A	B	C	D	E	F
Year and Month	Average price (cents)	Three-month (centered)		Twelve-month (centered on 7th month)	
		Total	Average C ÷ 3	Total	Average
1917					
Jan.	55				
Feb.	51	141	47		
Mar.	35	125	42		
Apr.	39	114	38		
May	40	120	40		
June	41	123	41		
July	42	129	43	579	48
Aug.	46	141	47	591	49
Sept.	53	154	51	603	50
Oct.	55	166	55	612	51
Nov.	58	177	59	616	51
Dec.	64	189	63	618	52
1918					
Jan.	67	194	65	620	52
Feb.	63	174	58	627	52
Mar.	44	150	50	635	53
Apr.	43	129	43	641	53
May	42	128	43	650	54
June	43	134	45	666	56
July	49	146	49	683	57
Aug.	54	162	54	691	58
Sept.	59	177	59	679	57
Oct.	64	197	66	683	57
Nov.	74	219	73	689	57
Dec.	81	230	77	700	58
1919					
Jan.	75	207	69	711	59
Feb.	51	174	58	719	60
Mar.	48	148	49	725	60
Apr.	49	150	50	729	61
May	53	156	52	737	61
June	54	164	55	744	62
July	57	171	57	753	63
Aug.	60	180	60		
Sept.	63	195	65		
Oct.	72	216	72		
Nov.	81	243	81		
Dec.	90				

[a] U. S. Bureau of Labor Statistics, *Bulletin* 270, pp. 62-65.

second or middle month of the three, as in column D of Table LV. Then the first month is dropped and the fourth added and the resulting new average placed opposite the third month, March. The computation may be lessened by noting at each shift the difference between the figure added and the one dropped, dividing the difference by the number of months averaged, and then adding the result, signs considered, to the last previous average.

If we examine the three-month moving average in column D, we see that it shows about as much seasonal variation as the original data. This indicates that we have not taken the correct period; for we have not eliminated the seasonal movement. In calculating a moving average we must take a period approximating the typical length of the wave to be eliminated. Ordinarily this can be determined by estimating the typical period from crest to crest or from trough to trough. For egg prices, we know the wave length to be about *twelve months*. In column F of Table LV is a twelve-month moving average centered in the seventh month.[1] This is plotted in Chart 32 as Curve B.

CHART 32

TWELVE-MONTH MOVING AVERAGE

MONTHLY AVERAGE PRICE OF FRESH EGGS PER DOZEN *

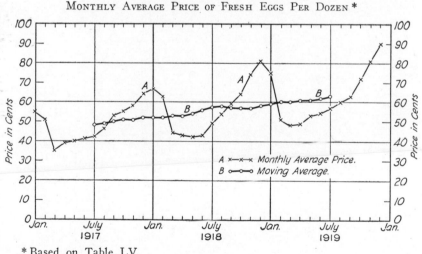

A x—x—x Monthly Average Price.
B o—o—o Moving Average.

* Based on Table LV.

---

[1] To be strictly accurate, the average should be centered between the sixth and seventh months and then a second moving average, with a two-month

In plotting the moving average, it is sometimes *projected* to the terminus of the period averaged,[1] but the more usual practice is to *center* it as shown in the foregoing example.

Weighted moving average. Occasionally in calculating a moving average, weights are given to the data for the periods nearest to the point at which the average is centered, these weights being either arbitrarily chosen or distributed according to the relative frequencies around the mean of a normal frequency distribution.[2]

The straight-line trend by the method of least squares. A second method of determining the secular trend is to calculate the straight line which best fits the given data. The line of best fit is usually considered to be the line of least squares—that is, the line so drawn that the sum of the squares of the vertical

CHART 33

STRAIGHT-LINE TREND BY METHOD OF LEAST SQUARES

COMPUTED FROM MONTHLY AVERAGE PRICE PER DOZEN OF FRESH EGGS[*]

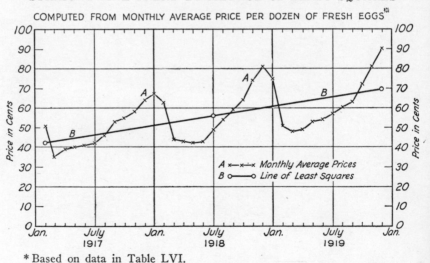

* Based on data in Table LVI.

period, be calculated to bring the averages opposite the original figures. Cf. G. R. Davies, *Economic Statistics,* footnote, p. 103.

[1] See the moving averages calculated in the *Review of Economic Statistics,* 1919, pp. 10-12, in testing for the best indicator of the secular trend.

[2] Professor W. M. Persons tested a moving average with weights of five, four, three, two, and one, in constructing a business index. See also discussion of "progressive mean" in G. R. Davies, *Economic Statistics,* footnote, pp. 104-105.

deviations of the curve representing the actual data from the given line is less than the sum of the squared deviations from any other line. The one line which satisfies these conditions may be found by the following process, the computation for which is given in Table LVI and the result graphically shown in Chart 33, line labeled B.

TABLE LVI

DETERMINATION OF LINE OF LEAST SQUARES AND DEVIATIONS THEREFROM

for the

Monthly average price per dozen of strictly fresh eggs in the United States during the period 1917-1919 [a]

A	B	C	D	E	F	G
Year and month	Monthly average price in cents	Months from the midpoint in time	Product of price and time deviation (B × C)	Squares of time deviation	Ordinate of the secular trend	Deviation from the trend (B − F)
	y	x	xy	x²	Y	y − Y
Total....	1,960		+ 2,872	3,570		
1917						
Feb.	51	− 17	− 867	289	42.4	+ 8.6
Mar.	35	− 16	− 550	256	43.2	− 8.2
Apr.	39	− 15	− 585	225	44.0	− 5.0
May	40	− 14	− 560	196	44.8	− 4.8
June	41	− 13	− 533	169	45.6	− 4.6
July	42	− 12	− 504	144	46.4	− 4.4
Aug.	46	− 11	− 506	121	47.2	− 1.2
Sept.	53	− 10	− 530	100	48.0	+ 5.0
Oct.	55	− 9	− 495	81	48.8	+ 6.2
Nov.	58	− 8	− 464	64	49.6	+ 8.4
Dec.	64	− 7	− 448	49	50.4	+ 13.6
1918						
Jan.	67	− 6	− 402	36	51.2	+ 15.8
Feb.	63	− 5	− 315	25	52.0	+ 11.0
Mar.	44	− 4	− 176	16	52.8	− 8.8
Apr.	43	− 3	− 129	9	53.6	− 10.6
May	42	− 2	− 84	4	54.4	− 12.4
June	43	− 1	− 43	1	55.2	− 12.2
July	49	0	0	0	56.0	− 7.0
Aug.	54	+ 1	+ 54	1	56.8	− 2.8
Sept.	59	+ 2	+ 118	4	57.6	+ 1.4
Oct.	64	+ 3	+ 192	9	58.4	+ 5.6
Nov.	74	+ 4	+ 296	16	59.2	+ 14.8
Dec.	81	+ 5	+ 405	25	60.0	+ 21.0
1919						
Jan.	75	+ 6	+ 450	36	60.8	+ 14.2
Feb.	51	+ 7	+ 357	49	61.6	− 10.6
Mar.	48	+ 8	+ 384	64	62.4	− 14.4
Apr.	49	+ 9	+ 441	81	63.2	− 14.2
May	53	+ 10	+ 530	100	64.0	− 11.0
June	54	+ 11	+ 594	121	64.8	− 10.8
July	57	+ 12	+ 684	144	65.6	− 8.6
Aug.	60	+ 13	+ 780	169	66.4	− 6.4
Sept.	63	+ 14	+ 882	196	67.2	− 4.2
Oct.	72	+ 15	+ 1,080	225	68.0	+ 4.0
Nov.	81	+ 16	+ 1,296	256	68.8	+ 12.2
Dec.	90	+ 17	+ 1,530	289	69.6	+ 20.4

[a] Bureau of Labor Statistics, *Bulletin* no. 270, pp. 62-65.

The steps in the computation of a straight-line trend by the method of least squares are:

(1) *Find the midpoint in time of the period* for which the trend is to be calculated.

For convenience in computation, let us drop January, 1917, in our table of egg prices, and take a period of thirty-five months of which July, 1918, is the midpoint. (If thirty-six months are taken, the midpoint, of course, lies between June and July, 1918.) July, 1918, then becomes our point of *origin*, with the months to the right considered positive values of x, those to the left, negative. Thus August, 1918, is + 1 on the abscissa or horizontal axis; September, 1918, is + 2; December, 1919, + 17, while June, 1918, is — 1, and February, 1917, is — 17 (see column C of Table LVI).

(2) *Average the original monthly data* for the entire period of thirty-five months. The usual algebraic symbol for this average is b. The value of b by the formula: $b = \dfrac{\Sigma y}{n}$ (Formula 34), is found to be 56 cents. b is one point on the desired straight line, hence the next step is to—

(3) *Plot b* as the ordinate of the straight line for July, 1918.

(4) *Compute the rise or fall* of the line of least squares from the determined point by use of the formula:

$$m = \frac{\Sigma\, xy}{\Sigma\, x^2} \quad\dotfill\quad \text{(Formula 35),}$$

in which the significance of the several terms is as follows:

$m =$ The slope of the line (the monthly rise or fall) measured by the vertical spread between any two successive monthly points on the line.

$\Sigma\, xy =$ The sum, signs considered, of the products obtained by multiplying the price for each month by the deviation of that month from the origin, or July 1, 1918, as shown in column D, Table LVI.

$\Sigma\, x^2 =$ The sum of the squares of the deviations in months from the midpoint (see Column E, Table LVI, and table of sums of squares in Appendix D).

Substituting the values shown in Table LVI in the formula given above, we find for m a value of 0.8¢ —

$$\frac{2872}{3570} = 0.8¢$$

The ordinate for the trend of any given month is then found by adding to b (56 cents), which is the ordinate for July 1, 1918, the product of 0.8 by the deviation in months from the midpoint. The results of this multiplication and addition are shown in column F of Table LVI. The line of least squares can be drawn by connecting any two of the points so determined.

To summarize the process just described, the equation of any straight line may be expressed by the formula:

$$y = mx + b \dots\dots\dots\dots \text{(Formula 36)},$$

in which b represents the point at which the line intersects the Y-axis, and m, the slope of the line. When these values are found, the determination of the corresponding values of x and y is a mere matter of successive substitution of the various values of x and the solution of the equation for y.

Short-cut methods for a straight-line trend. If only a rough accuracy is adequate, the straight-line trend of a series may be approximated with the eye and drawn without mathematical computations. We may call this the *strictly free-hand* method.

Another approximation may be obtained by the method of *semi-averages*.[1] The entire period is bisected and an average calculated for each half and plotted as ordinates at the midpoints of the first and second halves of the period, respectively. Applied to the egg prices in Table LVI, the method of semi-averages gives 48.9 and 63 cents as the ordinates of the straight-line trend, these ordinates to be plotted between September and October, 1917, and between March and April, 1919, respectively. If the reader will plot these amounts on Charts 32 and 33 and draw the straight line connecting them, he will see that it corresponds closely to the moving average and the line of least squares.

A similar approximation is obtained by drawing a straight

---

[1] G. R. Davies, *Economic Statistics,* p. 102.

line in such a way that in each half of the period one half of the points lie above the line and one half below.

Complex trends.[1] No method of calculating the trend should be applied blindly without consideration of the degree to which the resulting trend line really conforms to the nature of the data. In some cases, for example, the economist finds it necessary to fit more complex curves than the straight line, or to break the data into two periods, in order fairly to represent the trend.[2]

When the data evidence a constant ratio of increase, it is convenient to fit a straight line to the logarithms of the data rather than a compound interest curve to the original data, for the straight line correctly represents the trend when fitted to the logarithms and it is easier to project.

Free-hand trends.[3] Inasmuch as the determination of what type of curve best fits a given set of data is largely a matter of judgment, some statisticians believe that the most useful method of trend fitting is the determination of the general sweep of the data by a free-hand trend drawn with the aid of irregular, or "French," curves. Also, a moving average or a moving median, as a preliminary approximation, is helpful in the construction of a free-hand trend.

Summary of trend fitting. The reader may well be puzzled as to which of the several possible ways of approximating a trend is to be considered most appropriate, hence it may be helpful to recapitulate some of the significant considerations.

1. The *moving average* is useful as an approximation, particularly where it is desired to eliminate a cycle with a rather regular wave length, or as an aid to the construction of a free-

[1] For discussion of methods of approximating the parabola or a compound interest curve to fit a given set of data, see G. R. Davies, *Economic Statistics,* pp. 110-115. A good discussion of the parabola and logarithmic curve is given in Raymond Pearl, *Medical Biometry and Statistics,* chap. xvi.

[2] The price movement from 1879 to 1924, consisting of a decline to the middle of the nineties and a rise thereafter, affords an illustration of a series which could not properly be represented by a single straight line trend.

[3] Cf. G. R. Davies, *Economic Statistics,* pp. 100-102; and an unpublished manuscript by Dr. W. I. King, on "Principles Underlying the Isolation of Cycles and Trends," in which the use of the free-hand curve is defended and attention called to the usefulness of the moving median.

hand trend.   It is, however, somewhat unsatisfactory when there is no determinable wave length or when the original curve shows marked changes in direction other than those due to the cycle which it is desired to eliminate.   Also, as will be seen by reference to Chart 32, it cannot be extended to either end of the period without some additional approximation by free-hand, or by assumption of values beyond the months for which data are given.

2. The *straight-line trend* is often appropriate for short periods, but is apt not to be a good fit to a long series.

3. The fitting of trends by *mathematical formulas,* for either the straight line or more complex types, has the advantage that, once the type of curve is chosen, the placing of the line becomes a matter of mechanical computation rather than of judgment.   The mathematical curve, particularly the straight line, is convenient for extrapolation, that is, for estimation of the movement of the variable beyond the earliest or latest data given.   Also, where there is good reason to believe that the general movement of the series is determined by causes operating regularly enough to obey approximately a mathematical law, which may be represented by an equation, the mathematical curve is clearly the most logical.

4. Where a quick approximation is desired, or where the trend is irregular, there is much to be said for a judicious application of *free-hand* methods.

Representation of short-time deviations.   If it is desired to show the fluctuations remaining after adjustment has been made for the long-time trend, this can be done by subtracting the trend from the original data and plotting the resulting figures as positive or negative deviations from a horizontal zero line, as in Chart 34.   This process is spoken of as subtracting the curve or straight line representing the trend from the original curve, and may be accomplished either by measuring the vertical distance on the graph between the trend line and the original data curve for each month, or by finding the numerical amount of this difference from Table LVI.   Thus Column G, Table LVI, is the result of subtracting the ordinates of the trend in Column F from the corresponding monthly price figures in Column B, and Chart 34 is the graph of these deviations.

CHART 34 *

SHORT-TIME FLUCTUATIONS

DEVIATIONS OF MONTHLY AVERAGE PRICE PER DOZEN OF FRESH EGGS FROM THE LINE OF LEAST SQUARES

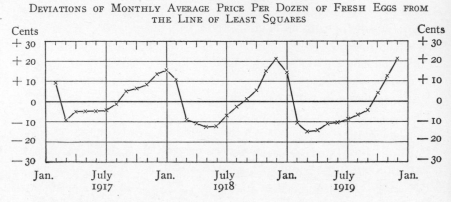

* Based on Table LVI, column G.

THE NATURE OF SEASONAL VARIATION

By seasonal variation is meant the fluctuations in chronological data which follow the round of the seasons, exhibiting tendencies to be above normal in certain months of the year and below in others. These fluctuations may be directly due to the seasonal changes, as the seasonal movement in the production or sale of ice, or somewhat more indirectly due to seasonal causes, as illustrated by the fluctuations in bank clearings with the changes in agricultural activity due to the round of the seasons. These movements are of great interest to the student of economic and social data. The business man wishes to know if the slump in his business in summer is typical of the industry to which he belongs or of his own past experience. He wishes to know at what seasons the interest rates customarily rise and when the prices of his raw products are usually lowest. The economist studies the degree to which currency expands to meet the seasonal demands upon it; the sociologist finds significant seasonal movements in the statistics of births, deaths and crimes. For example, "vagrancy and mendicity increase in winter (as in general all economic criminality does), when forced unemployment is at its height, and needs are most pressing, while they diminish in summer." [1]

Specific and normal seasonal variation. In approaching the problem of how to ascertain the presence and extent of seasonal variation, let us distinguish between the attempt to determine the actual seasonal fluctuation of a given series for a certain month or months and the attempt to determine the typical seasonal movement which, judging from past experience, we may reasonably expect that series to exhibit in the future. An attempt might be made to estimate the specific seasonal movement by subtracting from the actual figures the influence, so far as it is calculable, of all the other factors. In fact, however, the usual object of the statistician is to determine, not the specific seasonal variation, but rather a normal or typical seasonal fluctuation. He may seek the latter either as a means to a fuller understanding of the seasonal aspect of the given phenomenon, or, more frequently, that he may eliminate the normal seasonal variation as a step toward the isolation of the business cycle.

Ratio charting. [2] If the object sought is to ascertain the absence or presence of a relatively consistent seasonal variation, rather than to get a numerical measure of its amount, a helpful procedure is to plot the monthly data for each year on semi-logarithmic or ratio paper and arrange the curves one above another so that the similarities in the January to February, February to March movement, etc., can be readily compared. The use of ratio charting makes equal ratios of change present a similar appearance on the charts (see Chapter VI).

METHODS OF COMPUTING NORMAL SEASONAL VARIATION

Of several methods which have been devised by statisticians in an effort to determine the normal seasonal variation, the three most important are (1) the *simple average method,* adjusted for trend; (2) the *typical deviation from trend-cycle method;* and (3) *the link-relative method.*

[1] Wm. A. Bonger, *Criminality and Economic Conditions,* p. 547.
[2] Compare the *Review of Economic Statistics,* 1919, pp. 20-21, with charts drawn on ratio paper and arranged to show seasonal tendencies.

Simple average method. The most obvious and easy method of making a rough approximation of the influence of seasonal movements upon a given phenomenon is to find the average for each respective month for a period of years and express that average as a percentage of an average for the entire twelve months. The weaknesses of this simple method are that the results are influenced by the long-time trend, by cyclical movements, and by any exceptional items which may occur. If the secular trend is upward, each December will tend to be higher than the preceding January, all aside from any seasonal influence. Furthermore, inasmuch as the arithmetic average is affected relatively much by large items, any exceptional item, even if due to distinctly non-seasonal causes, will have a marked influence on the average.

The influence of the secular trend on the average may be removed by calculating the average annual trend and adjusting the twelve monthly averages by reducing February by one-twelfth of the annual trend, assuming it is a rising trend; March, by two-twelfths, etc.[1]

Typical deviation from a trend-cycle curve. A second method of estimating the normal seasonal variation is to determine the typical deviation from a trend-cycle curve—that is, from a curve designed to represent the most probable course of the given variable in so far as it is determined by the secular trend and the business cycle. Such a curve may be drawn freehand or a twelve-month moving average may be used. This method was used in the correction for seasonal variation of the indexes of the production of basic commodities published by the Federal Reserve Board,[2] the steps in the procedure being: (1) the computation of a twelve-month moving average, centered at the seventh month; (2) the computation for each month of the percentage of the monthly production data as related to the moving average; (3) the determination of the median of these percentages for each calendar month; (4) the adjustment of the twelve medians to total 1,200; (5) the determination of a seasonal base number for

[1] Cf. G. R. Davies, *Economic Statistics*, pp. 116-120.
[2] *Federal Reserve Bulletin*, 1922, pp. 1414-1421.

each calendar month by multiplying the average production in 1919 by the twelve medians; and (6) the computation of an index number, adjusted for seasonal variation, by dividing the original production figures by the respective seasonal base numbers. A numerical illustration of the nature and use of seasonal base numbers is given in the Appendix to this chapter, Tables LVII and LIX.

Particularly when the twelve-month moving average is adjusted by judicious free-hand smoothing to offset its tendency to cut corners and to minimize the amplitude of the fluctuations of the business cycle, the typical deviation method would seem to be a distinctly logical manner of approach.[1]

The link-relative method. In his exhaustive analyses of the statistical methods best adapted to the study of economic series with a view to determining the influence of the business cycle, Professor Warren M. Persons comes to the conclusion that the seasonal variation should be determined by the link-relative method.[2] The essence of this method is the determination of the typical month-to-month relationship by dividing the figure for each month by that for the preceding month and taking the median of the resulting quotients for each respective month as the type. The use of the median rather than the arithmetic average tends to lessen the influence of exceptional items, which is especially to be desired as an examination of the actual data indicates that the exceptional items are apt to be due to nonseasonal causes. The medians for each of the twelve calendar months are welded into a connected series by consecutive multiplication and adjusted to give twelve seasonal index numbers with the average of the year as a base. A more detailed description of this somewhat involved process is given in the appendix to this

[1] The moving-average method is credited in the *Federal Reserve Bulletin*, 1922, p. 1414, to Mr. Frederick R. Macaulay, of the National Bureau of Economic Research, and the writer understands that Mr. Macaulay has devised unpublished improvements of the method as outlined above, designed to correct for the eccentricities of the moving average.

[2] W. M. Persons, "Indices of Business Conditions," *Review of Economic Statistics*, 1919. This treatise is an unusual example of a high type of statistical analysis, in the completeness with which the data and methods are given and in the significance of the results for the understanding of economic conditions.

chapter.   The method of computation there elaborated differs in some respects from the process used by Professor Persons, particularly with reference to the method of eliminating the normal seasonal variation after it has been determined, but the essential features in the computation of the typical seasonal movement are as devised by him.   As the link-relative method is being used extensively in the currently published analyses of various aspects of the business cycle, the reader who wishes to understand current statistical literature will find it profitable to examine the appendix carefully.

A changing normal seasonal variation.   It may be noted that if, as not infrequently happens, the normal seasonal variation itself changes as the years pass, there is needed a still further refinement in the methods of dealing with it.   For an example of such a change, there has been a striking decrease in the seasonal fluctuation of interest rates on sixty-to-ninety day commercial paper since the inauguration of the Federal Reserve System.[1]

Elimination.   The normal seasonal variation, after it has been determined, may be eliminated either by the use of seasonal base numbers or by multiplying each monthly ordinate of the secular trend by the appropriate seasonal percentage—that is, the typical percentage for the corresponding month—and ascertaining the deviations from the trend as thus corrected.   The seasonal base-number method has been briefly described in connection with the typical-deviation-from-the-trend-cycle method of finding the normal seasonal, and is described more fully in the following appendix, where it is applied in connection with the link-relative method.   The other method of elimination was used by Professor Persons in the construction of the "Harvard" index of business conditions, described in the following chapter.

[1] Federal Reserve Agent, New York, *Monthly Review of Credit and Business Conditions,* February 1, 1922.

One method of adjusting for a changing normal is explained in an unpublished (April, 1924) article by W. I. King, on "An Improved Method for Measuring the Seasonal Factor."

APPENDIX A—CHAPTER XIII

THE LINK-RELATIVE METHOD[1]

THE following explanation is designed to indicate the link-relative method of reducing a series of original monthly data to index numbers from which the influence of the seasonal variation has been as far as possible eliminated. The object of such elimination is to facilitate the study of the fluctuations due to the business cycle. The process described does not include the elimination of the long-time trend from the final index numbers. If that is desired, a further step is required, but in many instances worth-while indications of cyclical influences can be determined without the additional labor involved in the computation of the secular trend. In tracing the steps in the process, the reader should keep in mind that the object is to obtain a *typical* seasonal movement for the twelve months in the year and then to eliminate that movement from the original data. Chicago bank clearings for the years 1890 to 1914, inclusive, are used to illustrate the process.

All tables used in this computation are grouped at the close of this Appendix. The steps in the process are as follows:

1. *Obtaining and recording the monthly data.* The desired data can be obtained from the sources indicated in Chapter XVII. To avoid the labor and chance of error involved in recopying, the computer will find it helpful to make the original entry of the data

[1] The particular variation of the link-relative method here described is an adaptation of the method used by Professor Warren M. Persons in his construction of an index of business conditions, and was prepared by Mr. Mark H. Ingraham for the use of Professor John R. Commons and associates in a study of the business cycle, with particular reference to its relation to employment conditions.

It may be noted that the term *relative* is ordinarily used in statistical literature to refer to percentage relatives, while the computations in this chapter are chiefly in terms of decimal fractions not reduced to percentages. However, as the phrase *"link-relative method"* has been associated with the process here described, it is retained as interchangeable with the expression *link ratio*.

in the columns of a table ruled like the form in Table LVII, at the close of this Appendix. For the sake of brevity, in Table LVII the data are shown only for the years 1890 and 1891, but a similar computation was made for each year from 1890 to 1914. (The balance of the original data is in Table 103.[1] Link relatives for the entire period were computed and used in finding the medians in Table LVIII.)

2. *Calculation of the link relatives.* Divide the figure for each month by that of the immediately preceding month and record the quotient as the link relative for the month used as the dividend. To illustrate, the February, 1890, link relative for Chicago bank clearings (Column C, Table LVII) is obtained thus:

$$\frac{\text{Link relative for}}{\text{February, 1890}} = \frac{\text{February clearings}}{\text{January clearings}} = \frac{253}{296} = .85$$

This fraction, .85, could be expressed as 85 per cent, indicating that the February clearings fell below the January clearings by 15 per cent, but the link ratios are not reduced to percentages in this explanation.

3. *Determination of the median link relative for each month.* In order to determine the typical proportions between each successive pair of months, it is necessary to take some sort of an average of the link relatives for each respective month in the year. For this purpose the median is chosen, because the mode is too indefinite when the total number of items is small, and the arithmetic average gives too much weight to exceptional or freak items, such as those which appeared at the outbreak of the war and which are not due to seasonal influences.

The median link relative is found by classifying the relatives, according to months, in a frequency table with small class intervals. Thus in Table LVIII we have the frequency distribution of the link relatives for clearings, computed from the data given in Table LVII and Table 103, and grouped in class intervals of .01. Each tally in this table represents a link relative of the size indicated by the corresponding stub.

As there are twenty-five years in the series (except for the January relatives, which are only twenty-four in number), the

[1] Table 103 is in Appendix B.

thirteenth item in the array is the median, and this is found by counting up from the lower extreme of each month-distribution, beginning at the top of the table. The resulting medians are recorded at the bottom of Table LVIII, and again in Column B of Table LIX.

It should be noted that the medians can be considered as giving a significant indication of the seasonal variation only when there is a fairly clear zone of concentration shown by the tally of the link relatives.

4. *Calculation of a preliminary or crude seasonal index.* The median link relatives express merely the typical relation between a given month and the preceding month. For use in eliminating the seasonal variations, it is necessary by serial multiplication to weld these links into a chain which will show the typical relations of the twelve months expressed in terms of a common base. To this end, let us list the median relatives as given in Table LIX, Column B, in the following form. The symbol L_1 is used as a convenient symbol for the January link relative, L_2 for the February link relative, etc.

Month	Median link relative	Symbol for link	Result of serial multiplication	
			Symbol	Amount
Jan.	.97½	L_1	C_1	1.000
Dec.				
Feb.	.86	L_2	C_2	.860
Jan.				
Mar.	1.17	L_3	C_3	1.006
Feb.				
Apr.	.96	L_4	C_4	.966
Mar.				
May	1.05	L_5	C_5	1.014
Apr.				
June	.97	L_6	C_6	.984
May				
July	.99	L_7	C_7	.974
June				

As a starting point, we take the January link relative as a base (C_1) from which to calculate a serial relative for all twelve months.

Then, to get the February serial relative (C_2), we multiply the base (1.000) by the February link relative (.86), giving $C_1 L_2$ or C_2, with a value of .860. Likewise the March serial relative is the product of the February serial relative and the March link relative ($C_2 L_3$), or .860 × 1.17, giving C_3 or 1.006. In this manner all the twelve links are welded together

Month	Median link relative	Symbol for link	Result of serial multiplication	
			Symbol	Amount
Aug. / July	.96	L_8	C_8	.935
Sept. / Aug.	1.02	L_9	C_9	.954
Oct. / Sept.	1.12	L_{10}	C_{10}	1.068
Nov. / Oct.	.96	L_{11}	C_{11}	1.025
Dec. / Nov.	1.05	L_{12}	C_{12}	1.076
Jan. / Dec.	.97½	L_{13}	C_{13}	1.049

to form an index number with January as a base, the twelfth serial number (C_{12}) being 1.076. Lastly we multiply by .975, the January link relative, to get a second January serial number (C_{13}) with a value of 1.049.

We started with January as 1.000; we end with January as 1.049. The discrepancy is presumably due to a secular trend upward and must be eliminated, as we wish an index of seasonal variation, not of seasonal variation and secular trend combined.

5. *Elimination of the influence of the secular trend to get an adjusted serial index.* To eliminate the discrepancy in the seasonal index numbers just found, and recorded in Column C of Table LIX, the discrepancy (0.049) is divided by twelve and the quotient (0.0041) is subtracted, in multiples of 1 to 12, beginning with February. The amounts which must be subtracted from each month are shown in Column D, and the results of subtraction in Column E. We have now an index number series which starts with January as a base—that is, January == 100— and with the influence of the long-time trend eliminated as far as possible.[1]

6. *Shifting the base from January to the average for the year.* The adjusted serial relatives in Column E are next shifted to a new base, the average for the twelve numbers, by dividing each serial relative by that average. The results are shown in Column F, and plotted in Chart 35.

[1] In his application of the link relative method, Professor Persons distributed the discrepancy on the compound-interest principle, which is more accurate than the simpler method here used, but the difference does not seem to justify the additional computation where the discrepancy due to the trend is not great.

CHART 35

TYPICAL SEASONAL VARIATION IN CHICAGO BANK CLEARINGS

(Based on Table LIX, Column F)

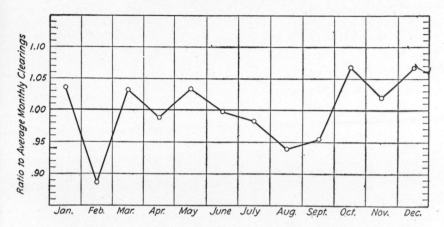

7. *Calculation of seasonal base numbers.*[1] Let us assume that we wish to compute index numbers for Chicago bank clearings, using 1890 as a base and eliminating the seasonal fluctuations. The average monthly clearings during the twelve months of that year were $341,000,000. Multiplying this figure by the twelve seasonal index numbers recorded in Column F, Table LIX, we get a series of seasonal base numbers, which can be used in the calculation of a final index number adjusted for seasonal fluctuations.

8. *Calculation of a seasonally adjusted index number.* As a last step in our process, we divide the original data for each month by the seasonal base number for the given month; that is, we divide each January clearings figure by the seasonal base number for January (353), each February clearings figure by the February base number (302), and proceed in like manner for each of the twelve months. The final results for the years 1890 and 1891 are given in Table LVII, Column E.

---

[1] Steps (7) and (8) are not a part of the link relative method as developed by Professor Persons. His method of applying the seasonal index numbers is outlined in the following chapter.

TABLE LVII

PARTIAL RECORD OF COMPUTATION OF AN INDEX NUMBER OF CHICAGO BANK
CLEARINGS ADJUSTED SEASONALLY BY THE LINK RELATIVE METHOD

(For computation of Column D, see Table LIX)

A	B	C	D	E
Year and month	Clearings [a] (Millions of dollars)	Link relative	Seasonal base number	Index number adjusted seasonally $(B \div D) \times 100$
1890				
January	296	...	353	84
February	253	.85	302	84
March	305	1.21	352	87
April	324	1.06	337	96
May	375	1.16	352	107
June	359	.96	340	106
July	351	.98	335	105
August	342	.97	320	107
September	360	1.05	325	111
October	406	1.13	364	112
November	364	.90	347	105
December	359	.99	364	99
1891				
January	346	.96	353	98
February	293	.85	302	97
March	334	1.14	352	95
April	348	1.04	337	103
May	391	1.12	352	111
June	375	.96	340	110
July	363	.97	335	108
August	362	1.00	320	113
September	398	1.10	325	122
October	422	1.06	364	116
November	402	.95	347	116
December	424	1.05	365	116

[a] From table 103, Appendix B.

TABLE LVIII
LINK RELATIVE FREQUENCY TALLY
CHICAGO BANK CLEARINGS

Based on Table LVII, Column C, and similar links computed from Table 103

RATIO	JAN. DEC.	FEB. JAN.	MAR. FEB.	APR. MAR.	MAY APR.	JUNE MAY	JULY JUNE	AUG. JULY	SEPT. AUG.	OCT. SEPT.	NOV. OCT.	DEC. NOV.
Under .81											I (70)	
.81	I	II										
.82						I		I				
.83		II										
.84		II										
.85		卌					I	II				
.86		II ※		I								
.87		I		I								
.88		I									I	
.89		III				I					I	
.90	I	I				I	I	I			II	
.91		II				I		IIII				
.92		II		I		II	I	I			I	
.93	II			III			I	II	I			
.94	I	I		I	II	I		I			II	
.95	III			II			III		I		II	
.96	IIII	I		IIII ※	I	IIII	II	I ※			III ※	
.97	※				I	II ※	II	II	II		I	
.98				II	II	I	I		I		卌	
.99	IIII			III	I	III	IIII ※		I		I	III
1.00	I			I	II	I	I	I	IIII		II	I
1.01	I			I	I		I	I	I		I	
1.02	I					III	IIII	II ※			I	
1.03	III			I	I	I			II			III
1.04	I			II	I	I	I					III
1.05					III ※		II	I	IIII			卌I ※
1.06				I	I	I	II		II	III		II
1.07		I		I	I		II	I		I		I
1.08									II	II		
1.09		II			II					I		
1.10					II				I	II		I
1.11										III		III
1.12		II			II					II ※		
1.13		II								I		I
1.14		III			II					I		
1.15		I								II		
1.16	I	I			I					I		
1.17		I ※					I	I				I
1.18		II								II		
1.19		II								II		
1.20		III		I						I		
Over 1.20		卌								I		
※ MEDIAN	.975	.86	1.17	.96	1.05	.97	.99	.96	1.02	1.12	.96	1.05

TABLE LIX

RECORD OF STEPS IN THE CALCULATION OF SEASONAL BASE NUMBERS FROM
THE MEDIANS OF LINK RELATIVES : CHICAGO BANK CLEARINGS

(Based on Table LVII)

A	B	C	D	E	F	G
Month	Median link relative	Crude serial relative	Monthly adjustment for secular trend (—.0041)	Adjusted serial relative (Jan. = 1.00)	Adjusted serial relative (Average of year = 1.00 [a])	Seasonal base numbers (Average of 1890 = 1.00 [b])
Jan.	.97½	1.000	...	1.000	1.035	353
Feb.	.86	.860	—.004	.856	.886	302
Mar.	1.17	1.006	—.008	.998	1.033	352
Apr.	.96	.966	—.012	.954	.988	337
May	1.05	1.014	—.016	.998	1.033	352
June	.97	.984	—.020	.964	.998	340
July	.99	.974	—.025	.949	.982	335
Aug.	.96	.935	—.029	.906	.938	320
Sept.	1.02	.954	—.033	.921	.953	325
Oct.	1.12	1.068	—.037	1.031	1.067	364
Nov.	.96	1.025	—.041	.984	1.019	347
Dec.	1.05	1.076	—.045	1.031	1.067	364
Jan.	.97½	1.049	—.049	1.000	....	...

[a] The average of the twelve monthly index numbers in Column E is .966.
[b] The average monthly clearings for the year 1890, computed from the data given in table 103, are 341 million dollars.

REFERENCES

1. COPELAND, M. T., *Quar. Jour. Econ.*, vol. 29, pp. 554-562, esp. 554-556.
2. DAVIES, G. R., *Introduction to Economic Statistics,* chap. v, "Trends and Cycles."
3. Federal Reserve Agent, New York, *Monthly Review,* February 1, 1922, "Credit Conditions," pp. 1-2.
4. KEMMERER, E. W., *Seasonal Variations in the Relative Demand for Money and Capital in the United States,* Senate Document 588, 61st Congress, 2d Session, pp. 13-15.
5. KING, W. I., *Elements of Statistical Method,* pp. 191-196.
6. PEARL, RAYMOND, *Introduction to Medical Biometry and Statistics,* chap. xvi, "Simple Curve Fitting."
7. PERSONS, W. M., *"Indices of Business Conditions"* in *Review of Economic Statistics,* Preliminary vol. i (1919), especially pp. 9-31.

CHAPTER XIV

BUSINESS CYCLES AND BAROMETERS

THERE is an increasing recognition on the part of business men and economists in general that a thorough understanding of the dynamic aspects of economic phenomena is to be attained largely through an analysis of that undulating movement in business activity which is customarily known as the business cycle. It is not the intention here to inquire into the causes of the business cycle, nor to describe the successive phases of prosperity, decline, depression, and recovery which mark its progress, but merely briefly to suggest some of the statistical methods which may be used in the analysis of the cyclical movements of economic activity. The term cyclical is not used with any implication of a definite periodicity to the movement. There is some difference of opinion among economists as to whether the undulatory movement of business activity has a regular wave-length, but all agree as to the existence and importance of the undulations or cycles.

STATISTICAL METHODS OF ISOLATING THE CYCLICAL MOVEMENT

Before a phenomenon can be studied satisfactorily, it must, so far as possible, be isolated. We have previously noted that the constituent elements in a time series are ordinarily a secular trend, a seasonal movement, various irregular or random fluctuations, and the business cycle. Also, we have noted various methods of determining the amount and direction of the long-time trend and the typical seasonal variation. How, then, may we proceed to eliminate these two factors in order to facilitate the study of the cyclical factor?

Eliminating the secular trend from annual data. If we are working with annual data, the seasonal factor is not present, hence we proceed to eliminate the influence of the trend in order to leave the net influence of the cycle (plus, of course, the influence of the irregular factors which cannot be removed by statistical methods). This may be done either by *subtracting* the trend from the original data, or by *dividing* the original data by the trend. The subtraction process is similar to that used in the preceding chapter in calculating the short-time or seasonal fluctuations of egg prices from the three-year trend (see Chart 34 and Table LVI, Column G).

If, on the other hand, it is desired to express the fluctuations of the cycle in terms of proportions of the trend from which they deviate, then the division method is used; that is, either the original item for a given year, or the deviation from the trend, is divided by the ordinate of the secular trend for that year, and so on for the entire period. The results of this division are ordinarily expressed in percentages.

The three parts of Chart 36 illustrate various ways of plotting the cyclical movement in annual data. Fig. A shows the annual production of crude steel in the United States as a whole and in the plants of the United States Steel Corporation taken separately. Also the straight-line secular trends, determined by the method of least squares, are shown for each series. Fig. B shows the deviations from the trends, with the trends as the zero or horizontal base line and the deviations expressed in millions of tons. In Fig. C these deviations are expressed in percentages of the ordinates of the respective trends at each given date, thus bringing out more clearly the similarity of the cyclical fluctuations of the two curves.

Determining the cycle from monthly data. For use in the analysis of the details of the business cycle, monthly data are more suitable than annual data, as many of the significant fluctuations are obscured in the annual averages. It then becomes necessary to remove not only the secular trend, but also the seasonal movement before the character of the cyclical fluctuations can be readily determined. One method of eliminating both the secular trend and the seasonal fluctuations is outlined later in this chapter, in the discussion of the business index computed by Professor W. M. Persons and published in the *Review of Economic Statistics*.

CHART 36

CYCLES IN ANNUAL PRODUCTION
CRUDE STEEL IN THE UNITED STATES: 1901-1921 *

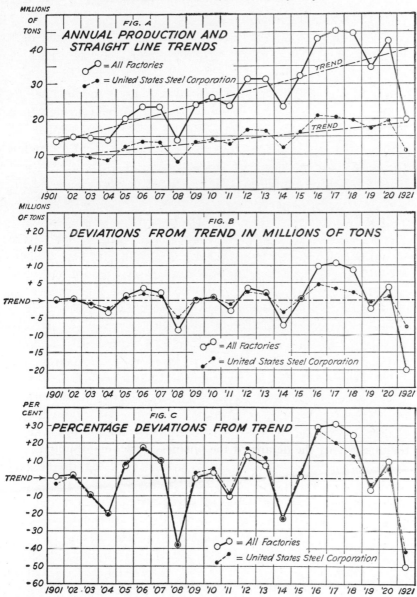

* Based on Tables LX and LXI.

TABLE LX

COMPUTATION OF CYCLES OF ANNUAL PRODUCTION OF CRUDE STEEL IN THE
UNITED STATES: 1901-1921 [a]

(Data for Chart 36)

A	B	C	D	E
	Production in millions of tons	Ordinate of trend $y = 1.32x + 26.6$	Deviation from trend	
Year			Millions of tons	Per cent of trend
1901	13.5	13.4	+ 0.1	+ 0.7
1902	14.9	14.7	+ 0.2	+ 1.4
1903	14.5	16.0	— 1.5	— 9.4
1904	13.9	17.4	— 3.5	— 20.1
1905	20.0	18.7	+ 1.3	+ 7.0
1906	23.4	20.0	+ 3.4	+ 17.0
1907	23.4	21.3	+ 2.1	+ 9.9
1908	14.0	22.6	— 8.6	— 38.1
1909	24.0	24.0	.0	.0
1910	26.1	25.3	+ 0.8	+ 3.2
1911	23.7	26.6	— 2.9	— 10.9
1912	31.3	27.9	+ 3.4	+ 12.2
1913	31.3	29.2	+ 2.1	+ 7.2
1914	23.5	30.6	— 7.1	— 23.2
1915	32.2	31.9	+ 0.3	+ 0.9
1916	42.8	33.2	+ 9.6	+ 28.9
1917	45.1	34.5	+ 10.6	+ 30.7
1918	44.5	35.8	+ 8.7	+ 24.3
1919	34.7	37.2	— 2.5	— 6.7
1920	42.1	38.5	+ 3.6	+ 9.4
1921	19.8	39.8	— 20.0	— 50.3

[a] Statistical Abstract of the United States, 1922, p. 194.

THE REDUCTION OF CYCLES OF SEVERAL SERIES TO A COMPARABLE BASIS

For purposes of comparative study, it is often desirable to reduce two or more cycles to relatives with a common unit of expression. This may be partially accomplished by expressing the series to be compared in terms of percentages, either with

TABLE LXI

COMPUTATION OF CYCLES OF ANNUAL PRODUCTION OF CRUDE STEEL BY THE
UNITED STATES STEEL CORPORATION: 1901-1921

(Data for Chart 36)

A	B	C	D	E
			Deviation from trend	
Year	Production in millions of tons [a]	Ordinate of trend $y = .48x + 14.0$	Millions of tons (B — C)	Per cent of trend (D ÷ C)
1901	8.9	9.2	— 0.3	— 3.3
1902	9.8	9.7	+ 0.1	+ 1.0
1903	9.2	10.2	— 1.0	— 9.8
1904	8.4	10.6	— 2.2	— 20.8
1905	12.0	11.1	+ 0.9	+ 8.1
1906	13.5	11.6	+ 1.9	+ 16.4
1907	13.3	12.1	+ 1.2	+ 9.9
1908	7.8	12.6	— 4.8	— 38.1
1909	13.4	13.0	+ 0.4	+ 3.1
1910	14.2	13.5	+ 0.7	+ 5.2
1911	12.8	14.0	— 1.2	— 8.6
1912	16.9	14.5	+ 2.4	+ 16.6
1913	16.7	15.0	+ 1.7	+ 11.3
1914	11.8	15.4	— 3.6	— 23.4
1915	16.4	15.9	+ 0.5	+ 3.1
1916	20.9	16.4	+ 4.5	+ 27.4
1917	20.3	16.9	+ 3.4	+ 20.1
1918	19.6	17.4	+ 2.2	+ 12.6
1919	17.2	17.8	— 0.6	— 3.4
1920	19.3	18.3	+ 1.0	+ 5.5
1921	11.0	18.8	— 7.8	— 41.5

[a] American Iron and Steel Institute, Annual Statistical Report, 1921, p. 67.
—Production of steel ingots and steel castings in gross tons.

some one year as a common fixed base, or as percentages of the
trend for each respective series. However, even after such reduction to percentages is accomplished, the cycles may not be close
enough together for easy comparison, due to the fact that the
several series differ in the amplitude (the vertical crest-to-trough

distance) of their cycles. In his analysis of fundamental business statistics, preparatory to the construction of a composite
business index, Professor Persons found that the percentage
deviations from the trend, adjusted seasonally, have a wide range
of distribution for some series and a narrow range for other
series.

> "For instance," he says,[1] "during the period of 1903-
> 1916 New York bank clearings ranged from — 49 per
> cent to + 64 per cent; outside bank clearings, from
> — 23 per cent to + 33 per cent; and the rate of interest
> on ten railway bonds, from — 4 per cent to + 11 per
> cent. This difference in range means that a deviation of
> + 10 per cent in one series indicates quite a different
> thing from what is indicated by a similar percentage de-
> viation in another series. That is, in *judging* the mean-
> ing of fluctuations of different series, percentages are
> not proper units to use. The problem, therefore, is to
> express the deviations of different series in comparable
> terms. What is a 'normal' fluctuation for each series?
> To answer this question a unit must be constructed for
> each series, which unit must depend upon the dispersion
> of percentage deviations in such series, so that the
> greater the dispersion the greater the unit. The range
> of the items is not a good measure of dispersion because
> it does not depend upon the distribution of the items
> between the maximum and the minimum. We need a
> measure of dispersion that, like an average, depends
> upon all items of the series. Of various measures
> which have been used by statisticians, the *standard
> deviation* is, without question, the most important and
> satisfactory."

Professor Persons finds,[2] for the three series named above,
the standard deviations of their percentage fluctuations from the
line of secular trend to be

[1] *Review of Economic Statistics,* January, 1919, p. 36.
[2] *Ibid.,* pp. 36, 190.

New York clearings............... 20.3 per cent
Outside bank clearings............ 8.62 " "
Yield of ten railroad bonds......... 2.82 " "

Accordingly, *to reduce these cycles to a comparable basis, each is divided by its standard deviation.* This brings the curves close together and makes it relatively easy to determine the extent to which they fluctuate in sympathy.

The actual study of the degree of sympathetic movement between the cycles is carried on by the various methods of correlation described in Chapter XV.

If it is desired to use a measure of dispersion which does not give so much influence to large deviations, the average deviation, instead of the standard deviation, may be used as the divisor.

CHART 37

METHODS OF COMPARING CYCLES *

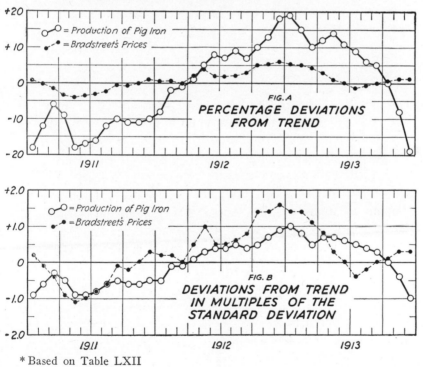

FIG. A
PERCENTAGE DEVIATIONS
FROM TREND

FIG. B
DEVIATIONS FROM TREND
IN MULTIPLES OF THE
STANDARD DEVIATION

* Based on Table LXII

TABLE LXII

MONTHLY CYCLES OF PIG IRON PRODUCTION AND "BRADSTREET'S" PRICES [a]

(Data for Chart 37)

Year and month	Percentage deviation from trend		Percentage deviation divided by standard deviation	
	Pig-iron production	Bradstreet's prices	Pig-iron production (S.D. = 19.15)	Bradstreet's prices (S.D. = 3.68)
1911				
January	— 18	+ .7	— .9	+ .2
February	— 12	— .2	— .6	— .1
March	— 6	— 1.4	— .3	— .4
April	— 9	— 3.4	— .5	— .9
May	— 18	— 4.0	— .9	— 1.1
June	— 17	— 3.5	— .9	— 1.0
July	— 16	— 3.0	— .8	— .8
August	— 12	— 2.2	— .6	— .6
September	— 10	— .5	— .5	— .1
October	— 11	— .6	— .6	— .2
November	— 11	.0	— .6	.0
December	— 10	+ 1.0	— .5	+ .3
1912				
January	— 8	+ .6	— .5	+ .2
February	— 2	+ .6	— .1	+ .2
March	— 1	— .1	— .1	.0
April	+ 1	+ 2.0	+ .1	+ .5
May	+ 5	+ 3.8	+ .3	+ 1.0
June	+ 8	+ 1.8	+ .4	+ .5
July	+ 7	+ 1.9	+ .4	+ .5
August	+ 9	+ 2.1	+ .5	+ .6
September	+ 7	+ 2.8	+ .4	+ .8
October	+ 10	+ 5.0	+ .5	+ 1.4
November	+ 13	+ 5.2	+ .7	+ 1.4
December	+ 18	+ 6.0	+ .9	+ 1.6
1913				
January	+ 19	+ 5.2	+ 1.0	+ 1.4
February	+ 15	+ 5.0	+ .8	+ 1.4
March	+ 10	+ 4.2	+ .5	+ 1.1
April	+ 12	+ 2.9	+ .7	+ .8
May	+ 14	+ 1.0	+ .7	+ .3
June	+ 11	+ .1	+ .6	.0
July	+ 9	— 1.3	+ .5	— .4
August	+ 6	— .6	+ .4	— .2
September	+ 5	+ .1	+ .3	.0
October	0	+ .5	.0	+ .1
November	— 8	+ 1.2	— .4	+ .3
December	— 19	+ 1.2	— 1.0	+ .3

[a] The data in this table are from the *Review of Economic Statistics,* Preliminary vol. i, 1919, pp. 67, 71, and 194. The trends used are based upon the data for the years 1903-16, inclusive. The pig-iron figures are corrected for seasonal variation; but such correction was not made for *Bradstreet's* prices, as the seasonal variation therein is minor.

Chart 37 illustrates the effect of dividing cycles in terms of percentage deviations by the standard deviation of the respective series. Fig. A shows the percentage deviations from trend of the production of pig iron and of *Bradstreet's* prices. A general similarity of movement is obvious, but the fluctuations of pig iron are so much more violent that comparisons become somewhat difficult. In Fig. B, however, the two curves are thrown together by dividing each by the standard deviation of the percentage deviations. We now see that the fluctuations of prices in 1902 and 1913 were even more violent than those of pig-iron production when the normal amount of fluctuation is taken as a criterion.

SINGLE-SERIES BUSINESS BAROMETERS

The fluctuations of the business cycle are so important a factor in the condition of business that it is appropriate at this point to deal briefly with the various so-called barometers of business. The alert business man who seeks to make the greatest possible success studies not only the conditions of his own industry, but also the general business conditions as reflected in the movement of fundamental business statistics or business barometers. Strictly speaking, we may distinguish between *business thermometers* and *business barometers*. Business thermometers record the present condition of business; business barometers forecast future movements. In practice, the term business barometer is often used indiscriminately to cover either concept.

What statistical series are good indicators of business conditions? Professor Day [1] compares three leading series with his general index of physical production and comes to the conclusion that the best single-series indicator of physical production is the freight tonnage handled by railroads. The other two series, revenue net ton-miles and deflated bank clearings, are influenced not only by the physical volume of goods traded, but also by the frequency with which such goods are exchanged. "Bank clearings are an extremely good barometer of present conditions and are watched with keen interest by all successful merchants and

[1] *Review of Economic Statistics,* 1921, pp. 20-21. ("Deflated" means divided by the price curve.)

manufacturers," [1] but Professor David F. Jordan points out that while bank clearings show accurately how business has been in the immediate past, they "offer little assistance in determining how it will be in the immediate future." [2] In his *Business Forecasting,* Professor Jordan treats in turn of barometers of agriculture, of industrial production, of marketing, of labor conditions, of business profits, of the exchanges, and of finance, and comes to the conclusion that, "No single barometer can be accepted as definitely indicative of coming events. The 'shadow which is cast before' must be sought in diverse developments rather than through one factor alone." [3] "Agricultural production," he says, "is the most important single factor which influences business conditions." Also, "the all-importance of the element of price in modern business makes changes in price levels of major significance in barometric work. No other factor more truly reflects the trend in business activity. . . . The prices of industrial securities, especially those of companies chiefly interested in raw materials and producers' goods, offer the best criterion for judging the impending course of events," and, "prices on the commodity exchanges reflect an even more scientific study of future probabilities than do those on the stock exchanges." The series mentioned are but a few of those which are considered significant in the attempt to forecast future conditions.

Composite Barometers of Business Conditions

The number and variety of single-series barometers of business conditions just mentioned suggest the desirability of computing, if possible, a single barometer, or a small group of barometers, which will faithfully record the combined influence of the important business series and by their movements indicate to business men what changes lie ahead. Composite curves or groups of curves designed to give indications of future business conditions are now published by several agencies. Three of these are briefly outlined below, each selected because of some distinc-

[1] R. W. Babson, *Business Barometers for Forecasting Conditions,* 1916, p. 19.
[2] D. F. Jordan, *Business Forecasting,* p. 193.
[3] *Ibid.,* pp. 227-233.

tive feature. It should be noted that none of these barometers are intended to be used as mechanical forecasters, but merely as statistical summaries of probabilities estimated from past experience; and, furthermore, that it is not a necessary implication that the three which are singled out for illustrative purposes are all necessarily superior to those not discussed.

The Harvard (Review of Economic Statistics) business index.[1] The Harvard business index, computed under the direction of Professor Persons and published in the *Review of Economic Statistics,* is of special interest to the student of statistical method because of the commendable fullness with which the process of construction is described. The original data used, the processes to which they are subjected, and the reasons for the choice of the particular methods employed, are set forth to enable the reader to retrace the steps taken and form his own judgment concerning the validity of the conclusions reached. The material analyzed in the preliminary study consisted of twenty-three important economic series for which consecutive monthly data could be obtained during the pre-war period (in most cases data for the years 1903-1916 were used). The data were subjected to the following processes: [2]

1. The *secular trend was determined,* in most instances by computing a straight-line trend by the method of least squares.

2. The *seasonal variation* was calculated for each series by the link-relative method.

3. The *original data* were then *corrected for secular and seasonal movements* by

   (a) multiplying each monthly ordinate of the secular trend by the index of seasonal variation for that month;

   (b) subtracting the resulting product from the corresponding original item; and

---

[1] For details as to method of construction see W. M. Persons, "Indices of Business Conditions," in *Review of Economic Statistics,* 1919, pp. 5-107, and "An Index of General Business Conditions," *ibid.,* pp. 111-205. This explanation is in itself almost a complete text-book of the fundamental processes in statistical methods, and no one who wishes to keep abreast of current developments in statistical science can afford not to be familiar with it.

[2] *Review of Economic Statistics,* 1919, especially 117-139

(c) expressing the result as a percentage of the ordinate of the secular trend, thus securing "percentage deviations of the original items from the corresponding ordinates of the secular trend corrected for seasonal variation."

4. The cycles of corrected percentage deviations were *divided by their respective standard deviations* in order to secure comparable cyclical fluctuations.[1]

5. The *correlation,* or similarity in direction and degree of movement, of each of these cycles when compared with the other series analyzed, was *studied by graphic and mathematical methods* of determining correlation (see Chapter XV, *infra*).

6. The *cycles were combined into groups* by putting together those series which exhibited a tendency to fluctuate simultaneously and in sympathy. The result, after the omission of several series, which, for one reason or another, did not appear suitable for use in the current index, and including certain modifications made in May, 1923,[2] is three groups of series, each represented by a graph and designated respectively as:

A. The *speculative group,* consisting of
   (1) New York City bank debits.
   (2) Price of industrial stocks.

B. The *business group,* consisting of
   (3) Bank debits for 140 cities outside New York City;
   (4) Commodity prices.

C. The *banking group,* consisting of
   (5) Rate on 4-6 months paper;
   (6) Rate on 60-90 day paper.

The barometric value of these index numbers lies in the fact that between each group there is a more or less regular lag in time. In the period studied, "the major movements of speculation preceded those of business by four to ten months, and the movements of business preceded those of banking by two to eight

---

[1] See charts of the cycles, in terms of standard deviations, on pp. 200-205, *Review of Economic Statistics,* 1919.
[2] *Review of Economic Statistics,* July, 1923.

months. The sequence of movements holding for upward swings and crests also held for downward swings and troughs." [1]

Consequently, it is believed that a rise in the speculative curve forecasts a rise in the business curve; a rise in the business curve anticipates a rise in the banking curve, and so on.

The Brookmire Economic Service [2] formerly published a forecasting chart of the same general type as the present Harvard business index, with three curves—Banking, Speculation, and General Business—grouped according to the principle of the time sequence of correlated series. In this sequence, however, the origin was interpreted to be with banking conditions rather than, as in the Harvard barometer, with speculation. In recent years, the Brookmire chart has been modified in an effort to get a forecaster such that major changes in direction can be distinguished from minor changes. Six series are used: (1) speculation, measured by the prices on the New York Stock Exchange of forty industrial and railroad stocks multiplied by the number of shares sold; (2) the physical volume of activity, measured by a composite of several series; (3) the ratio of imports to exports; (4) the turnover of bank deposits; (5) commercial-paper rates; and (6) foreign money rates as typified by those in the London money market.

These six series are corrected for seasonal variation and, when necessary, for secular trend, and combined into the "Forecasting Line" of their Barometer Chart No. 1, in such a way that so long as the economic phenomena represented by the composite curve remain above normal, it moves steadily upward, and so long as they continue below normal the curve moves downward; hence a change of direction in the curve represents, not merely a minor change in direction of the constituent series, but that they have passed their normal. The compilers of this curve interpret it as usually forecasting major changes in industrial stock prices by about one month and changes in *Bradstreet's* index of commodity prices by about seven months.

---

[1] *Review of Economic Statistics,* 1921, explanation to chart, p. 1.
[2] For fuller explanation of the Brookmire forecaster, see Ray Vance, *Business and Investment Forecasting,* chap. v.

The "Babsonchart." [1] In addition to the regular publication of many of the single series usually considered to be important barometers of business conditions, Babson's Statistical Organization publishes a *composite series* designed to indicate business conditions and represented graphically by the "Babsonchart." The general principle upon which the chart is constructed seems to be that in economic phenomena "action and reaction are equal" and that, consequently, when there has been a period of supernormal prosperity, the succeeding period of depression, or below-normal business, will equal the period of prosperity when both duration and intensity are considered. The extent of the periods of prosperity and depression, indicated on the chart by shaded areas, is computed from a normal trend line (the X-Y line) which represents Babson's estimate of the secular trend in business activity. The series used in forming the composite series are new buildings, crops, check transactions, immigration, total foreign trade and money (adjusted scales), failures, commodity prices, railroad earnings, stock prices, and an index of Canadian business conditions. In the judgment of the writer, there is not as clear a scientific basis for the method of forecasting used in this barometer as is furnished by the principle of time sequence which is basic to the Brookmire, Harvard, and some of the other barometers.

Business barometers are also published in the *Standard Daily Trade Service,* the *Annalist,* and *Management and Administration.* The last named series is prepared by Professor Lewis H. Haney, Director of the New York University Bureau of Business Research.

Special Studies and Future Possibilities

We have been able in this chapter to do little more than intimate the significance of the statistical aspects of the business cycle. For fuller discussion the reader should turn to the growing volume of special literature on the business cycle, notably the

---

[1] Cf., for example, Babson's *Report,* August 29, 1922, "Barometer Letter and the Babsonchart"—"Business this week is thirty-two points below the X-Y line, compared with thirty points below the line a week ago and fifty-six points a year ago."

study by Professor Warren M. Persons on the construction of a business index, the treatise by Professor Wesley C. Mitchell on *Business Cycles*, the volume by Professor David F. Jordan on *Business Forecasting*, and to the numerous other books and magazine articles on the subject, a few of which are listed in the "References" at the close of the chapter. Among the more technical treatises we should mention *Economic Cycles: Their Law and Cause*, by Professor H. L. Moore. In this he attempts to determine the periodicity of the rainfall cycle and trace its relation to the business cycle. The mere mention of a few of the studies of special phases of the business cycle suggests the many points at which it touches current economic and social problems. For example, in recent years Professor W. A. Berridge has published several studies on "Cycles of Employment and Unemployment"; [1] Professor G. R. Davies has inquired into the "Social Aspects of the Business Cycle"; [2] Professor Alvin H. Hansen has traced, by statistical means, the relation between cycles of strikes and price movements; [3] and the National Bureau of Economic Research has published two volumes [4] dealing with the business cycle and unemployment. One of these embodies the results of an investigation made for the President's Conference on Unemployment; the other is an intensive study, by Dr. W. I. King, of employment conditions in the United States from January, 1920, to March, 1922. Many other statistical studies dealing with various aspects of the business cycle may be found in recent numbers of the *Review of Economic Statistics*, the *Journal of the American Statistical Association*, or other similar economic publications.

[1] W. A. Berridge, *Cycles of Unemployment in the United States, 1903-1922*, and articles in the *Review of Economic Statistics*, January, 1922; and the *Journal of the American Statistical Association*, March, 1922, pp. 42-55, and June, 1922, pp. 227-240.

[2] *Quarterly Journal*, University of North Dakota, January, 1922, pp. 107-121.

[3] *American Economic Review*, December, 1921, pp. 616-621.

[4] *National Bureau of Economic Research:* vol. iv, *Business Cycles and Unemployment*, including report and recommendations of a committee of the President's Conference on Unemployment; vol. v, W. I. King, *Employment, Hours and Earnings in Prosperity and Depression. United States, 1920-1922.*

REFERENCES

BUSINESS CYCLES AND BAROMETERS

1. BABSON, ROGER W., *Business Barometers for Forecasting Conditions,* chap. iv, "The Theory of Fundamental Statistics."
2. BERRIDGE, W. A., *Cycles of Unemployment in the United States,* 1903-1923.
3. DAVIES, G. R., *Introduction to Economic Statistics,* 123-127.
4. ——— "Social Aspects of the Business Cycle," *Quarterly Journal,* published by the Univ. of North Dakota, January, 1922, pp. 107-121.
5. HANSEN, A. H., "Cycles of Strikes," *American Econ. Rev.,* December, 1921, 616-621.
6. ——— *Cycles of Prosperity and Depression in the United States, Great Britain, and Germany. A Study of Monthly Data, 1902-1908,* Univ. of Wisconsin Studies in the Social Sciences and History, No. 5, 1921.
7. JORDAN, D. F., *Business Forecasting.*
8. MITCHELL, W. C., *Business Cycles.*
9. MOORE, H. L., *Economic Cycles: Their Law and Cause.*
10. National Bureau of Economic Research, Inc.
    Vol. iv, *Business Cycles and Unemployment.*
    Vol. v, *Employment, Hours and Earnings in Prosperity and Depression—United States, 1920-22,* by W. I. King.
11. PERSONS, W. M., "Indices of Business Conditions," in *Review of Economic Statistics,* Preliminary vol. i, 1919, pp. 5-107; "An Index of General Business Conditions," *ibid.,* pp. 111-205.
12. ——— *The Index of General Business Conditions: A Non-Technical Explanation.*
13. VANCE, RAY, *Business and Investment Forecasting.*

CHAPTER XV

CORRELATION[1]

Just as the study of history is valuable largely as a guide to the future, so likewise, to a considerable extent, may statistics be looked upon as an historical method of study, by which, out of past experience, we formulate statements of the most probable future occurrences. By statistical analysis the economist hopes to obtain forecasting formulas which will afford practical aid in anticipating coming changes in economic conditions. He wants to be able to anticipate the most probable change in the price of corn with a given change in the quantity produced, or the most probable change in interest rates with a given change in bank reserves. Measures or coefficients of correlation are bases for such forecasting formulas, in that they express the relations which have existed in the past, in concise quantitative form convenient for use in estimating future probabilities.

Let us introduce our study of correlation by examining Chart 38. The reader will note that there is a marked uniformity in the movements between the curve representing the production of cotton and the curve representing the movement of the price of cotton. When the production curve rises, the price curve usually falls; when the production curve falls, the price curve rises. This relative consistency in the movement of the two curves is one type of correlation, called inverse correlation because of the tendency to movement in opposite directions. Let us examine more closely the nature of this phenomenon.

[1] The development of the theory of correlation is to be credited largely to a group of biometricians whose studies in inheritance led them to devise means of measuring the extent to which the characteristics of parents are inherited by their children and the extent to which the children tend to revert to the average type. In the group of those to whom the methods explained in this chapter are to be credited should be mentioned particularly Sir Francis Galton, Karl Pearson, and G. U. Yule. For a brief statement of the history of the development of the theory of correlation see W. M. Persons, *Indices of General Business Conditions*, p. 130.

CHART 38

INVERSE CORRELATION

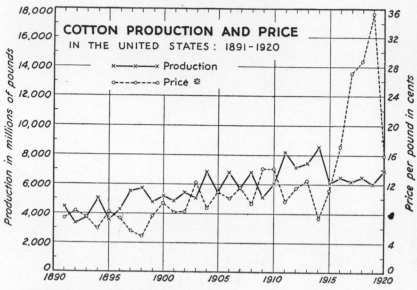

* Numerical data in Table LXIII.

We may tentatively define correlation as the typical amount of similarity, in direction and degree, of variations in corresponding pairs in two series of variables. On close analysis, the reader will recognize that there are three questions raised by this definition: (1) from what standard or *norm* are the variations to be compared measured; (2) what is meant by the *direction* of variation; and (3) what is the meaning of the phrase *degree* of correlation and how is it measured?

THE NORM FROM WHICH DEVIATIONS ARE MEASURED

We shall find it convenient to recognize definitely at the outset of our analysis three norms from which variation in chronological statistics may, according to the nature of the particular problem, appropriately be measured. These are the mean, the trend, and the item next preceding in time.

Variations from the mean of the series. If we wish to inquire into the extent to which variations in the length and

TABLE LXIII

COTTON PRODUCTION AND PRICE IN THE UNITED STATES: 1891-1920 [a]

Year	Production in millions of pounds	Price per pound (cents)	Year	Production in millions of pounds	Price per pound (cents)
1891	4,450	7.3	1906	6,800	10.0
1892	3,350	8.4	1907	5,700	11.5
1893	3,700	7.5	1908	6,800	9.2
1894	5,000	5.9	1909	5,150	14.3
1895	3,550	8.2	1910	6,000	14.0
1896	4,250	7.3	1911	8,150	9.6
1897	5,500	5.6	1912	7,150	11.5
1898	5,700	4.9	1913	7,400	12.5
1899	4,750	7.6	1914	8,500	7.3
1900	5,150	9.3	1915	6,050	11.2
1901	4,850	8.1	1916	6,400	17.3
1902	5,400	8.2	1917	6,200	27.1
1903	5,000	12.2	1918	6,500	28.8
1904	6,850	8.7	1919	6,000	35.4
1905	5,400	10.9	1920	6,950	15.8

[a] From U. S. Bureau of the Census, Bulletin 147, *Cotton Production and Distribution: Season of 1920-1921*, pp. 77-78. The production data, which were given in bales in the Census bulletin, have been converted into pounds in table LXIII and recorded to the nearest 50 million pounds.

The price data are for upland cotton. "For the years 1910 to 1920, inclusive, the price per pound for upland cotton represents the average price received for cotton by the growers as computed by the Department of Agriculture; for the years 1902 to 1909 it is the average price of the average grade marketed in New Orleans prior to April 1 of the following year; for the years 1890 to 1901, inclusive, it is the average price of middling cotton on the New Orleans Cotton Exchange." *Ibid.*

breadth of leaves, the height and weight of men, the size of wheat farms and the production cost per bushel—are similar in direction and degree, then we measure the variations from the arithmetic *mean*. We ask whether a wheat farm that is in size above the average has a production cost per bushel that is above or below average cost, and so on. This phase of correlation we shall designate as *static* correlation, as a matter of contrast with correlation involving the time element.

As we have previously noted, the greater part of the work of the economic statistician is concerned with the analysis of time series. The correlation between the long-time movements of two chronological series may be determined by the same method as that used for static correlation—that is, by comparing deviations from the mean. If the secular trends of the two series have been calculated, a simple method of determining the general character of the correlation of the long-time movements is by direct comparison of the slopes of the secular trends. If this were done for the data in Chart 38, we should expect to get evidence of correlation similar in direction, for both curves show a general tendency to rise.

Variations from the trend. The comparison of variations of two series from their trends is an important phase of statistical method as applied to economic statistics. This may be illustrated from the study made by Professor Warren M. Persons of the cyclical fluctuations of twenty important business series.[1] In order to determine which series fluctuated in sympathy, he correlated each of the twenty series with one or more of the other nineteen and in this way determined which series have associated fluctuations and, particularly, fluctuations which are substantially similar, not only in character, but also in time of occurrence. The comparisons in these cases were made between the series after seasonal variation and the secular trend had been eliminated, hence the variations compared are deviations, not from the arithmetic average, but from the trend.

First differences. In certain economic problems we are interested, not so much in deviations from the average, or in deviations from the trend, but in deviations from the immediately preceding item. Does an increase in the price of wheat bring a corresponding increase in the acreage of wheat planted in the succeeding year? Does a change of 1 per cent in the price of wheat bring a corresponding change in the price of flour? Is a rise or fall of 10 per cent in one index number accompanied by

[1] *Review of Economic Statistics,* 1919, especially pp. 120-127. See also chap. xiv, *supra.*

an equivalent movement in another index number? [1] Here we
have the question of the correlation of first differences; the variations to be considered are fluctuations from the preceding item.
Professor Persons calls attention to the fact that the following
frequently quoted definition of correlation by Bowley refers to
the correlation of first differences: [2]

> "When two quantities are so related that the fluctuations
> in one are in sympathy with the fluctuations of the other, so
> that an increase or decrease of one is found in connection
> with an increase or decrease (or inversely) of the other, and
> the greater the magnitude of the changes in the one, the
> greater the magnitude of the changes in the other, the quan-
> tities are said to be correlated."

We shall return presently to the method of computing the
correlation of first differences for the data represented in Chart 38.

TYPES OF CORRELATION

The second problem in correlation is that of direction or
type. Correlation may be either *direct* or *inverse*. If two series
tend to fluctuate in the same direction, one increasing when the
other increases, and decreasing when the other decreases, we have
direct correlation. However, if one decreases when the other increases, we have inverse correlation. We should expect direct
correlation between wholesale and retail prices; between unemployment and the amount of crime; between prosperity and the
number of marriages. We should, on the other hand, expect
inverse correlation between bank clearings and unemployment;
between market interest rates and prices of five-per-cent bonds;
and, as indicated in Chart 38, between crop production and the
unit price of farm products.

MEASUREMENT OF THE DEGREE OF CORRELATION

The degree of correlation. It is not enough, however, to
say that there is inverse correlation between crop production and

---

[1] For an example of the use of coefficients of correlation of first differences
for testing the closeness of movement between index numbers, see U. S.
Bureau of Labor Statistics Bulletin 284, p. 105.

[2] *Review of Economic Statistics,* 1919, p. 122. The definition given above
is quoted from A. L. Bowley, *Elements of Statistics,* p. 316, 1901 ed.

prices; we wish to know also whether this inverse relation is
invariable and, even if always inverse, whether or not both series
always vary to the same degree.   Is an increase in production
always accompanied by a change in price bearing some constant
ratio to the change in production?   Or is the relative change in
the two series variable, and if so, how can we express the most
probable relation in the paired variations?   Correlation may be
perfect, high, low, or entirely absent.   If two series always fluctuate in the same direction and in a constant ratio to each other,
there is perfect direct correlation.   If they always fluctuate in
opposite directions and to the same degree, there is perfect inverse
correlation.   If there seems to be only random association between the fluctuations, so that an increase in one series is equally
likely to be accompanied by either an increase or decrease in
the other, then we have the absence of correlation.

It is customary in mathematical terminology to use the figure
(1) as the symbol of certainty or perfection.   Hence perfect direct correlation is symbolized as (+ 1) correlation, perfect
inverse correlation as (— 1), and (0) represents no correlation.
In fact, however, practically all series show some similarity in
movement but do not reach perfect correlation.   The chief problem is to find some method of measuring the extent of this similarity.   To this end the coefficient of correlation has been devised.
It is computed in such a way that it reaches + 1 for perfect direct
correlation, — 1 for perfect inverse correlation, and 0 if there is
no relation evident.   All other values obtained range between + 1
and — 1.

The coefficient of concurrent deviations.   If we are interested only in the *direction* of the deviations and not in their
size, then we may use the coefficient of concurrent deviations, the
formula for which is as follows: [1]

$$r = \pm \sqrt{\pm \frac{2c - n}{n}} \quad \dots\dots\dots\dots\dots\dots \text{(Formula 37)},$$

[1] Adapted from W. I. King, *Elements of Statistical Method*, pp. 207-211.
This formula may also be used to measure the correlation between *changes
in direction* of two curves.   Cf. G. R. Davies, *Introduction to Economic Statistics*, pp. 132-134.

where,

> r = the coefficient of correlation,
> n = the number of pairs of items,
> c = the number of concurrent deviations, that is to say, the devia-
> tions of both paired items are positive (+) or both are
> negative (—).

If the reader will turn to Table LXVII later in this chapter, he will note that there is a comparison made between the year-to-year fluctuations in the production and price of cotton. There are twenty-four pairs of items in all, and if all first differences were concurrent, Formula 37 would give: $r = \sqrt{\dfrac{48 - 24}{24}} = +1$.

If the quantity (2c-n) is negative, a minus sign is used in front of it to make it positive, so that the square root can be extracted; then the minus sign is reintroduced by giving it to the square root. In Table LXVII only four of the years show a change in the same direction; hence the value of the coefficient of concurrent deviations becomes—

$$r = \pm \sqrt{\pm \dfrac{2\,(4) - 24}{24}} = -\sqrt{-(-2/3)} = -\sqrt{2/3} = -.82.$$

The Pearsonian, or sum-product, method.[1] If any considerable degree of precision is desired, the concurrent deviation method of finding the coefficient of correlation is inadequate, in that it gives no influence to the size of the deviation. The slight divergences in the same direction in 1900, 1901, and 1902 are given just as much weight in determining the coefficient as the larger deviations in opposite direction in 1904, 1911, and 1915, etc. To remedy this weakness the sum-product formula for the coefficient, usually known as the Pearsonian coefficient of correlation, has been devised. This is the method of correlation ordinarily used by statisticians, and it is, therefore, important that we understand the computation and interpretation of the Pearsonian coefficient.

To illustrate the method, let us take first an artificially simplified case of static correlation, in which we assume data con-

---

[1] This method is often designated as the product-moment method.

cerning the bushels of wheat produced on five farms (Table LXIV, Column II) and the cost per bushel on each farm (Column V). These are, of course, hypothetical data selected to reduce the illustrative computations to a simple form. The reader will note that a deviation of two bushels per acre from the mean production per acre for all farms (eighteen bushels) is accompanied by a deviation of one cent per bushel in the cost, in the opposite direction, and that this ratio is true for each farm. Evidently this is a case of perfect inverse correlation and the mathematical expression of this relation should be — 1. The formula for the coefficient of correlation is

$$r = \frac{\Sigma\, xy}{n(S.D._x)(S.D._y)}, \text{ or } r = \frac{\Sigma\, xy}{n\, \sigma_x \sigma_y} \ldots \ldots \text{(Formula 38)},$$

where

$r =$ the coefficient of correlation,
$xy =$ the product of a pair of deviations,
$\Sigma\, xy =$ the sum of such products,
σ_x or $S.D._x =$ the standard deviation of the x series,
σ_y or $S.D._y =$ the standard deviation of the y series,
$n =$ the total number of pairs compared.

The data for finding these quantities are given in Table LXIV below.

TABLE LXIV

COMPUTATION OF THE PEARSONIAN COEFFICIENT OF CORRELATION

(Hypothetical data)

I	II	III	IV	V	VI	VII	VIII
	Wheat production per acre			Cost of production per bushel			Product of deviations (III)×(VI)
Farm	Bushels	Deviation from mean	Deviations squared	Cost in cents	Deviation from mean	Deviations squared	
		x	x^2		y	y^2	xy
Total			80			20	— 40
A	12	— 6	36	39	+ 3	9	— 18
B	16	— 2	4	37	+ 1	1	— 2
C	18 (Mean)	0	0	36 (Mean)	0	0	0
D	20	+ 2	4	35	— 1	1	— 2
E	24	+ 6	36	33	— 3	9	— 18

Substituting the values found in the above table in Formula 38 for the coefficient of correlation, we have

$$r = \frac{\Sigma \, xy}{n\sigma_x \, \sigma_y} = \frac{-40}{5\sqrt{\frac{80}{5}}\sqrt{\frac{20}{5}}} = \frac{-40}{40} = -1, \text{ or perfect inverse correlation.}$$

In Formula 38, x and y represent deviations from the means. Another form of the correlation equation, identical in meaning with Formula 38, uses $(x - \bar{x})$ and $(y - \bar{y})$ to represent the respective deviations from the means. This form of the Pearsonian formula, which is used in subsequent illustrations, is

$$r = \frac{\Sigma(x - \bar{x})(y - \bar{y})}{n\sigma_x \, \sigma_y} \ldots\ldots\ldots\ldots\ldots\ldots(\text{Formula 39}),$$

where

x = an item in one of the original series; y, the corresponding item in the other series,

$\bar{x}$ = the mean of the x-series,

$\bar{y}$ = the mean of the y-series,

hence the deviation from the mean is expressed, not by x and y, as in Formula 38, but by $(x - \bar{x})$ and $(y - \bar{y})$.

We may make the meaning of the coefficient of correlation more obvious if we call attention to the fact that what Formulas 38 and 39 give is the *mean sum-product,* or the mean of the sum of the products of the paired deviations, when each deviation is first divided by the standard deviation of its series. The standard deviation of the x-series is $\sqrt{\frac{80}{5}}$ or 4, of the y-series, $\sqrt{\frac{20}{5}}$ or 2.

Dividing each series by its standard deviation we have—

TABLE LXV.—DEVIATIONS IN MULTIPLES OF THE STANDARD DEVIATIONS

(Based on Table LXIV)

Farm	Production	Cost	Product
A	— 1.5	+ 1.5	— 2.25
B	— 0.5	+ 0.5	— 0.25
C	0.0	0.0	0.00
D	+ 0.5	— 0.5	— 0.25
E	+ 1.5	— 1.5	— 2.25
			$\Sigma = -5.00$

The sum-product of the deviations is — 5. The number of pairs is also 5; hence the mean sum-product is — 1. By a different order of procedure we have again obtained — 1, the coefficient for perfect correlation.

The significance of (r) may be stated also in terms of its *geometric meaning*. To this end, let us first plot the data in Table LXIV on a chart with units in bushels and cents like the original data. In Fig. A of Chart 39, the vertical axis represents the mean of the x-series (eighteen bushels per acre). The horizontal axis represents the mean of the y-series (thirty-six cents per bushel). The deviations for Farm A are — 6 and + 3, respectively, giving the point A on the scale. The points B, C, D, and E are located in like manner. The line AE is the line of regression or the line which best fits the plotted points. In this case, and in all cases of perfect correlation, the points all lie on the line, hence there is no difficulty in drawing it. This line may be expressed by the regression equation, which is

$$Y = r\left(\frac{\sigma_y}{\sigma_x}\right)X, \text{ or } (y-\bar{y}) = r\left(\frac{\sigma_y}{\sigma_x}\right)(x-\bar{x})\ldots..\text{(Formula 40)},$$

where

X, or $(x-\bar{x})$ = a given deviation of the variable x from its mean, or the abscissa of a point on the regression line (Chart 39, Fig. A),

Y, or $(y-\bar{y})$ = the most probable deviation in y, or the ordinate of the regression line corresponding to the given deviation in x,

r = the coefficient of correlation.

Substituting the values for these quantities previously found, we have

$$Y = (-1)\left(\frac{2}{4}\right)X, \quad \text{or } Y = -\frac{1}{2}X,$$

which means that for any given value of X there is an opposite deviation of one-half as many units in Y. The reader can verify this relation by reference to Table LXIV. For each deviation of one unit from the mean in bushels produced there is a deviation of half a unit in price (in the opposite direction). This we may call the statistical law connecting bushels produced and cost per bushel.

CHART 39
PERFECT INVERSE CORRELATION*

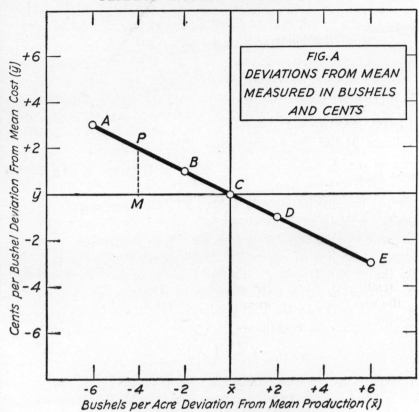

FIG. A
DEVIATIONS FROM MEAN
MEASURED IN BUSHELS
AND CENTS

Cents per Bushel Deviation From Mean Cost ($\bar{y}$)

Bushels per Acre Deviation From Mean Production ($\bar{x}$)

Unit = One Standard Deviation

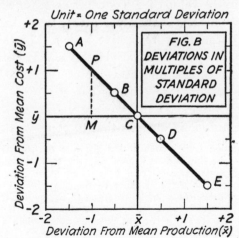

FIG. B
DEVIATIONS IN
MULTIPLES OF
STANDARD
DEVIATION

Deviation From Mean Cost ($\bar{y}$)

Deviation From Mean Production ($\bar{x}$)

*Based on Tables LXIV and LXV.

In Fig. B of Chart 39, the scale units are the standard deviations. As a result the standard deviations are eliminated from the equation of the line A-E, and we may write

$$Y = r(X), \text{ or } r = \frac{Y}{X}$$

In other words, when the scale units are the standard deviations, the coefficient of correlation is the fraction found by dividing the ordinate of the line of regression by its abscissa, e.g. $\frac{MP}{CM}$ in Fig. B, Chart 39; or we may say that it is the slope of the regression line.

The hypothetical data in Table LXIV give perfect correlation, but in actual data the correlated points will not all lie on a straight line, nor will the correlation formula give $(+ 1)$ or $(- 1)$ as the result. The line of regression then becomes the line which best fits the scattered points.[1] To find this line and consequently the law of most probable relation between the items in the two series, we calculate (r) by the sum-product formula and insert its value in the regression equation—

$$Y = r \left(\frac{\sigma_y}{\sigma_x} \right) X$$

This gives us the best estimate we can make from the statistical analysis of the available data as to the probable deviation which will be found in the value of Y (cost per acre, for example) with a unit deviation in X (bushels per acre), when both deviations are measured from their respective means. In this sense, the regression equation for two variables is a forecasting formula, giving the best estimate for the value of one variable when the corresponding value of the other is known.

Correlation table. If the variate values to be correlated are very numerous, it is obvious that to compute the correlation

---

[1] In this discussion it is assumed that the line of *best fit* is the line of least squares, that is, the line so drawn that the sum of the squares of the deviations of the plotted points from it is a minimum. Expositions of the mathematical reasons for the acceptance of the line of least squares as best for this purpose will be found in the treatises on the method of least squares cited in the "References" for Chapter X. It should also be noted that the line of best fit is not always a straight line. For some data a curved line of regression is more accurate.

from the deviation for each individual item would be too laborious. A more practicable method is to arrange the items in frequency groups in a correlation or double-entry table similar in form to Table LXVI, and compute the correlation by using these groups as units, with due allowance for the relative frequencies.[1] Often, also, the general character of the relation between the variables can be determined by inspection of the correlation table or of a scatter tally arranged in similar form. Even a superficial inspection of Table LXVI reveals a general tendency to direct correlation—that is, for short men to be light in weight and tall men to be heavy.

TABLE LXVI.—CORRELATION TABLE

HEIGHT AND WEIGHT OF NINETY UNIVERSITY OF WISCONSIN MALE STUDENTS

(Based upon Table 104, Appendix B)

Weight in pounds	All heights	Height in inches					
		62.0 to 63.9	64.0 to 65.9	66.0 to 67.9	68.0 to 69.9	70.0 to 71.9	72.0 to 73.9
Total	90	1	18	23	26	16	6
100.0–109.9	3	1	1	1			
110.0–119.9	9		5	4			
120.0–129.9	23		6	12	5		
130.0–139.9	22		6	4	8	4	
140.0–149.9	14			2	6	4	2
150.0–159.9	14				6	6	2
160.0–169.9	2					1	1
170.0–179.9	3				1	1	1

Correlation of first differences. Let us now turn our attention to the method of computing the coefficient of correlation of first differences, and in this connection we shall try to make

[1] For more detailed discussion of the use of the correlation table, see G. U. Yule, *Theory of Statistics*, 6th ed., chap. ix, and C. J. West, *Introduction to Mathematical Statistics*, chap. vii.

more obvious the real significance of the coefficient, which doubtless still appears to the reader as a somewhat abstract concept.

TABLE LXVII—CORRELATION OF FIRST DIFFERENCES
Computed from data in Table LXIII

	A	B	C	D	E	F	G	H	I
	Production of cotton				Price of Cotton				Product of deviations (B × F)
Year	First differences (millions of pounds)	Deviation from mean (+ 70)	Deviation squared	Deviation divided by S.D.[a]	First differences (cents)	Deviation from mean (+ 0.2)	Deviation squared	Deviation divided by S.D.[a]	
	x	(x − x̄)	(x − x̄)²	$\frac{(x - \bar{x})}{\sigma_x}$	y	(y − ȳ)	(y − ȳ)²	$\frac{(y - \bar{y})}{\sigma_y}$	(x − x̄)(y − ȳ)
Total	+ 1,600		34,973,600		+ 3.9		+ 158.85		− 63,322
1892	− 1,100	− 1,170	1,368,900	− .97	+ 1.1	+ 0.9	.81	+ .35	− 1,053
1893	+ 350	+ 280	78,400	+ .23	− 0.9	− 1.1	1.21	− .43	− 308
1894	+ 1,300	+ 1,230	1,512,900	+ 1.02	− 1.6	− 1.8	3.24	− .70	− 2,214
1895	− 1,450	− 1,520	2,310,400	− 1.26	+ 2.3	+ 2.1	4.41	+ .82	− 3,192
1896	+ 700	+ 630	396,900	+ .52	− 0.9	− 1.1	1.21	− .43	− 693
1897	+ 1,250	+ 1,180	1,392,400	+ .98	− 1.7	− 1.9	3.61	− .74	− 2,242
1898	+ 200	+ 130	16,900	+ .11	− 0.7	− 0.9	.81	− .35	− 117
1899	− 950	− 1,020	1,040,400	− .85	+ 2.7	+ 2.5	6.25	+ .97	− 2,550
1900	+ 400	+ 330	108,900	+ .27	+ 1.7	+ 1.5	2.25	+ .58	+ 495
1901	− 300	− 370	136,900	− .31	− 1.2	− 1.4	1.96	− .54	+ 518
1902	+ 550	+ 480	230,400	+ .40	+ 0.1	− 0.1	.01	− .04	− 48
1903	− 400	− 470	220,900	− .39	+ 4.0	+ 3.8	14.44	+ 1.48	− 1,786
1904	+ 1,850	+ 1,780	3,168,400	+ 1.47	− 3.5	− 3.7	13.69	− 1.44	− 6,586
1905	− 1,450	− 1,520	2,310,400	− 1.26	+ 2.2	+ 2.0	4.00	+ .78	− 3,040
1906	+ 1,400	+ 1,330	1,768,900	+ 1.10	− 0.9	− 1.1	1.21	− .43	− 1,463
1907	− 1,100	− 1,170	1,368,900	− .97	+ 1.5	+ 1.3	1.69	+ .51	− 1,521
1908	+ 1,100	+ 1,030	1,060,900	+ .85	− 2.3	− 2.5	6.25	− .97	− 2,575
1909	− 1,650	− 1,720	2,958,400	− 1.43	+ 5.1	+ 4.9	24.01	+ 1.91	− 8,428
1910	+ 850	+ 780	608,400	+ .65	− 0.3	− 0.5	.25	− .19	− 390
1911	+ 2,150	+ 2,080	4,326,400	+ 1.72	− 4.4	− 4.6	21.16	− 1.79	− 9,568
1912	− 1,000	− 1,070	1,144,900	− .89	+ 1.9	+ 1.7	2.89	+ .66	− 1,819
1913	+ 250	+ 180	32,400	+ .15	+ 1.0	+ 0.8	.64	+ .31	+ 144
1914	+ 1,100	+ 1,030	1,060,900	+ .85	− 5.2	− 5.4	29.16	− 2.10	− 5,562
1915	− 2,450	− 2,520	6,350,400	− 2.09	+ 3.9	+ 3.7	13.69	+ 1.44	− 9,324

[a] The S. D. for cotton production = 1207; for price, 2.57.

In Table LXVII are given the first differences for cotton production and price, and paired differences are plotted in Chart 40, designated as a *"scatter diagram."* The figures in Columns A and E of Table LXVII represent the change in production, as compared with the preceding year, and the corresponding change

CHART 40*

SCATTER DIAGRAM

FIRST DIFFERENCES OF COTTON PRODUCTION AND PRICE
1891 – 1915

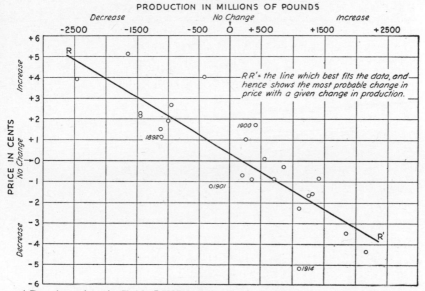

* Based on data in Table LXVII, Columns A and E.

in price; and, likewise, each plotted point on Chart 40 graphically represents the first differences in production and price for some one year. For example, the circle marked 1892 represents the fact that the first difference for 1892 is — 1,170 million pounds, a decrease to that extent from 1891, and that price increased that year 1.1 cents, measured vertically from the "No change" line. In a similar way each circle represents both the production change and the price change for a given year. In general the circles indicate that a decrease in production is accompanied by an increase in price, but the relation is variable in degree. We wish to find some expression which will represent the most probable change in price with a given change in production—that is, we wish to find the line which best fits the data. This is the line of least squares, (RR'), or the line so drawn that the sum of the squares of the deviations of the plotted points from it is a minimum; hence the slope of the line RR′ is given by the equation which represents the slope of the line of least squares, which is

$$m = \frac{\Sigma(x-\bar{x})\,(y-\bar{y})}{\Sigma\,(x-\bar{x})^2}\ldots\ldots\ldots\ldots\text{(Formula 41)},$$

where

$m =$ the slope of the line of least squares,

$(x-x) =$ a deviation of a first difference in production from the mean of the first differences,

$(y-\bar{y}) =$ the corresponding deviation of first differences in price,

or, substituting the value of these quantities as given in Table LXVII, we have

$$m = \frac{-63,322}{34,973,600} = -.00181.$$

If we keep in mind that we are speaking of the extent to which the change in production or price in the given year exceeds or falls short of the average year-to-year change, we may interpret the numerical value (—.00181) of m in the above equation as indicating that when the change in production varies from the average change by one million pounds, then the most probable variation in price is a variation in the opposite direction of —.00181 cents. This relation could be used as a coefficient of correlation or statement of the relation between the two series, but would be ill-adapted to comparisons with coefficients calculated for other series. Furthermore, dependent as it is on the particular units in which the data are expressed, that is, cents and millions of pounds, it does not clearly indicate the degree to which price fluctuates in sympathy with production. To improve these defects the formula for m, the slope of the line of least squares, is translated into r, which is the slope of the line best fitting the points when the deviations of each are measured from the mean and expressed in multiples of their respective standard deviations. In Columns B and F of Table LXVII the deviations of the first differences from their respective means are given, and in Columns D and H, the results of dividing each series of deviations by its respective standard deviation. Chart 41 represents the data in Columns D and H plotted with circles representing the paired values, and RR′ is the line of best fit to these plotted

CHART 41 *

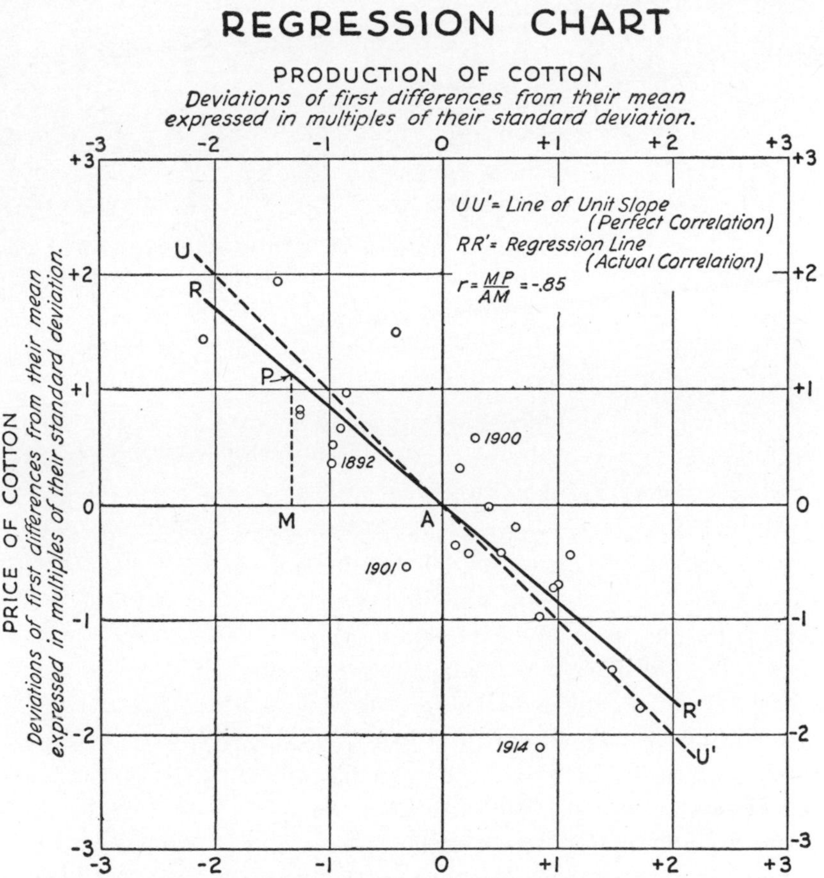
REGRESSION CHART
PRODUCTION OF COTTON
Deviations of first differences from their mean expressed in multiples of their standard deviation.
PRICE OF COTTON
Deviations of first differences from their mean expressed in multiples of their standard deviation.
UU' = Line of Unit Slope (Perfect Correlation)
RR' = Regression Line (Actual Correlation)
r = MP/AM = -.85
U
R
P
M
A
R'
U'
1900
1892
1901
1914
-3
-2
-1
0
+1
+2
+3

* Based on data in Table LXVII, Columns D and H.

points. Let r represent the slope of this line RR′. The data plotted in this chart are deviations from the mean divided by the standard deviation, hence Formula 41, for the slope of the line of least squares, becomes

$$r = \frac{\Sigma\left(\frac{x-\bar{x}}{\sigma_x}\right)\left(\frac{y-\bar{y}}{\sigma_y}\right)}{\Sigma\left(\frac{x-\bar{x}}{\sigma_x}\right)^2} \text{..........(Formula 42),}$$

but the denominator of this equation reduces to unity, hence the formula may be rewritten

$$r = \Sigma \left[\left(\frac{x - \bar{x}}{\sigma_x} \right) \left(\frac{y - \bar{y}}{\sigma_y} \right) \right] = \frac{\Sigma(x - \bar{x})(y - \bar{y})}{n\, \sigma_x\, \sigma_y}.$$

This last equation is merely the familiar Pearsonian equation (Formula 39) for the coefficient of correlation. In other words, the Pearsonian coefficient of correlation is the slope of the straight line which best represents the plotted points portraying the associated deviations of two series when these deviations are expressed in multiples of their standard deviations. Substituting the quantities in Table LXVII, the numerical value of this slope is found from Equation 39 to be

$$r = \frac{-63,322}{24\sqrt{\dfrac{34,973,600}{24}}\sqrt{\dfrac{158.85}{24}}} = \frac{-63,322}{24(1207)(2.57)} = -.85.$$

More concretely, if the reader will measure the length of the lines AM and MP in Chart 41, he will note that the line MP is .85 as long as AM. In other words, a deviation of one unit in production is accompanied by an opposite deviation of .85 in price. Or we may say the slope of the regression line is —.85 for the first differences of cotton production and price.

Correlation of deviations from secular trends. We have noted the application of the Pearsonian method of correlation to two cases, one of perfect static correlation, the other of correlation of first differences. With appropriate modifications the sum-product method may be applied also to the study of deviations from secular trends. On page 282, in Columns A and D, are given the ordinates of the respective secular trends [1] of cotton production and prices. In Columns B and E are given the deviations from the secular trends. The formula for the coefficient of correlation for such deviations is [2]

[1] The steps in the computation of these trends are not shown. They are computed by the method of least squares for a straight line trend, as described in chap. xiii.

[2] It should be noted that the correlation of deviations from the straight-line trend determined by the method of least squares is essentially the same as the correlation of deviations from the mean of the deviations, in that the mean of the deviations from such a trend is zero.

$$r = \frac{\Sigma(y-Y)_1\,(y-Y)_2}{n\sigma_1\,\sigma_2}\dots\dots\dots\text{(Formula 43)},$$

where r = the coefficient of correlation,

$(y-Y)_1$ = a deviation of the ordinate of the first series from its secular trend,

$(y-Y)_2$ = a deviation of the ordinate of the second series from its secular trend,

σ_1 = the standard deviation of the deviations from trend of the first series,

σ_2 = the corresponding S.D. for the second series, and

n = the number of years or other periods compared.

Substituting in above formula from Table LXVIII, we have

$$r = \frac{-23,809.5}{25\sqrt{\dfrac{14,350,000}{25}}\sqrt{\dfrac{85.66}{25}}} = -.679.$$

When deviations from straight-line trends have been expressed in multiples of their standard deviations, as is frequently done for purposes of comparison (see Chapter XIV), the formula for r reduces to

$$r = \frac{\Sigma xy}{n}\dots\dots\dots\dots\dots\dots\text{(Formula 44)},$$

where x and y represent deviations expressed as multiples of their respective standard deviations.

Short-cut process. In actual statistical practice it will usually be found convenient to compute the coefficient by a short-cut process rather than by the direct process illustrated in the correlation of first differences. To avoid burdening the text with further detail, the explanation of this short-cut process is placed in Appendix A to this chapter, but it should not be neglected by the reader who wishes to make correlation computations.

The standard error of the regression equation.[1] We have seen that the coefficient of correlation enables us, through the regression equation, to state the most probable change in one variable, given a certain change in another. But we still need some measure of the degree to which the actual occurrences vary

---

[1] This "standard error" is merely the standard deviation of the deviations of the actual plotted points from the line RR′, Chart 40, measured vertically. When all points lie on the straight line, as in Chart 39, there are no deviations and hence no error in estimating from the regression equation.

TABLE LXVIII

CORRELATION OF DEVIATIONS FROM STRAIGHT-LINE TRENDS [a]

Year	A	B	C	D	E	F	G
	Production of cotton			Price of cotton			Product of deviations (B × E)
	Trend (millions) (of tons)	Deviation from trend	Deviation squared	Trend (cents)	Deviation from trend	Deviation squared	
	Y_1	$(y - Y)_1$	$(Y - Y)_1{}^2$	Y_2	$(y - Y)_2$	$(y - Y)_2{}^2$	$(y - Y)_1(y - Y)_2$
Total			14,350,000			85.66	− 23,809.5
1891	3,812	+ 638	407,044	6.8	+ 0.5	.25	+ 319.0
1892	3,963	− 613	375,769	7.0	+ 1.4	1.96	− 858.2
1893	4,114	− 414	171,396	7.2	+ 0.3	.09	− 124.2
1894	4,265	+ 735	540,225	7.4	− 1.5	2.25	− 1,102.5
1895	4,416	− 866	749,956	7.6	+ 0.6	.36	− 519.6
1896	4,567	− 317	100,489	7.8	− 0.5	.25	+ 158.5
1897	4,718	+ 782	611,524	8.0	− 2.4	5.76	− 1,876.8
1898	4,869	+ 831	690,561	8.2	− 3.3	10.89	− 2,742.3
1899	5,020	− 270	72,900	8.4	− 0.8	.64	+ 216.0
1900	5,171	− 21	441	8.6	+ 0.7	.49	− 14.7
1901	5,322	− 472	222,784	8.8	− 0.7	.49	+ 330.4
1902	5,473	− 73	5,329	9.0	− 0.8	.64	+ 58.4
1903	5,624	− 624	389,376	9.2	+ 3.0	9.00	− 1,872.0
1904	5,775	+ 1,075	1,155,625	9.4	− 0.7	.49	− 752.5
1905	5,926	− 526	276,676	9.6	+ 1.3	1.69	− 683.8
1906	6,077	+ 723	522,729	9.8	+ 0.2	.04	+ 144.6
1907	6,228	− 528	278,784	10.0	+ 1.5	2.25	− 792.0
1908	6,379	+ 421	177,241	10.2	− 1.0	1.00	− 421.0
1909	6,530	− 1,380	1,904,400	10.4	+ 3.9	15.21	− 5,382.0
1910	6,681	− 681	463,761	10.6	+ 3.4	11.56	− 2,315.4
1911	6,832	+ 1,318	1,737,124	10.8	− 1.2	1.44	− 1,581.6
1912	6,983	+ 167	27,889	11.0	+ 0.5	.25	+ 83.5
1913	7,134	+ 266	70,756	11.2	+ 1.3	1.69	+ 345.8
1914	7,285	+ 1,215	1,476,225	11.4	− 4.1	16.81	− 4,981.5
1915	7,436	− 1,386	1,920,996	11.6	− 0.4	.16	+ 554.4

[a] The trends in Columns A and D are computed by the method of least squares from the data for 1891-1915 in table LXIII. (See Formulas 35 and 36, chap. xiii.) They are: $y = 5624 + 151x$, for production; and $y = 9.2 + .2x$, for price.

$$r = \frac{\Sigma (y - Y)_1 (y - Y)_2}{n\, \sigma_1\, \sigma_2} = \frac{- 23,809.5}{25 \cdot \sqrt{\dfrac{14,350,000}{25}} \sqrt{\dfrac{85.66}{25}}} = - .679$$

from the "most probable" occurrence. This measure is found in the standard error, the formula for which is

$$S_y = \sigma_y \sqrt{1 - r^2} \dots\dots\dots\dots\dots \text{(Formula 45)},$$

where

S_y = the standard error of the regression equation,
σ_y = standard deviation of the y series.

Substituting in this equation the values for σ_y and r which we have computed for the data in Table LXVII, we have

$$S_y = 2.57 \sqrt{1 - (-.85)^2} = 1.35 \text{ cents.}$$

Hence 1.35 cents is the "standard error" in estimating the change in annual average price from a given change in production in the years 1891-1915.

The probable error. The coefficient which we have obtained for the first differences in cotton production and price was calculated from a sample of twenty-four years. If we took a different sample we should probably get a somewhat different result. The usual measure of the probable variations of the coefficient from sample to sample is found in the "probable error," which depends on two factors, the size of the coefficient and the size of the sample. The formula for it is this:

$$\text{P.E.}_r = 0.6745 \; \frac{(1 - r^2)}{\sqrt{n}} \dots\dots\dots\dots \text{(Formula 46).}$$

The significance of the probable error has been noted in Chapter X. Briefly stated, it means that if many similar samples were taken, half of the coefficients found would, on the average, if the differences between the samples are due merely to random selection, fall within the range—

$$-.85 \pm 0.6745 \; \frac{[1 - (-.85)^2]}{\sqrt{24}} \text{ or } -.85 \pm .04.$$

The probable error throws additional light on the significance of a given coefficient of correlation, hence a coefficient should, if all the available information is to be stated, be written as $r \pm \text{P.E.}$[1]

[1] The practice of stating the probable error of a coefficient of correlation is not quite so rigidly adhered to for the correlation of time series as for static correlation; also it has been suggested that a modified form of the probable error formula should be used in connection with the correlation of first differences. Cf. *Biometrika*, x., p. 278.

The time lag or lead. The above somewhat tedious digression into the theory of the coefficient of correlation should not divert our attention from the central fact, which is that we are often desirous of getting a quantitative measure of the degree of sympathy of fluctuation between two series, and that the coefficient of correlation is the accepted device for that purpose. In economic statistics there often appears a factor not previously mentioned, and that is the lag, or the tendency for the influence of one phenomenon to be evident in another only after the passage of time. When immigration is not closely regulated, it ebbs and flows with the tide of prosperity in this country, but the effect is not instantaneous. Professor W. M. Persons in the construction of the business index previously discussed had occasion to make extensive study of the lag between various series. The coefficient of correlation affords a convenient device for this purpose when the lag is not entirely regular and hence not readily determinable by simple inspection. By computing coefficients of correlation for pig-iron production and the interest rates on sixty-to-ninety day paper, using varying periods for the lag of the interest rate behind pig-iron production, he obtained the following results: [1]

Lag of interest rate (months)	Coefficient of correlation	Lag of interest rate (months)	Coefficient of correlation
None	$+.34$	Seven	$+.73$
Three	$+.67$	Eight	$+.70$
Four	$+.72$	Nine	$+.65$
Five	$+.75$	Twelve	$+.45$
Six	$+.75$		

It is apparent that the maximum correlation ($+.75$) between pig-iron production and the interest rate occurs when the production of pig-iron is paired with the interest rate some five or six months later. The approach to the fascinating problem of forecasting future business conditions is largely by way of analysis of the timing, or relations of lag and lead, between important economic series. This relation, it may be noted, is not

[1] *Review of Economic Statistics,* 1919, p. 124. For the procedure preliminary to this study of correlation, see chaps. xiii and xiv.

necessarily the same on the upturn and on the decline of the business cycle.

THE USE AND INTERPRETATION OF THE COEFFICIENT AS HIGH OR LOW

In a problem like the one just cited, it is not necessary to put a direct valuation on the coefficient of correlation. All that is necessary to determine the predominant lag is to find which lag gives the highest coefficient. In many cases, however, the statistician wishes to know whether he should consider a coefficient of .25, or .40, or .50, or .60, etc., as low, moderate, or high. It is somewhat hazardous to venture the formulation of a guiding principle for the interpretation of the coefficient, for its significance will vary somewhat with the type of data involved. The meaning of the term is more definite when the regression equation is given, but it is more customary to use the coefficient as the expressed measure of correlation. The following rules have been suggested for its interpretation: [1]

"1. If r is less than the probable error, there is no evidence whatever of correlation.[2]

"2. If r is more than six times the size of the probable error, the existence of correlation is a practical certainty."

3. In those cases in which the probable error is relatively small, "if r is less than .30 the correlation cannot be considered at all marked," and in such cases

4. "If r is above .50 there is decided correlation."

The following enumeration of some of the correlations which have been determined will suggest the use of the coefficient and something of the size of the coefficients to be expected. Professor G. R. Davies [3] finds the correlation between the "price cycle and the marriage rate" to be $+.67 \pm .08$; between the manufacturing cycle and liquor consumption (with six months

---

[1] W. I. King, *Elements of Statistical Method,* p. 215.

[2] The first and second rules may be phrased as follows: (1) if r is less than the probable error, there is *little* evidence that the correlation shown is not due merely to chance; and (2) if r is more than six times the size of the probable error, it is a practical certainty that the correlation evidenced is not accidental.

[3] *Quarterly Journal,* University of North Dakota, January, 1922, p. 111.

lag to the latter), $+ .78 \pm .06$; between the price cycle and crime, $- .41$ and $\pm .13$; between "the manufacturing cycle and unemployment," $- .84 \pm .05$. Professor A. L. Bowley finds a coefficient of $+ .65 \pm .09$ for "the value of imports into the United Kingdom per head of the population with the marriage rate in England and Wales," using deviations from a five-year trend.[1] Professor W. C. Mitchell studies the reliability of various index numbers by comparing their fluctuations and finds, for example, a coefficient of $+.964$ between the Bureau of Labor Statistics index number and *Bradstreet's*, and $+.992$ between the Bureau's number and *Dun's*.[2] Professor Moore finds "that the correlation between the predicted yield-ratio of cotton and the actual yield-ratio is . . . for September, $r = + .685$."[3] Numerous other examples might be cited, but these will suffice to indicate the varied uses to which the coefficient is put.

Multiple and partial correlation.[4] In more advanced texts and in the special monographs on the subject the reader will find discussions of additional devices used in estimating correlation, including formulas for multiple correlation, involving the problem of estimating the most probable value of a given variable from two or more other variables by which it is influenced; or the reverse problem of partial correlation—that is, of determining correlation between two variables with the influence of a third variable eliminated. For further information on this and other phases of the subject of correlation, including the method of rank correlation for series which do not lend themselves readily to precise quantitative measurement, and for ways of measuring correlation where the relation between the variables is not well represented by a straight line, the references given in the footnotes to this paragraph and in the chapter references following will be found helpful.

[1] A. L. Bowley, *Elements of Statistics,* 4th ed., p. 386.
[2] W. C. Mitchell, Index Numbers, *op. cit.,* 1921 ed., p. 104.
[3] H. L. Moore, *Forecasting the Yield and Price of Cotton,* p. 147.
[4] Cf. Truman L. Kelley, *Statistical Method,* chap. xi, "Multiple Correlation"; Raymond Pearl, *Introduction to Medical Biometry and Statistics,* chap. xv, "Partial Correlation"; and, for an application to an economic problem, G. C. Haas, *Sale Prices as a Basis for Farm Land Appraisal,* Technical Bulletin 9, The University of Minnesota Agricultural Experiment Station.

APPENDIX A.—CHAPTER XV

SHORT-CUT METHOD FOR COEFFICIENT OF CORRELATION

WE shrink somewhat at the amount of calculation which would seem to be involved in the computations of the means, the standard deviations, and the sum-product, that were made for the first differences of cotton production and price in Table LXVII. To avoid part of that computation, we may avail ourselves of a short-cut formula which has been worked out for the coefficient of correlation, as follows:[1]

$$r = \frac{\Sigma\,x'y' - nd_{\bar{x}}d_{\bar{y}}}{\sqrt{\Sigma(x')^2 - nd_{\bar{x}}^2}\;\sqrt{\Sigma(y')^2 - nd_{\bar{y}}^2}} \quad \ldots\ldots \text{(Formula 47)},$$

where
    $x'y'$ = a product of paired deviations from the assumed average,
    $\bar{x}$ = the true mean of the x series,
    $\bar{y}$ = the true mean of the y series,
$d_{\bar{x}}$ and $d_{\bar{y}}$ = the deviations of the assumed means from the true means.

If the assumed means are both zero, $d_{\bar{x}} = \bar{x}$, and $d_{\bar{y}} = \bar{y}$; hence by taking zero for the assumed mean for both series we are enabled to proceed directly to the computation of the factors in Formula 47 without first finding the deviation of each item from a mean, for the first differences themselves become the assumed deviations (Columns A and C, Table LXIX). If the true means are not known, they can be found from Columns A and C by the short-cut method for the mean. This is done at the foot of Table LXIX. From the computations below that table we note that we again obtain a coefficient of — .85 for the first differences of cotton production and price. (Compare with results in Table LXVII and accompanying discussion.) [2]

[1] Adapted from H. L. Moore, *Forecasting the Yield and the Price of Cotton*, pp. 40-42.
[2] For convenience in computation the "true" means in table LXVII are taken as + 0.2 for price and + 70 for production, the latter being accurate only to tens. In table LXIX the means are carried to one more place and

TABLE LXIX.—SHORT-CUT METHOD FOR THE COEFFICIENT OF CORRELATION

FIRST DIFFERENCES OF COTTON PRODUCTION AND PRICE

(From Table LXVII, Columns A and E)

	A	B	C	D	E	F
	Production		Price		Products of paired deviations	
Year	First differences	Squared deviation from assumed average $(E_x = 0)$	First differences	Squared deviation from assumed average $(E_y = 0)$	Positive	Negative
	x	$(x - E_x)^2$, or $(x')^2$	y	$(y - E_y)^2$, or $(y')^2$	$+ x'y'$	$- x'y'$
Total	+ 1,600	35,080,000	+ 3.9	159.45	+ 1,345	− 64,410
1892	− 1,100	1,210,000	+ 1.1	1.21		− 1,210
1893	+ 350	122,500	− 0.9	.81		− 315
1894	+ 1,300	1,690,000	− 1.6	2.56		− 2,080
1895	− 1,450	2,102,500	+ 2.3	5.29		− 3,335
1896	+ 700	490,000	− 0.9	.81		− 630
1897	+ 1,250	1,562,500	− 1.7	2.89		− 2,125
1898	+ 200	40,000	− 0.7	.49		− 140
1899	− 950	902,500	+ 2.7	7.29		− 2,565
1900	+ 400	160,000	+ 1.7	2.89	+ 680	
1901	− 300	90,000	− 1.2	1.44	+ 360	
1902	+ 550	302,500	+ 0.1	.01	+ 55	
1903	− 400	160,000	+ 4.0	16.00		− 1,600
1904	+ 1,850	3,422,500	− 3.5	12.25		− 6,475
1905	− 1,450	2,102,500	+ 2.2	4.84		− 3,190
1906	+ 1,400	1,960,000	− 0.9	.81		− 1,260
1907	− 1,100	1,210,000	+ 1.5	2.25		− 1,650
1908	+ 1,100	1,210,000	− 2.3	5.29		− 2,530
1909	− 1,650	2,722,500	+ 5.1	26.01		− 8,415
1910	+ 850	722,500	− 0.3	.09		− 255
1911	+ 2,150	4,622,500	− 4.4	19.36		− 9,460
1912	− 1,000	1,000,000	+ 1.9	3.61		− 1,900
1913	+ 250	62,500	+ 1.0	1.00	+ 250	
1914	+ 1,100	1,210,000	− 5.2	27.04		− 5,720
1915	− 2,450	6,002,500	+ 3.9	15.21		− 9,555

$$\bar{x} = 0 + \frac{1600}{24} = + 67 \qquad \bar{y} = 0 + \frac{3.9}{24} = + .16$$

$$r = \frac{\Sigma x'y' - nd_{\bar{x}}d_{\bar{y}}}{\sqrt{\Sigma(x')^2 - nd_{\bar{x}}^2} \ \sqrt{\Sigma(y')^2 - nd_{\bar{y}}^2}} =$$

$$\frac{- 63,065 - 24(-(7)(-.16)}{\sqrt{35,080,000 - 24(-67)^2} \ \sqrt{159.45 - 24(-.16)^2}} = \frac{- 63,322}{74,530} = - .85$$

The use of zero as the arbitrary mean is, of course, not necessary if any other figure is more convenient.

REFERENCES

1. BOWLEY, A. L., *Elements of Statistics,* 4th ed., part II, chap. vi, "Theory of Correlation" (mathematical); chap. vii, "Examples of Correlation"; chap. viii, "Partial and Multiple Correlation" (mathematical).
2. DAVIES, G. R., *Introduction to Economic Statistics,* chap. vi.
3. DAVENPORT, C. B., *Statistical Methods,* 3d ed., chap. iv.
4. ELDERTON AND ELDERTON, *Primer of Statistics,* chap. v. A good statement of general principles.
5. KELLEY, T. L., *Statistical Method,* chaps. viii, ix, x, xi.
6. KING, W. I., *The Elements of Statistical Method,* chaps. xvii, xviii.
7. MOORE, H. L., *Forecasting the Yield and the Price of Cotton,* especially chap. ii.
8. PEARL, RAYMOND, *Introduction to Medical Biometry,* chap. xiv, "The Measurement of Correlation," chap. xv, "Partial Correlation."
9. PERSONS, W. M., "An Index of Business Conditions," in *Rev. of Economic Statistics,* 1919, pp. 120-127, 130-138.
10. RUGG, H. O., *Statistical Methods Applied to Education,* chap. ix.
11. SECRIST, H., *An Introduction to Statistical Methods,* chap. xii.
12. THORNDIKE, E. L., *An Introduction to the Theory of Mental and Social Measurements,* 2d ed., chap. xi.
13. WEST, C. J., *Introduction to Mathematical Statistics,* chaps. vii-x, xii-xiii; bibliography pp. 145-150.
14. WHIPPLE, G. C., *Vital Statistics,* chap. xiii.
15. YULE, G. U., *An Introduction to the Theory of Statistics,* chaps. ix-xii.

read as $+67$ and $+.16$, respectively. As may be verified by the short-cut formula, the correction of the data in table LXVII for this slight difference in the means would not change the coefficient from $-.85$.

CHAPTER XVI

OBTAINING STATISTICAL DATA

IN terms of effort required or of influence on results, the gathering of facts may properly be said to be the most important phase of statistical procedure. If the facts utilized are inadequate or essentially inaccurate, the most ingenious and scientific methods of subsequent analysis can do little to make their use profitable. Refined statistical analysis is wasted, or worse than wasted, if applied to false data.

The determination of the proper method of securing statistical facts is largely a question of applying common sense to the particular circumstances, and common sense is acquired in the school of experience, rather than in the classroom. However, the school of experience, while it may be effective, is also wasteful. One must try too many experiments before learning the best way, and hence it may help to economize time and effort to note what practical rules have been formulated from the experience of others. If much of the subsequent discussion seems trite, the reader will keep in mind that it represents merely an attempt to present the conclusions reached in the application of common-sense standards to the practical problems involved in the search for statistical facts.

PLANNING AN INVESTIGATION

A predetermined plan of procedure is essential for profitable work. No careful statistician proceeds with a piece of statistical research without first laying out his plan, picturing the end, the means, and the process. The preparation for the actual work of the investigation will usually include the following steps:

(1) *Definition of the purpose of the investigation.* Statistical method is essentially inductive, but the inductive method does not imply a blind searching for facts. A

290

working hypothesis must be set up as a guide to their selection. If you are planning to make a statistical survey of your home county, you must first define your purpose. Do you wish to make a commercial survey to determine the potentialities of the county as a market for vacuum cleaners, victrolas, or sewing machines; or is it to be a survey of social conditions to determine to what extent the community is equipped with recreational or educational facilities? And, if for the former purpose, what shall be taken as indicators of potential demand? Average income, value of property, number of homes electrically wired? In brief, what quantitatively measurable factors can be selected as evidence for the particular fact to be investigated?

(2) *Examination of available literature and collected data.* Before completing his plan, the organizer of the investigation will wish to read the accounts of similar investigations, and also to discover and examine any data which may have been collected in the field of his proposed inquiry. Possibly some of the contemplated work has already been satisfactorily done. (See discussion of "Library method" below.)

(3) *Determination* of the available *primary sources* of additional information.

(4) *Choice of methods* to be used in obtaining facts from primary sources.

In determining the method most appropriate to his purpose, the statistician will be guided chiefly by considerations of adequacy, time, and expense. Often the statistician will not be justified in using the information most readily obtainable, either because it is inadequate or because it is inaccurate. In other cases, an approximate accuracy may be sufficient, and speed or economy the dominant considerations.

(5) *Selection of the working force.*

(6) *Preparation* of the necessary *forms and instructions* for their use in the field.

(7) *Instructions for editing the schedules* after they are
returned by the enumerator or other informant.

The above sketch of the elements of the plan of a statistical
investigation will emphasize the suggestion previously made that
the plan is a highly important part of the process. The steps
enumerated can scarcely be carried out successfully without a
preliminary hypothesis as to the results which will be obtained
and the outlining of the analysis to which the data are to be
subjected subsequent to the obtaining of the schedules from informants. This part of the work requires the best skill of the
statistician, of the director of the statistical force. Let us examine more carefully the *methods of obtaining data* from which
the statistician must choose in planning an investigation. These
methods may be conveniently designated as (1) the *library* or
secondary source method, (2) the *field* method, and (3) the
correspondence method.

THE LIBRARY METHOD

The library method involves the use of secondary sources, of
compilations of facts prepared by some previous investigator.
To these the statistician should apply principles of criticism similar to those used by the historian in the examination of docu-
ments. He should strive to develop the habit of alert, critical
questioning applied to both the external and internal evidence
presented concerning the compilation under consideration. There
is a natural tendency, due to credulity and intellectual sloth, to
assume that a printed table of figures is correct and pertinent to
the purpose to which it is devoted. The careful user will, however, apply the following *tests* before resting content with secondary data.[1]

1. Is the series *homogeneous* throughout the period for
   which it is available or for which it is to be utilized; that
   is, have the definitions of the statistical terms or units
   involved been unchanging; and, if the series is based upon
   a sample, has the degree to which the sample is representative been constant?

[1] Cf. W. I. King, *Elements of Statistical Method*, p. 61, for a similar list.

2. Is the validity of the data possibly affected by intentional or unintentional *bias?* If the compiler or publisher of the statistics has an interest in the results shown by the data, the chances of bias are increased. It is for this reason, among others, that the results of investigations conducted by the government are often considered the most reliable for scientific use.

3. Are there *other elements of inaccuracy,* due, for example, to the imperfection of the sources or of the methods used in the collection of the data?

4. To summarize, are the data as *adequate* for the problem in hand as data which might be obtained from primary sources? Do they extend over a sufficiently long period and evidence the desired degree of accuracy and homogeneity? [2]

In applying the above tests, the statistician usually finds it profitable to have recourse to the sources in which the data are originally published, rather than to second-hand summaries, as the original publisher is more apt to give full explanations of the nature and limitations of the data. The earliest data issued, however, are apt to be provisional and should be checked for revisions made later upon the basis of more complete information, care being taken to ascertain whether the changes are real revisions or merely typographical errors. Where possible, the data should be checked for self-consistency. For example, monthly data may be checked by comparisons with annual totals. If data for each period appear in more than one issue of the publication, errors due to misprints may often be detected by recording the data from one issue and checking the recording by comparison with the figures given in a different issue.

In the following chapter a list of the more important periodic secondary sources of statistical data is presented. The student of the social sciences should familiarize himself with these publications sufficiently to enable him to find the available information on a given subject as need for the information arises.

[2] See also H. Secrist, *Statistics in Business,* chap. iii, for the standards to which facts should conform to make them useful for statistical analysis.

If an examination of the available secondary data leads the investigator to reject them as inadequate to his purpose, he must then seek for facts from *primary sources,* "made to order" compilations as contrasted with the "ready made" tabulations found in secondary sources. He must go, or send, after the data. This may be done either by the *field method* or by *correspondence.*

THE FIELD METHOD

The first problem is, *where is the desired information?* Facts, the raw material of the statistical process, are to be found in official or private records or stored in the memories of individuals, or, in a few cases, are to be obtained only by direct observation. To illustrate:

1. *Official records.* When official data are assembled and tabulated, as in the census, we think of them as secondary sources, but when they appear in the form of individual, unclassified records, as birth, death, and marriage certificate records, they may reasonably be designated as primary sources. If one wished to make a study of the distribution of wealth at death in a given county, he would go to the probate records of each estate.[1]

2. *Private records.* In many statistical studies, reliance must be placed upon other than public records. Thus, unemployment may be studied by examination of the time records kept by employers; farm statistics may be compiled from the records kept by the farmer; and cost of living budgets, from private expense accounts.

3. *Individual unrecorded knowledge.* In a still larger number of inquiries, there are no adequate records available and reliance must be placed upon facts verbally stated by individuals. The greater part of the information in the population census is obtained directly from the statements of individuals based on unrecorded knowledge, opinion, or estimate. Under the direction of Professor D. D. Lescohier,[2] agents of the Department of

[1] Cf. W. I. King, *The Wealth and Income of the People of the United States,* pp. 64-98.

[2] For report of the results of this investigation during the summer of 1920 see *Harvest Labor Problems in the Wheat Belt,* by D. D. Lescohier, U. S. Dep't of Agriculture Bull. no. 1020.

Agriculture made, in the post-war period, a study of the harvest labor problem. Much of the information obtained in that survey was received by interviewers in personal talks with harvest hoboes. Needless to say, the interviewer must use discretion in the use of information from such sources, for the hobo is proverbially gifted with a highly developed imagination. But in all field work much depends upon the ingenuity of the interviewer in leading his informant to give real facts or to indicate errors by means of corroboratory questions.

4. *Direct Observation.* The retailer planning to establish a new store will often make a study of the traffic past potential sites. This is done by direct observation of the number and types of passers-by. In a similar manner the U. S. Bureau of Public Roads is making at various points in the country traffic studies on the highways to determine the character and extent of the travel thereon.

The personnel of the investigating force. In the field method, then, facts may be obtained by examination of records, public or private, by the interview method, or by direct observation. The investigation may be conducted personally by the organizer of the investigation or by agents or enumerators. The first method, that of *personal investigation,* is well suited to small intensive studies where intimate familiarity with the object and problems of the investigation and the maintenance of uniformity of viewpoint are important. The authoritative exemplification of the intensive method is found in the family budget investigations of Le Play,[1] thus described by Professor R. C. Chapin, in his study, *The Standard of Living Among Workingmen's Families in New York City,* pp. 7-9:

> "Le Play . . . carried the intensive study of family accounts to the highest degree of excellence. From 1829 to 1856 he spent a large portion of his vacations (he was a professor of metallurgy in Paris) in traveling through the countries of Europe, studying the condition of workingmen's families. His method was

---

[1] See brief discussion in W. I. King, *op. cit.,* pp. 48-49; also Henry Higgs, in *Q. J. Econ.,* vol. iv, p. 408, and M. F. Le Play, *Les Ouvriers Européens.*

to make in each place careful inquiry of clergy, teachers, and others until he found what was considered to be a really typical family, whether a Sheffield cutler or a Dutch fisherman, and then he would arrange to live with the family for some weeks if necessary, observing their whole manner of living. He would ask questions, make notes of what he saw and heard, and when he had gathered his material, would prepare a family monograph, containing in fifteen or twenty octavo pages a photographic picture of the given family group. . . . He made studies during the long period of his activity of some 300 families, but carried only fifty-seven of them to the point where he was willing to have them published."

Ordinarily the investigator will be under the necessity of enlisting others to help him conduct the work, and to a large extent the degree of success will depend upon the selection of the *agents or enumerators*. If the enumerator is not blessed with a high standard of intellectual integrity and interest in the investigation, he will be tempted to follow the line of least resistance in filling out the schedules, and the results will be worthless. Only when he is endowed with tact, good judgment, honesty, and zeal can best results be expected.

Scope of the inquiry. Enumerations may aim to be either complete or partial. The United States Census is designed to be a *complete enumeration* of the population. Of course, the results are never perfect; some persons are omitted and some are counted twice, but the intent is to make as full a canvass as possible. The draft registration was another attempt to make a full canvass of those men falling within the prescribed age limits. Again, in a social survey the purpose may be to make a complete enumeration of certain features of a community.[1] Such an enumeration may also be looked upon as a sample if the object is to draw conclusions which may be applied to other communities.

The greater number of investigations are of the *sampling*

[1] For discussion of social surveys, see F. S. Chapin, *Field Work and Social Research*, chap. v, with bibliography, p. 126.

type. The investigator selects a portion of the whole which he
believes will be sufficiently representative and by means of a
partial canvass seeks to obtain data from which he can draw
conclusions applicable to the whole from which the sample is
drawn. Thus in market analysis the market potentialities are
sometimes estimated by the use of a test letter sent to a sample
chosen from the prospective customers (see Chapter II).

**Study of the conditions under which the inquiry is to be
conducted.** Before preparing the forms needed and determining the scope of the inquiry in detail, the statistician in
charge will study the conditions under which the inquiry is to be
conducted, as those conditions will materially affect the amount
and character of information he may profitably attempt to get.
What is the grade of intelligence of the informants and enumerators, and how familiar are they with the subject matter of the
inquiry? What is the degree of interest on the part of the
informants in the objects sought? What is their probable bias,
if any? What degree of compulsion, explicit or implied, may be
exercised or threatened?

To illustrate, a few years ago, during a strike, a study was
made of the budgets of workingmen's families in Madison, Wisconsin, by the legal firm in charge of the interests of the strikers.
The inquiry was conducted by the questionnaire method. In
this case it is a reasonable presumption that the informants were
interested in filling out the schedules, as they had a pecuniary
interest in the use to which they were to be put, but it is by no
means clear that the element of bias would be lacking or that the
record of receipts and expenditures would be adequate for accurate statements of the amount and distribution of expense.

Definition of the statistical units.[1] Before any field work
is done, the meaning of each important term used must be carefully and accurately defined. If a study is to be made of the
changing size and ownership of farms, it is necessary to have a
definite understanding of just what a farm is and what consti-

---

[1] A thorough analysis of the nature and uses of statistical units is found
in H. Secrist, *An Introduction to Statistical Methods,* chap. iii. See also his
Readings, chap. iii; Bowley, *Elements of Statistics,* 4th ed., pp. 18-20; W. I.
King, *op. cit.,* chap. v; F. S. Chapin, *op. cit.,* 167-172.

tutes ownership. Are a garden plot, a two-acre truck farm, a
ten-acre orchard, a twenty-acre alfalfa field, an eighty-acre wheat
field, and a thousand-acre ranch all to be considered as farms,
and if not, just where is the line to be drawn? If a farm is held
under a land contract, or under a life tenure, does that constitute
ownership? Obviously the statistical units in terms of which
the data are to be gathered must be so defined that the results
will be interpreted in like manner by all the enumerators and
informants. The more important qualities of the statistical unit
may be summarized as:

(1) *Appropriateness* to the purpose of the study.
(2) *Clarity.* The terms must be so clearly defined that persons of the grade of intelligence possessed by the enumerators and informants will not mistake their meaning.
(3) *Measurability.* A unit must be chosen which is capable
of definite determination, which is ascertainable within the
limits of time and effort available. If one wishes to compare statistically the religious tendencies of two periods or
communities he must measure those tendencies, not in their
intangible influence on the inner man, but in their concrete
evidences in church membership, and similar measurable
facts which may be taken as some indication of religious
tendencies.
(4) *Comparability.* If possible, the units should be so defined
that the results will be comparable with those of similar
investigations. Thus, the results of two inquiries into the
cost of living of the families of workingmen can be readily
compared only when the term "family" is defined alike in
both investigations.

Forms. The results of interviews should be recorded in
standardized forms or schedules carefully worked out in advance.
More detailed suggestions for the preparation of schedules are
made below in connection with questionnaires to be sent by mail.
Most of the suggestions made apply with equal force to schedules to be used by enumerators. It is not quite so essential that
the questions be few in number or simply worded, as it is possible
for the enumerator to get answers to more questions than the

informant will answer without prompting. However, each additional question means additional expense.

Where compactness is important or special care must be taken not to divulge the information received, a *coded card* may be used to advantage, with numbers or symbols for the questions or answers, or both, but the danger of incorrect entries is increased by the use of a code.

THE OFFICE OR CORRESPONDENCE METHOD

The office method involves the substitution of inquiry by mail, wire, or wireless, for field investigation. It is ordinarily less satisfactory than the field method, but can be conducted with less expense, and in a few cases the suspicions of the prospective informant can be allayed more readily by a well-stated printed explanation than by the enumerator in a personal interview. The office method is used for an almost inconceivable variety of investigations. Governmental agencies use it to get the necessary information for assessing income taxes or recording industrial accidents. Newspapers use it in obtaining "straw votes" during political campaigns. Business men use the mail questionnaire to sound out the conditions of the market. Private investigators seek for information on the changing size of families, etc.[1]

In the use of the office method, the investigator may organize an *established corps of correspondents* who report to him by mail or wire either at regular stipulated intervals or on the happening of certain occurrences. In the United States crop reporting service, reports are received periodically through the growing season from a large number of correspondents over the crop area.[2]

---

[1] Cf. the inquiry on "Changes in the Size of Famiiles," conducted by Professors E. A. Ross and R. E. Baber, by means of family history questionnaires. A summary of the results of this investigation appears in the February, 1924, issue of the *Century* magazine.

[2] For a discussion of the crop reporting system, which is, of course, only in part the office method, see H. Secrist, *Readings,* pp. 64-90, adapted from *Government Crop Reports; their Value, Scope and Preparation,* U. S. Department of Agriculture, Bureau of Crop Estimates, Circular 17, Revised, pp. 8-26.

Also, H. L. Moore, *Forecasting the Yield and the Price of Cotton,* chap. iii.

The estimates used are based on condition reports received from "a corps of paid state field agents and crop specialists and a large body of voluntary crop reporters composed of the following classes; county reporters, town-

Again, large operators on the commodity exchanges sometimes maintain a corps of correspondents who keep them informed of conditions affecting the supply or demand for the given commodity.   In this connection we should also note the *registration service* [3] which the various states and cities are, with the encouragement of the federal government, gradually establishing. Where a registration law is in effect, the attending physician is required to report deaths and births, together with such other pertinent information as may be stipulated.   Needless to say, the development of an adequate and comprehensive registration service is the first essential to a statistical study of the important subjects of changing death and birth rates and similar population problems.

The mail questionnaire.

For the greater number of inquiries the establishment of a regular corps of informants is impracticable and the investigator relies on mail questionnaires sent to *irregular correspondents,* and it is this type of inquiry which we have particularly in mind in the following discussion.

Many questionnaires are not essentially statistical in nature, in that they are designed to elicit qualitative information rather than quantitative, but there is an extensive and growing use of the mail questionnaire or schedule for obtaining data of a statistical nature.   The very multiplicity of such inquiries hazards the success of any one project.   The sender of a questionnaire must take care in formulating it, or its destination will certainly be the waste-paper basket.

(1) *The preface or explanation.*   In the first place, the questionnaire should be accompanied by an explanatory letter, or a preface, in which the sender should state as clearly, tactfully and persuasively as possible the purpose of his inquiry, the authority, if any, under which the inquiry is directed, and any inducement or reward which he is able to offer the informant for furnishing

ship reporters, individual farmers, and several lists of reporters for special inquiries."—H. Secrist, *op. cit.,* p. 69.

   [3] G. C. Whipple, *Vital Statistics,* chap. iv; also C. L. Wilbur, *The Federal Registration Service of the United States: Its Development, Problems and Defects,* U. S. Bureau of the Census, 1916.

the information. The promptness with which a reply is desired and the degree of accuracy necessary should be stated, though the latter point may, in some cases, be indicated with greater effectiveness in the text of the questions.

(2) *The questions.* The type of questions to be asked, the number used, and the effort required in answering must necessarily vary with each inquiry, but the framer of the questionnaire may achieve better results if he keeps in mind the following suggestions:

(a) *Number.* The questions should be few in number, as few as consistent with the purpose of the inquiry. If there comes to the desk of a busy man a short inquiry which does not seem to demand too much time to answer, he may attend to it immediately. If there are many questions, he is apt to lay it aside for the present, even if he intends ultimately to answer. A task postponed is easily forgotten; hence a few-question schedule promptly answered is worth more than a long one with a greater percentage of casualties. In some cases it has even been found advisable to use a one-question method.[1, 2]

(b) *Form of the questions.* The questions should be as brief as is consistent with clarity, and preferably answerable by the words "Yes," "No," or an easily ascertained number.

It is essential that they be unambiguous. It is almost inconceivably difficult to frame questions which will be interpreted alike by all to whom they are directed. Statisticians sometimes find it profitable to send out a preliminary set of questionnaires in order to test the interpretation which the reader will put on the questions asked.

(c) *Content of the questions—what to include.* The questions asked should be *adequate* to bring out the essential information. It is in the adjustment between the conflicting demands

---

[1] Asher Hobson, "The Use of the Correspondence Method in Original Research," *Quar. Pub. Amer. Stat. Assoc.*, vol. 15, pp. 210-218.

[2] Not always can the questions be restricted to a small number. A striking exception is found in the long schedule sent to the retail clothiers of the country in the retail-clothing survey conducted by the Northwestern University Bureau of Business Research. This schedule occupies some fifteen printed pages (see vol. vi of the *Retail Clothing Survey*, pp. 585-599).

of brevity and adequacy that the ingenuity of the statistician is taxed to the utmost.

Where bias or inaccuracy are apt to appear in the answers, it will be found profitable to use *corroboratory questions,* asking the same thing in different ways so that the answers can be compared. To cite an obvious example, in population inquiries, the age in years and the date of birth may be asked for corroboratory purposes.

(d) *Content of the questions—what not to include.* Unnecessarily *inquisitorial* or *irritating* questions should be avoided. Also, the informant should not be asked to make *computations* which can readily be made after the receipt of the schedule. Care should be taken to avoid so phrasing questions that the probability of *bias* in the reply is increased.

(3) *Definition of terms and units.* Somewhere in the schedule should appear a definition of all terms or units whose significance might otherwise be incorrectly interpreted. These should appear in the questions at the point used, if convenient; otherwise, in some reasonably conspicuous place. As previously suggested, the explanations should include a statement of the degree of numerical accuracy expected in the answers.

(4) *Mechanical form of the schedule.* Put the questionnaire on a good grade of paper, not so light that it tears easily, nor on cardboard which does not file or mail readily. The usual *typewriter size,* 8½ by 11 inches, is preferable, so that the informant may conveniently insert his replies with the typewriter. If possible, it is desirable to furnish a duplicate for the records of the informant.

Such columns for figures as appear in the schedule should be simply and clearly arranged, with an eye to the convenience of the person filling them in and also to facilitate the office handling of the schedules.

The probability of prompt return of the schedules is increased by the use of a stamped return envelope, or, where it does not appear appropriate to furnish return postage, at least an addressed envelope. If you do not care enough for a reply to provide convenient facilities, you can scarcely expect the other person to go to much trouble to answer your inquiry.

Editing Instructions

Questionnaires, whether they are filled out by enumerators or received from correspondents, should be carefully edited before the results are tabulated. Let us assume that a questionnaire has been used to obtain facts concerning living conditions in a rural community. What objects should be sought in the office examination of these schedules? Editing has in mind four general purposes: increased accuracy, consistency in facts, uniformity in expression, and completeness.[1]

(1) *Accuracy.* Certain replies raise a presumption of error. Ten phonographs in one family or six bathtubs in a six-room house would be obvious grounds for incredulity. Apparent errors of this kind should be corrected by further inquiry or on the basis of other evidence in the schedule, not on the mere opinion of the editor. If correction cannot be satisfactorily made, the schedule should be eliminated, as a few accurate schedules are better than a larger number with material inaccuracies.

(2) *Consistency.* One type of error is evidenced by inconsistency in the answers. If a married person is reported as ten years of age, a person born in England described as a native in the U. S. census, or if the totals of figures do not agree with the separate items, there is need for editing to effect consistency.

(3) *Uniformity in expression.* Frequently numerical answers will be in varying units. Some may report the size of a residence in terms of stories, others in terms of the number of rooms, others in ground dimensions or cubic contents. Potato production may be stated in carloads, bushels, or pounds. Such answers must all be reduced to a common unit to make tabulation feasible.

(4) *Completeness.* Lastly, the editing of schedules involves the determination of whether or not essential questions have been left unanswered. If so, it may be necessary to send a second inquiry or an inquiry to other parties. Also, there may be percentage calculations or other computations to make before the schedules are ready for tabulation.

[1] Cf. Bailey and Cummings, *Statistics,* chap. iv.

When the editing is completed the schedules are then ready for the tabulation process, discussed in Chapter III.

Summary of the Relative Merits of the Several Methods of Gathering Facts from Primary Sources

The choice of method to be used will depend chiefly on the time and funds available, the extensiveness of the inquiry, the character of the informants, and the regularity of the inquiry.

If the investigation is *to cover a period of many years,* antedating the inquiry, it is probable that recourse to official records if there be such, will be preferable. Private records are not apt to be readily available for many years back and memories are treacherous.

If a thorough *intensive study* of a small number of items is desired, under conditions requiring the application of well-informed personal judgment, the method of *field investigation by one man* is probably best. If the study becomes extensive and the time and expense are limited, other methods must be used.

When it is intended to repeat a similar investigation at more or less *periodic intervals,* the method of establishing a corps of regular *correspondents* becomes feasible, and, particularly if an appeal may be made to the self-interest or pride of the informant, this method may be carried on without prohibitive expense.

The method of inquiry by *enumerators* is, on the whole, most satisfactory where the area to be covered and the amount of data to be obtained are *extensive.* It is chiefly by this method that the census is compiled. For an attempt at a full count over a large area, the expense of this method becomes prohibitive for a private investigator. For *smaller studies* the greater ease of getting returns from a large percentage of those to whom the inquiry is directed and the greater accuracy of the data obtained recommends the enumerator method even for private investigations.

However, for many of the investigations which governments, private firms, or individuals wish to conduct the only feasible method is an *inquiry by mail.* The expense per inquiry is relatively small; the inquiry may be spread over a large area; and where considerable time is required in the preparation of the answers the enumerator method is often not feasible.

REFERENCES

1. BAILEY AND CUMMINGS, *Statistics,* chaps. iii, iv.
2. BOWLEY, A. L., *Elements of Statistics,* 4th ed., part i, chap. iii.
3. CHAPIN, F. S., *Field Work and Social Research.*
4. HOBSON, ASHER, "The Use of the Correspondence Method in Original Research," *Amer. Stat. Assoc.,* vol. 15, pp. 210-218.
5. KING, W. I., *Elements of Statistical Method,* chaps. iv-vii.
6. KINGSLEY, D. J., "Keeping Questionnaires Out of the Waste Basket," *Printers' Ink,* February, 1922, p. 62.
7. SECRIST, HORACE, *An Introduction to Statistical Methods,* chaps. ii, iii, and iv.
8. —— *Readings and Problems in Statistical Methods,* chaps. ii, iii, and iv.
9. —— *Statistics in Business,* chap. iii.
10. WHIPPLE, G. C., *Vital Statistics,* chap. iv.
11. WHITE, PERCIVAL, *Market Analysis,* chap. ii.

CHAPTER XVII

PERIODIC SECONDARY SOURCES

THE seeker after truth in quantitative terms must, in the great majority of cases, rely upon *secondary sources* of data. By secondary sources we mean compilations of facts gathered together and to some degree sorted and classified.[1] They are "ready-made" facts which the statistician finds at least partially prepared for his use, usually in the form of tables. The volumes of the decennial census are one great secondary source of statistical data.

The secondary sources of statistical data may conveniently be classified as recurring and non-recurring. The recurring or periodic sources include connected series, issued at more or less regular intervals, such as the retail price series of the Bureau of Labor Statistics. The non-recurring sources include such extended studies into special fields as the volume prepared by Professor Kemmerer for the National Monetary Commission on "Seasonal Variations in the Relative Demand for Money and Capital in the United States,"[2] and various monographic studies such as essays, articles, and theses presenting statistical data on special subjects with interpretations thereof. With the exception of some special reports of the Bureau of the Census the sources of information discussed or listed in this chapter are of the recurring type.

To facilitate the use of secondary sources, there are given in this chapter (1) a discussion and list of the more important

[1] Professor H. Secrist defines secondary data as "those which have been collected, tabulated in simple or composite form, and made available for use, but which are removed one or more steps from the form in which they were reported and consequently do not show on their face the nature of the units employed, the purpose for which used, the treatment to which they have been subjected in analysis, etc."—*Statistical Methods,* p. 16.

[2] Senate Document 588, 61st Congress, 2d Session.

periodic or recurrent statistical publications and (2) a classification of economic and sociological data, with a partial bibliography of the sources of statistical information on each class of facts mentioned. The reader will find it helpful to expand this partial bibliography from the hints given in the discussion below and from his personal study. In the previous chapter we have touched on the tests which should be applied to secondary data to determine their fitness for a given purpose.

DISCUSSION OF IMPORTANT PERIODIC SOURCES OF STATISTICAL FACTS

To attempt to discuss the secondary sources of statistical data may be almost as futile as to attempt a verbal description of the beauty of a bit of landscape. Beauty must be seen to be appreciated; sources of data must be frequently used before their value is appreciated. Nevertheless, it may help to indicate some of the important sources of statistical facts. It is not feasible here to attempt a full characterization, or even a full enumeration, of periodic sources, but attention will be given to a few of the more important publications, particularly those which, because of their recent inauguration, may not be familiar to the average reader.

For purposes of discussion and classification herein, periodic statistical publications have been classified as United States Government publications; publications of state governments; commercial and trade papers; daily papers; private statistical services; and year books.

U. S. GOVERNMENT PUBLICATIONS

On the whole, the leading sources of statistical data used by the average person are the various government publications, particularly those of the Bureau of the Census, the Department of Commerce, the Bureau of Labor Statistics, and the Federal Reserve Board, though until recently there have been some very large gaps in the types of statistical data appearing in the government publications. Prior to the inauguration of the *Federal Reserve Bulletin,* for example, the government was doing little in the way of regular publication of financial statistics. For a fuller statement of the statistical activities and publications of the various government bureaus than is given below, the reader should consult a *Report on the Statistical Work of the United States Government,* issued by the Bureau of Efficiency.

THE BUREAU OF THE CENSUS

The *decennial census* is, of course, the great reservoir of facts concerning the people of the country and their possessions. It is to this that we turn for the authoritative facts of population, occupations, races, industries, etc., etc.

Nor should we overlook the *special publications* of the Bureau of the Census, such as the two volumes on *Wealth, Debt, and Taxation,* under date of 1913; the annual volumes in recent years on *Financial Statistics of Cities,* and, in a separate series, on *Financial Statistics of States.* These series form the chief source of statistical data for the student of public finance and taxation. There are also the annual volumes on *Mortality Statistics,* and, more recently, on *Birth Statistics,* both of which are of special interest to the student of sociology. Current mortality data appear in a *Weekly Health Index.*

The most recent of the important monthly statistical publications of the government is the *Survey of Current Business,* inaugurated in August, 1921, and published jointly by the Bureau of the Census, the Bureau of Standards, and the Bureau of Foreign and Domestic Commerce. This summarizes and brings together in one publication, and in attractive form, a large amount of statistical data appearing in other government publications, both federal and state, and in reports from trade associations, private organizations, and technical periodicals. The range of material covered will be indicated by the following partial list of statistics appearing in the April, 1923, number. In most instances the series are given in the form of ordinary numerical data and also in percentages or index numbers. The list follows:

Business indicators, such as pig-iron production and freight tonmiles; wholesale price comparisons; production, prices, stocks, etc., for textiles, metals, fuels, rubber, building construction, transportation, and other important industries; labor indices; cost of living; banking and business finance; and foreign exchange and trade of the United States.

This publication appears monthly in abridged edition, with a full quarterly edition; and also in the form of advance sheets covering data to be included in the next issue. Further information concerning production in a considerable list of industries is contained in other monthly releases issued by the Bureau of the Census.

BUREAU OF FOREIGN AND DOMESTIC COMMERCE

Special attention should be called to the *Statistical Abstract of the United States,* an annual volume giving data for the current and previous years—usually annual data—on a variety of subjects almost as extensive as the complete classification of facts submitted later in this chapter.

This Bureau has now commenced the publication of a *Commerce Yearbook,* the first issue containing data for the year 1922 and the first part of 1923.

The student of foreign trade will be especially interested in the weekly *Commerce Reports* and in the *Monthly Summary of Foreign Commerce of the United States.*

BUREAU OF LABOR STATISTICS

The Bureau of Labor Statistics publishes valuable series which are of importance to many others besides those specially interested in labor problems. The most important of these is the *Monthly Labor Review,* with data on wages, hours of labor, unemployment, wholesale and retail prices, etc., etc. This Bureau also publishes special series devoted entirely to wholesale prices, retail prices, wages, or similar subjects. Thus, *Bulletin* 335 is devoted entirely to the movement of wholesale prices in various commodities and by groups from 1890 to 1922; and *Bulletin* 334 contains a similar treatment of retail prices in the years 1913 to 1922.

DEPARTMENT OF AGRICULTURE

For current agricultural statistics, one turns to *Weather, Crops, and Markets.* This is a consolidation, dating from January, 1922, of three publications—the *Monthly Crop Reporter,* the *Market Reporter* and the *National Weather and Crop Bulletin.*

THE FEDERAL RESERVE BOARD

The *Federal Reserve Bulletin,* published monthly, contains, in addition to the statistics of banking conditions to be expected in such a publication, an increasing variety of statistics on general trade and business conditions.

This periodical, together with the *Survey of Current Business,* gives the student a convenient source of a large amount of statistical data which has hitherto been available only in private publications, if at all.

Many *other government publications* carry significant statistical data. Information on the oil and mining industries is obtainable from the Geological Survey reports. The printed monthly bulletin of the Bureau of Immigration has been discontinued in recent years, but the annual reports of the Commissioner General are available for facts as to immigration, and monthly statistics appear in the *Monthly Labor Review,* and in mimeographed bulletins. The reports of the Treasury Department contain data for public finance, and those of the Interstate Commerce Commission for railway statistics.

STATE BUREAUS

It is not feasible to attempt a complete description or even an enumeration of state publications with which the statistician may profitably familiarize himself. The publications of a few states are of appreciably superior merit. In the field of labor statistics, for example, one should at least be familiar with the publications of the Illinois, Massachusetts, New York, and Wisconsin industrial commissions. Of particular interest are the estimates of factory employment which are now being issued monthly by the labor departments of several states, including those just named.[1] On the whole our information concerning the extent of employment has been sadly inadequate, and any step which looks toward a substantial increase of the knowledge of employment conditions is to be applauded.

[1] A good list of publications containing data on employment is given in the *Federal Reserve Bulletin,* December, 1923, pp. 1278-1279.

COMMERCIAL AND TRADE PAPERS

Among the general commercial and financial weeklies we should note particularly the *Commercial and Financial Chronicle, Bradstreet's, Dun's Review,* and the New York *Annalist.* Each of these has its particular merits and special features. The *Commercial and Financial Chronicle* has probably the most complete descriptive analysis of those phases of public affairs which affect financial interests and has an annual *Financial Review* with valuable statistical data; *Bradstreet's* is known for its data on building permits and its index of wholesale prices; *Dun's Review* deals with movements in important industries, publishes a well-known series of statistics of business failures, and also has an index number of wholesale prices; the *Annalist* is the youngest of the group, beginning in 1913, and is on the whole the most popular in style.

Among the *foreign weeklies* of similar type, we may mention the *London Economist* and the *Statist,* for Great Britain, and, for France, *L'Economiste Français.* These give data, not only for Great Britain and France, but also for other European countries.

Several of the larger *banks* and other financial institutions are publishing periodicals with much statistical data. Some of these are listed in the accompanying classification.

Also of special interest and importance are the numerous specialized *trade papers,* such as the *Iron Age,* which are devoted primarily to the interests of some one industry. A large proportion of the price quotations used by the U. S. Bureau of Labor Statistics in its compilation of wholesale price indices are derived from publications of this type.

THE DAILY PAPERS

Several dailies, such as the *Wall Street Journal* and the New York *Journal of Commerce,* contain a large amount of statistical material and many of the important general daily newspapers publish in their financial columns daily statistics of many kinds, particularly as to the transactions of the stock, produce, and

money markets. The following partial list of statistics published daily in the New York *Times* will suggest the character of
the information furnished:

1. Stock and bond transactions on the New York Stock
   Exchange and on other exchanges.
2. Commodity exchange quotations, such as wheat.
3. Foreign-exchange quotations.
4. Interest rates.
5. Clearing-house exchanges.
6. The daily "Treasury Statement" (U. S. Government).

PRIVATE STATISTICAL SERVICES

We must not pass unnoticed the quite commendable service
which is being rendered by several private statistical services in
the compilation, presentation, and analysis of statistical data.
We may mention in this connection the *Babson* desk sheets and
reports, the *Brookmire* service, the annual volumes of *Moody's*
and *Poor's* with their accounting statements for individual firms,
and the several publications of the *Standard Statistics Co., Inc.*
(see Section V of the classified list on the following pages).

Of special interest to the trained student of business statistics
is the publication inaugurated in 1919 by the Harvard Committee on Economic Research and appearing quarterly under the
title of *The Review of Economic Statistics*. This publication
gives a considerable amount of original statistical data, but the
noteworthy feature is the character of the economic and statistical analysis to which the data are subjected. Most statistical
publications rest content with the publication of the data accompanied by a quite elementary analysis thereof; or in those few
cases in which more analysis is undertaken, as in the construction of the Babson business barometer, it is difficult for the
reader to trace the process by which conclusions have been
reached or to verify the validity of those conclusions by retracing
the process used in reaching them. The early numbers of the
Review of Economic Statistics, however, explain in great detail
the method to be used in handling the data, analyzing them into
their constituent elements, discovering relationships, and utilizing

those relationships in the construction of a business barometer and in other analytic processes. We touched on this subject in Chapter XIV, on "Business Cycles and Barometers." The following list of a few of the articles which have appeared in the *Review* will suggest the character of the publication—

1. "An Index Chart Based on Prices and Money Rates," January, 1922, pp. 7-11.
2. "Employment and the Business Cycle," January, 1922, pp. 12-51.
3. "The Iron and Steel Industry During Business Cycles," December, 1921, pp. 378-383.
4. "An Index of the Physical Volume of Production." (Consecutive studies, September, 1920-January, 1921.)
5. "An Analysis of Building Statistics for the United States," January, 1924, pp. 32-62.
6. Current statistics—monthly data for a large number of important series.

OTHER PRIVATE PUBLICATIONS

There are many other private statistical services which might be mentioned, such as the research reports of the Industrial Conference Board, dealing chiefly with wages and the cost of living since July, 1914. Another interesting development is the growth of special labor bureaus organized to furnish statistical and other technical aid to labor unions.

YEAR BOOKS

For annual data, the *Statistical Abstract of the United States,* the *Year Book* of the Department of Agriculture, and the several yearbooks published by private agencies furnish the most convenient sources of information.

LIST OF PERIODIC STATISTICAL PUBLICATIONS

The following list of publications gives the name of the publisher, the title, and the frequency of publication of the more important periodic sources of statistical data, including those discussed in the preceding pages.

In indicating the frequency of issue, De. is used to designate a decennial publication; A., annual; Q., quarterly; M., monthly; S.M., semi-monthly; W., weekly; and D., daily.

PERIODIC STATISTICAL PUBLICATIONS

(Partial list)

I. U. S. Government Publications. Washington, D. C.
    A. BUREAU OF THE CENSUS:
        1. *Survey of Current Business* (Q., with abridged monthly edition—published jointly with the Bureau of Standards and the Bureau of Foreign and Domestic Commerce).
        2. Decennial census—*e.g. Fourteenth Census of the U. S., 1920,* 11 volumes and abstracts (one for manufactures and one for the census as a whole).
        Population:
            Vol. I.—*Number and Distribution of Inhabitants.*
            Vol. II.—*General Report and Analytical Tables.*
            Vol. III.—*Composition and Characteristics of the Population, by States.*
            Vol. IV.—*Occupations.*
        Agriculture:
            Vol. V.—*General Report and Analytical Tables.*
            Vol. VI.—*Reports for States, with Statistics for Counties.*
                Part 1.—The Northern States.
                Part 2.—The Southern States.
                Part 3.—The Western States and the outlying Possessions.
            Vol. VII.—*Irrigation and Drainage.*
        Manufactures:
            Vol. VIII.—*General Report and Analytical Tables.*
            Vol. IX.—*Reports for States, with Statistics for Principal Cities.*
            Vol. X.—*Reports for Selected Industries.*
            (The census of manufactures is now taken in each odd year.)
        Mining:
            Vol. XI.—*Mines and Quarries.*
        Abstract of the Fourteenth Census.
        Abstract of the Census of Manufactures.

3. Annual publications of the Bureau of the Census.
   a. *Birth Statistics for the Birth Registration Area of the United States* (1915-date).
   b. *Financial Statistics of Cities Having a Population of over 30,000* (1905-date). See 1905 number for location of earlier bulletins.
   c. *Financial Statistics of States* (1915-date).
   d. *Mortality Statistics* (1900-date).

4. Special Reports—issued at irregular intervals.
   a. *Benevolent Institutions,* 1910.
   b. *The Blind in the U. S.,* 1910.
   c. *Census of Manufactures:* at five-year intervals, 1904 to 1919, and biennially thereafter.
   d. *A Century of Population Growth (1790-1900);* also *Census Monograph I—Increase of Population in the United States, 1910-1920,* by William S. Rossiter.
   e. *Chinese and Japanese in the U. S.,* 1910.
   f. *Cotton Production and Distribution,* Bulletins 125, 128, 131, 134.
   g. *Estimates of the Population of the U. S.,* Bulletins 122, 133, 138 (intercensal estimates).
   h. *General Statistics of Cities,* 1909 (Highway service); 1915 (governmental organizations, police departments, liquor traffic, municipally owned water systems); 1916 (recreation service).
   i. *Insane and Feeble Minded,* 1904, 1910.
   j. *Marriage and Divorce,* 1867-1906 (2 vols.).
   k. *Mortality from Cancer and Other Malignant Diseases:* 1914.
   l. *Negro Population in the U. S.,* 1790-1915.
   m. *Paupers,* 1904, 1910.
   n. *Prisoners and Juvenile Delinquents in the U. S.,* 1910.
   o. *Religious Bodies,* 1916 (2 vols.).
   p. *Specified Sources of Municipal Revenue,* 1917.
   q. *Statistical Atlas,* 1900, 1914.
   r. *Statistical Directory of State Institutions for the Defective, Dependent, and Delinquent Classes.*
   s. Transportation and other public utilities:
      Central Electric Light and Power Stations and Street and Electric Railways, 1912.
      Telegraphs, 1917.
      Telephones, 1907, 1917.

> *Telephones, Telegraphs and Municipal Signaling Systems*, 1912.
> *Transportation by Water*, 1906, 1916.
> t. *Wealth, Debt, and Taxation*, 2 vols., 1913.

B. BUREAU OF FOREIGN AND DOMESTIC COMMERCE:
1. *Commerce Yearbook*—new publication; first issue contains data for 1922 and part of 1923.
2. *Monthly Summary of Foreign Commerce of the U. S.*
3. *Commerce Reports* (W.), 1921 to date, formerly issued daily.
4. *Statistical Abstract of the U. S.* (A.).
5. *The Foreign Commerce and Navigation of the U. S.* (A.).
6. *Miscellaneous Series*—e.g., No. 103, *Annual Review of the Foreign Commerce of the U. S.*, 1919.
7. *Annual Report of Commissioner of Navigation.*
8. *Trade Information Bulletin*—supplement to Commerce Reports—*e.g.*, No. 40, "German Reparations, Budget and Foreign Trade."
9. *Trade and Economic Review*, supplement to Commerce Reports. Each number is devoted to one country—*e.g.*, No. 1 (1921) pertains to the United Kingdom.

C. BUREAU OF IMMIGRATION:
1. *Annual Report of the Commissioner-General of Immigration*, and monthly mimeographed releases.

D. BUREAU OF LABOR STATISTICS:
1. *Monthly Labor Review.*
2. Special series (partial list):
> *Retail Prices and Cost of Living Series*—e.g., No. 334. *Retail Prices, 1913-1922.*
> *Wholesale prices series*—e.g., No. 335, *Wholesale Prices, 1890-1922.*
> *Wages and Hours of Labor Series*—e.g., No. 279, *Hours and Earnings in Anthracite and Bituminous Coal Mining.*

E. BUREAU OF MINES (see also "Bulletins," "Technical Papers"):
1. *Monthly Statement of Coal-mine Fatalities in the U. S.*

F. DEPARTMENT OF AGRICULTURE:
1. *Weather, Crops, and Markets* (W.), January, 1922, to date.
2. *Year Book* (A.).

G. FEDERAL RESERVE BOARD:
1. *Federal Reserve Bulletin* (M.).
2. *Annual Report* (A.).

H. FEDERAL RESERVE AGENT, NEW YORK. (Similar reports are issued for the other Federal Reserve districts.)
  1. *Monthly Review of Credit and Business Conditions in the Second Federal Reserve District* (New York).

J. GEOLOGICAL SURVEY:
  Mineral Resources of the U. S. (A.).
    Part I. *Metals* ⎰ See bibliographical summary,
    Part II. *Non-metals* ⎱ 1917, pp. 17A-22A, Part I.

K. INTERSTATE COMMERCE COMMISSION.
  1. *Statistics of Railways in the United States* (A.).
  2. *Preliminary Statement of Class I Roads* (M.).

L. TREASURY DEPARTMENT.
  1. *Daily Statement of the U. S. Treasury* (N. Y. *Times*), Annual reports,—
  2. *Commissioner of Internal Revenue.*
  3. *Comptroller of the Currency.*
  4. *Director of the Mint.*
  5. *Secretary of the Treasury—Finance.*
  6. *Treasurer of the United States.*

II. Publications of State Governments (sample list).

LABOR:
  1. Illinois Department of Labor, *The Employment Bulletin* (M.).
  2. Industrial Commission of Wisconsin, *Wisconsin Labor Market* (M.).
  3. Massachusetts Department of Labor and Industries, *Massachusetts Industrial Review* (Q.).
  4. New York State Industrial Commission, *The Industrial Bulletin* (M.).

TAXATION:
  5. Minnesota Tax Commission, *Biennial Report.*
  6. Wisconsin Tax Commission, *Biennial Report,* and *Municipal Statistics Department Bulletins.*

HEALTH:
  7. New York State Department of Health, *Monthly Vital Statistics Review.*

III. Commercial and Trade Papers:

A. FINANCIAL WEEKLIES.
  1. *The Annalist—A Magazine of Finance, Commerce, and Economics.* New York (W.).
  2. *Bradstreet's—A Journal of Trade, Finance and Public Economy.* New York (W.).
  3. *The Commercial and Financial Chronicle.* New York (W.).

See also, *The Financial Review—Finance, Crops, Railroads, Trade, Commerce,* published by the Chronicle (A.). (The most recent issue is that for year 1920.)

4. *Dun's Review—A Weekly Survey of Business Conditions in the United States and Canada.* New York (W.).
5. *The Economist.* London (W.).
6. *L'Economiste Français* (in French). Paris (W.).
7. *The Statist—A Journal of Practical Finance and Trade.* London (W.).

B. PUBLICATIONS OF BANKS AND OTHER FINANCIAL INSTITUTIONS.
   1. *Commerce Monthly.* National Bank of Commerce, N. Y. (M.).
   2. *Economic Conditions.* The National City Bank, N. Y. (M.).
   3. *The Index.* N. Y. Trust Co. (M.).

C. SPECIAL TRADE JOURNALS[1] (publishers not listed):
   1. *The American Sugar Bulletin* (W.).
   2. *Coal Age* (W.).
   3. *Engineering and Mining Journal* (W.).
   4. *Iron Age* (W.).
   5. *Iron Trade Review* (W.).
   6. *Oil, Paint and Drug Reporter* (W.).
   7. *Railway Age* (W.).
   8. *The American Contractor* (W.).
   9. *Automotive Industries* (W.).
      (See *Crain's Market Data Book and Directory of Trade and Technical Publications,* C. D. Crain, Chicago.)

IV. **Daily Papers (Financial Columns):**

V. **Private Statistical Services:** (Partial list)
   1. Babson's Statistical Organization, Inc.
      a. *Babson's Statistical Tables and Charts* (desk chart) (M.).
      b. *Babson's Reports: Barometer Letter and the Babson-chart* (W.).
         Industries Bulletin (S.M.), and other bulletins.
   2. Brookmire Economic Service, Inc.
      The Brookmire Barometers (M.), *Analyst* (B.-W.), *Forecaster* (W.), *Monthly Report of Purchasing Power of Cities, Trade Bulletin* (B.-W.), *Trend Chart* (M.).

[1] See *Survey of Current Business* for list of government reports, reports from trade associations and private organizations, and technical periodicals— *e.g.,* February, 1924, pp. 217-220.

3. Bureau of Railway Economics:
   Railway Revenues and Expenses (M.).
4. Harvard University Committee on Economic Research.
   Harvard Economic Service, including—
     (a) *The Review of Economic Statistics* (Q.).
     (b) *Weekly Letter.*
5. Moody's Investor's Service. *Weekly Review of Financial Conditions;* also special reports and annual volumes with some statistical material.
6. National Industrial Conference Board, N. Y., Century Co.
   Research Reports—e.g., No. 63, "Changes in the Cost of Living, July, 1914—July, 1923."
7. Standard Statistics Co., Inc. New York.
   Standard Daily Trade Service (with Statistical Bulletin published quarterly with monthly supplements).
   Standard Corporation Service (card system, with daily news service and other supplements).
   Standard Bond Description Service (card cabinet and bond book, with various periodic supplements).

VI. Year Books (A.):
1. *The American Year Book.* Appleton, New York.
2. *The Chicago Daily News Almanac and Year-Book.* Chicago.
3. *The Statesman's Year-Book.* Macmillan, N. Y.
4. *The World Almanac and Encyclopedia.* The Press Pub. Co., The New York *World,* N. Y.

A Classification of Statistical Facts

In the attempt to master the great diversity of facts which, in the modern world, compete for the attention of the individual, the limitations of the human mind make it convenient to group facts according to classes, to arrange them according to common characteristics. In the accompanying "Classification of Periodic Statistics," an attempt has been made to insure a readier command of the sources of statistical data by grouping such data into fifteen major classes, with their respective subdivisions. This classification is neither entirely complete nor has a certain amount of overlapping been avoided, but the arrangement is such that it is thought the student of commercial or social facts will find it convenient to group his sources of information along the lines of this classification.

For each of the subdivisions in the following classification of periodic statistics, one or more sources of information have been suggested. This indication of sources is not intended to be comprehensive, but rather as a sample which the student will amplify from his reading. The principal abbreviations which may not be clearly self-explanatory are as follows:

Key to abbreviations:

Babson's ....*Babson's Statistical Tables and Charts* (desk chart).

C&F Chron ......*The Commercial and Financial Chronicle.*

Dun's ....*Dun's Review.*

Fed R Bul.......*Federal Reserve Bulletin.*

MLR ....*Monthly Labor Review.*

R Econ Stat......*Review of Economic Statistics.*

Standard DTS ...*Standard Daily Trade Service.*

Stat Abst ....*Statistical Abstract of the United States.*

Sur Cur Bus.....*Survey of Current Business.*

W C & Markets...*Weather, Crops, and Markets.*

A CLASSIFICATION OF PERIODIC STATISTICS

COMMERCIAL, ECONOMIC, AND SOCIOLOGICAL DATA, WITH PARTIAL BIBLIOGRAPHY

I. *Agricultural Statistics:*
   a. Crops.
      Acreage.
         (Agric. Year Book; Stat Abst; W C & Markets.)
      Conditions.
         (Babson's; bulletins of the various Fed. R. Agents; Fed R Bul; W C & Markets.)
      Estimates.
         (Agric. Year Book; W C & Markets.)
      Values.
         (Agric. Year Book; Stat Abst; W C & Markets.)
   b. Farm resources: land, machinery, live stock, etc.
         (Agric. Year Book; U. S. Census volumes on Agriculture.)
   c. Movements of crops and stock.
      Exports and imports.
         (Mo. Summary of Foreign Commerce; Stat Abst; W C & Markets.)
      Domestic receipts, shipments, and slaughter.
         (See preceding item; also C & F Chron; Sur Cur Bus.)
   d. Prices of farm products.
         (See Sec. 1-c above, and daily papers.)

e. Visible supply.
> (Bulletins of the various Fed R Agents; C & F Chron.; daily papers; Sur Cur Bus; W C & Markets.)

f. Tenancy.
> (U. S. Census, *e.g.*, vols. v and vi, 1920.)

2. *Business Conditions:*

a. Failures: number and liabilities.
> (Babson's; Bradstreet's; bulletins of the various Fed R Agents; Dun's; Fed R Bul.)

b. Composite indexes of business conditions.
> (Babson's; Brookmire's; F. W. Dodge Co., the Graphic Review; Management and Administration; R Econ Stat; Standard DTS.)

c. New construction.
> (Annalist; Babson's; Sur Cur Bus; F. W. Dodge Co., *Building Statistics* (a monthly pamphlet) and *The Graphic Review.*)

d. Unfilled tonnage of U. S. Steel Corporation.
> (Babson's; C & F Chron.)

3. *Capital Equipment:*
> (See 2-c above and 12-a below; Stat. of Railways in U. S.; U. S. Census decennial reports, Census of Manufactures; Wealth, Debt and Taxation.)

4. *Commodity Prices and Cost of Living:*

a. Cost of living indices.
> (Fed R Bul; MLR; Natl. Ind. Confer. Board; Sur Cur Bus.)

b. Farm products.
> (See Agric Stat, Sec. 1, above.)

c. Foreign price indices.
> (Babson's; Com. Reports; Fed R Bul; MLR.)

d. Retail prices.
> (Bulletins of the various Fed R Agents; Bureau of Labor special Bul. No. 315, "Retail Prices, 1913 to Dec., 1921"; MLR.)

e. Wholesale prices.
> (Annalist; Bradstreet's; bulletins of the various Fed R agents; Bureau of Labor Statistics *Bulletin* No. 335, "Wholesale Prices, 1890-1922"; Dun's; Fed R Bul; MLR; Standard DTS; various trade journals.)

5. *Consumption Facts:*

a. Estimates of consumption.
> (Stat Abst; see also "Production." Sec. 11 and "Trade," Sec. 14.)

b. Purchasing power.
> (See "Personal Incomes," Sec. 10.)

6. *Corporation Accounting and Financing:*
  a. Balance sheets.
     (Moody's Manual; Poor's Manual.)
  b. Incomes, earnings, and dividends.
     (Bradstreet's; C & F Chron; Dun's; Moody's Manual; Poor's Manual; Sur Cur Bus; Standard DTS.)
  c. New security issues.
     (Babson's; Bradstreet's; Bulletins of the twelve Fed R Banks.)
  d. Security market conditions.
     (Annalist; Bradstreet's; C & F Chron; daily papers; Dun's; Sur Cur Bus.)
     (1) Prices of individual stocks and bonds.
     (2) Average prices for groups.
       Same as preceding; (Standard DTS.)
     (3) Volume of transfers.
       Same as preceding.

7. *Labor Facts:*
     (In general: MLR; Sur Cur Bus; Research Reports of the National Industrial Conference Board; see also Sec. 13-h.)
  a. Accidents.
     (MLR; U. S. Bureau of Mines—Monthly Stat. of Coal Mine Fatalities.)
  b. Employment and unemployment.
     (Fed R Bul; Ill. Dept. of Lab.—"The Labor Bul"; Indus. Comm. of Wis.—"Wis. Lab. Market"; Mass. Dept. of Lab.—"Mass. Indus. Rev."; "MLR"; N. Y. State Indus. Comm.—"The Indus. Rev."; "Sur Cur Bus"; see also, "Publications of State Governments," in this chapter.)
  c. Earnings.
     (MLR; N Y State, *The Indus. Rev.*)
  d. Hours.
     (MLR; *e.g.,* Feb., 1921; U. S. Bureau Lab. Stat. Special Bul. 279. "Hours and earnings in Anthracite and Bituminous Coal Mining.")
  e. Strikes and lockouts.
     (MLR; Proceedings Amer. Fed. Lab.)
  f. Union membership.
     Same as preceding.
  g. Wage rates.
     MLR; Stat Abst; U. S. Department of Agriculture Year Book; special bulletins of Bureau of Lab. Stat.—*e.g.,* No. 279, "Hours and Earnings in Anthracite and Bituminous Coal Mining."

8. *Land and natural resources:*
     (Stat Abst; U. S. Census—decennial reports and "Wealth, Debt, and Taxation, 1913.")

9. *Money, Banking and Credit Statistics:*
    a. Banking resources and liabilities.
       (Annalist; Babson's; C & F Chron; Dun's; Fed R Bul.)
    b. Clearings and bank debits to individual accounts.
       (Annalist; Babson's; Bradstreet's; C & F Chron; Dun's; Fed R Bul.)
    c. Exchange rates—domestic.
       (Annalist.)
    d. Exchange rates—foreign.
       (Annalist; Bradstreet's; C & F Chron; daily papers; Dun's; Fed R Bul.)
    e. Foreign banking.
       (C & F Chron; Fed R Bul.)
    f. Interest and discount rates.
       (Annalist; Babson's; C & F Chron.; Fed R Bul.)
    g. Movement of money, interior.
       (C & F Chron.)
    h. Paper money issues.
       (Fed R Bul.)
    i. Precious metals.
       (1) Imports and exports.
          (Bradstreet's; Fed R Bul; Report of Director of Mint; U. S. For. Trade Reports, and Monthly Summary.)
       (2) Production.
          (Report of Director of Mint; U. S. Geol. Survey—Mineral Resources of U. S.)
       (3) Stocks.
          (C & F Chron; Report of Director of Mint.)

10. *Personal Incomes:*
       (See "Public Finance," Sec. 12.)

11. *Production Facts:*
       (See also Secs. 1, 14, 15.)
    a. Crop yields.
       (See "Agricultural Statistics," Sec. 1; Stat Abst; Sur Cur Bus; W C & Markets.)
    b. Fisheries.
       (Stat Abst.)
    c. Indices of physical production.
       (Fed R Bul; R Econ Stat; Sur Cur Bus.)
    d. Live stock products.
       (See "Agricultural Statistics," Sec. 1.)
    e. Manufactures.
       (R Econ Stat; Stat Abst; U. S. Census of Manufactures.)
    f. Mineral products extracted.
       (Fed R Bul; R Econ Stat; Stat Abst; U. S. Geol. Survey—Mineral Resources.)

g. Timber products.
(Stat Abst.)

12. *Public Finance:*
(C & F Chron; daily papers; Daily reports U. S. Treas.;
Fin. Stat. of States; Fin. Stat. of Cities; N. Y. *Times;* Stat
Abst; Sur Cur Bus; see also Publications of State Governments.)
a. Assessed values.
b. Debts.
c. Expenditures.
d. Revenues.
(Comm. Internal Revenue—Statistics of Income.)

13. *Sociological Statistics:*
a. Births.
(Stat Abst; U. S. Census—Birth Stat., 1915 to date; "Weekly
Health Index.")
b. Composition of population: age, color, race; defectives; marital
condition; nativity; sex.
(U. S. Census: decennial reports; The Blind in the U. S.,
1910; Chinese and Japanese in the U. S., 1910; Insane and
Feeble-minded, 1904, 1915; Negro Population in U. S., 1790-
1915.)
c. Criminal statistics.
(U. S. Census—"Prisoners and Juvenile Delinquents in U. S.,
1910.")
d. Disease.
(U. S. Public Health Reports. See also "Mortality Statistics," Sec. 13-j, below.)
e. Educational statistics.
(Stat abst.)
f. Geographical distribution (urban and rural by states.)
(U. S. Census.)
g. Growth of population.
(U. S. Census—decennial reports and bulletins 122, 133, 138;
and "A Century of Pop. Growth, 1790-1900.")
h. Immigration.
(Babson's; Bradstreet's; MLR; Report of U. S. Comm. General of Immigration, and monthly mimeographed statements;
Stat Abst; Sur Cur Bus)
i. Marriages and divorces.
(U. S. Census, "Marriage and Divorce, 1867-1906.")
j. Mortality statistics.
(Stat Abst; U. S. Census—Mortality Stat., 1900 to date;
"Weekly Health Index.")
k. Occupations.
(U. S. Census.)

    1. Political affiliation.
      (Stat Abst)

14. *Trade:*
      (See also "Transportation," Sec. 15, below.)
    a. Indices of physical volume of trade.
      (Fed. R. Bul.)
    b. Movements of commodities.
      (1) Exports and imports.
          (Annalist; Bradstreet's; Fed R Bul; Sur Cur Bus;
          U. S. Foreign Trade Reports and Monthly Summary of
          Foreign Commerce.)
      (2) Domestic receipts and shipments.
          (Fed R Bul; See "Agricultural Statistics," Sec. 1.)
      (3) Sales: Chain stores, Department stores, Mail Order
          stores, Wholesale Trade.
          (Bulletins of various Fed R Agents; Fed R Bul; Sur
          Cur Bus.)
    c. Stocks of goods on hand.
          (Bulletins of various Fed R agents; Fed R Bul; Sur
          Cur Bus; see "Agricultural Statistics," Sec. 1.)

15. *Transportation:*
    a. Earnings and expenses.
      (Babson's; C & F Chron; Interstate Com. Comm. Annual Re-
      ports; Railway Age.)
    b. Facilities: cars and locomotives in use.
      (Interstate Com. Comm. Annual Reports; Railway Age.)
    c. Rates and fares.
      (Fed R Bul.)
    d. Traffic and operation.
      (Interstate Com. Comm., Stat. of Railways in U. S.; Railway
      Age; R Econ Stat.)
    e. Car-miles, locomotive mileage, passenger mileage, train-miles,
      freight loaded, ton-miles.
      (See preceding.)

REFERENCES

1. AUSTIN, O. P., "Use of Statistical Publications of the Government in Working Out Problems of Commercial Investigation," in *Administration*, April, 1922, pp. 433-436.
2. COPELAND, M. T., *Business Statistics,* pp. 161-177, "Current Sources of Information in Produce Markets."
3. JORDAN, D. F., *Business Forecasting,* p. 259.
4. New York University Bureau of Business Research, *Source-Book of Research Data,* 1923.
5. PARMALEE, J. H., "Organizations that Collect Business Statistics," *Quar. Pub., Amer. Stat. Assoc.,* Vol. 15, pp. 566-73, sub-topic.

6. *Review of Economic Statistics*, January, 1919, pp. 5-6, 39-48.
7. ROBINSON, L. D., *Criminal Statistics in the United States.*
8. SECRIST, H., *Business Statistics,* chap. ii.
9. ——— *An Introduction to Statistical Methods,* pp. 16-19.
10. United States Bureau of Efficiency, *Report on the Statistical Work of the United States Government,* 1923.

APPENDIX A

The Literature of Statistical Method and Its Applications

In the following bibliography, while most of the general treatises on statistical method are listed, together with many of the economic and social studies which have involved the use of statistical method, the list, particularly as regards the periodical literature, is intended to be suggestive rather than complete. Books and other publications which have been frequently referred to in the chapter references are listed again below. The basis of classification is as follows:

CLASSIFICATION OF REFERENCES

   I. Treatises on statistical method.
  II. Statistical journals and publications.
 III. Business statistics.
 IV. Sociological statistics: vital, criminal, and dependency statistics.
  V. Economic statistics.

    1. Cycles and forecasting.
    2. Distribution of wealth and income
    3. Labor problems: wages, family budgets, cost of living, unemployment.
    4. Theory of index numbers and prices.
    5. Money and banking.
    6. Miscellaneous.

  VI. Graphic presentation.
 VII. History of statistics.
VIII. Theory of probability and least squares.
  IX. Computing tables.
   X. Unclassified.

I. Treatises on Statistical Method.

ALEXANDER, CARTER, *School Statistics and Publicity.* New York, Silver, Burdett & Co., 1919.

BAILEY, W. B., and CUMMINGS, J., *Statistics.* Brief. Chicago, A. C. McClurg Co., 1917.

BOWLEY, A. L., *Elements of Statistics,* 4th ed. New York, Scribner, 1920. Two volumes (or one combined). Vol. II, mathematical.

—— *An Elementary Manual of Statistics.* London, McDonald & Evans, 1910.

—— *The Measurement of Groups and Series,* London, 1903.

DAVENPORT, C. B., *Statistical Methods—with special reference to Biological Variation,* 3d ed. New York, Wiley, 1914.

DAVIES, G. R., *Introduction to Economic Statistics.* New York, Century Co., 1922.

ELDERTON, W. P., *Frequency Curves and Correlation.* London, 1906.

ELDERTON, W. P. and E. M., *Primer of Statistics.* New York, Macmillan, 1912. Good for brief survey of theory.

JONES, D. C., *A First Course in Statistics.* London, G. Bell & Sons, 1921.

KELLEY, T. L., *Statistical Method.* New York, Macmillan, 1923.

KING, W. I., *Elements of Statistical Method.* New York, Macmillan, 1912.

RIETZ, H. L., editor-in-chief, *Handbook of Mathematical Statistics.* Houghton Mifflin, 1924.

RUGG, H. O., *Statistical Methods Applied to Education.* Boston, Houghton Mifflin, 1917.

SECRIST, H., *An Introduction to Statistical Methods,* Macmillan, 1917.
——— *Readings and Problems in Statistical Methods.* Macmillan, 1920.

THORNDIKE, E. L., *An Introduction to the Theory of Mental and Social Measurements.* New York, Science Press, 1904.

WEST, C. J., *Introduction to Mathematical Statistics.* Columbus, R. G. Adams & Co., 1918. (Bibliography of mathematical articles, appendix.)

WESTERGAARD, HARALD, *Scope and Methods of Statistics, Quar. Pub. of Am. Stat. Assn.,* Vol. XV, 1916, pp. 225-291, and discussion.

YULE, G. U., *An Introduction to the Theory of Statistics.* London, C. Griffin & Co., 1922 (sixth edition). Excellent for theory.

ZIZEK, FRANZ, *Statistical Averages,* translated by W. M. Persons. New York, Henry Holt & Co., 1913. Standard treatise on averages.

II. Statistical Journals.

Not all of the following publications are devoted primarily to statistical literature, but they contain frequent articles with discussions or applications of statistical method.

American Economic Review (Quarterly). New Haven, Conn.

The Annalist (Weekly). New York.

Biometrika; A Journal for the Statistical Study of Biological Problems, 1901-date. Cambridge, England.

Federal Reserve Bulletin, Federal Reserve Board (Monthly).

Industrial Management. New York.

Journal of the American Statistical Association (Quarterly). Formerly, *The Quarterly Publication of the American Statistical Association.* Concord, N. H.

Journal of Political Economy. Chicago (Monthly).

Journal of the Royal Statistical Society. London.

Management and Administration. New York, Ronald Press.

Metron, an international quarterly review of statistics, published at Ferrara, Italy, beginning in 1920. The articles are in English, French, German or Italian.

Monthly Labor Review, Bureau of Labor Statistics.

Monthly Review, Federal Reserve Agent. New York.

Quarterly Journal of Economics. Boston.

The Review of Economic Statistics. Harvard University Committee on Economic Research, Cambridge, 1919, to date.

III. Business Statistics.

American Statistical Association Quarterly Publication (now the *Journal of the Am. Stat. Assn.*). See index, *e.g.,* Vol. XVI.

BODDINGTON, A. L., *Statistics and their Application to Commerce.* London, H. Foulk Lynch & Co., 1921.

Bureau of Business Research, Northwestern University School of Commerce, H. Secrist, Director, *Costs, Merchandising Practices, Advertising and Sales in the Retail Distribution of Clothing,* 6 vols. New York, Prentice-Hall, 1921.

COKEL, W. B., "Statistics in Business," *Administration,* May, 1921.

COPELAND, M. T., *Business Statistics,* Harvard University Press, 1917.

DAVID, D. K., *Retail Store Management Problems,* Pt. III, "Statistical Problems," pp. 120-214. New York, A. W. Shaw Co., 1922.

DUNCAN, C. S., *Commercial Research.* New York, Macmillan. 1919.

FREDERICK, J. G., *Business Research and Statistics.* Appleton, 1920.

PARMALEE, J. H., "The Utilization of Statistics in Business," *Am. Stat. Assn.,* Vol. XV, pp. 565-576.

ROTH, H. L., "The Application of Statistics to Advertising and Marketing," *Am. Stat. Assn.,* Vol. XV, pp. 436-465.

SECRIST, H., *Statistics in Business*—Their Analysis, Charting and Use. New York, McGraw-Hill, 1920.

WAHL, ALEXANDER, *A Study of Credit Barometrics.* Report for Federal Reserve Board. National Bank of Commerce, Detroit, Michigan.

WHITE, PERCIVAL, *Market Analysis.* New York, McGraw-Hill, 1921.

IV. Sociological Statistics.

Vital, criminal and dependency statistics. (See also "Labor Problems" and "Distribution of Wealth and Income.")

American Journal of Public Health (Monthly), official publication of the American Public Health Association. 1916-date. Boston.

BAILEY, W. B., *Modern Social Conditions.* New York, Century Co., 1906.

BONGER, WM. A., *Criminality and Economic Conditions,* Little Brown & Co., 1916.

BOWLEY, A. L., *The Nature and Purpose of the Measurement of Social Phenomena.* London, King & Son, 1915.

CHAPIN, F. S., *Field Work and Social Research*. New York, Century Co., 1920.

FALK, I. S., *The Principles of Vital Statistics*. Philadelphia, Saunders, 1923. ("Almost wholly devoted to the results of Vital Statistics.")

GILLIN, J. L., "The Social Survey and Its Further Development," *Am. Stat. Assn.*, September, 1915, pp. 603-610.

HEXTER, M. B., "Persistency of Dependency—A Study in Social Causation." *Am. Stat. Assn.*, Vol. XV, pp. 860-867.

KNIBBS, G. H., "The Mathematical Theory of Population, of its Character and Fluctuations and of the Factors which Influence Them, etc." Appendix A, Vol. I, Census of the Commonwealth of Australia, for April, 1911, Melbourne, 1917.

NEWSHOLME, ARTHUR, *Elements of Vital Statistics*. London, Allen & Unwin, 1923, new ed., rev.

PEARL, RAYMOND, *Introduction to Medical Biometry and Statistics*. Philadelphia, Saunders, 1923.

Public Health Reports. Weekly. Published by the U. S. Public Health Service.

ROBINSON, L. D., *Criminal Statistics in the United States*.

SMITH, R. MAYO, *Statistics and Sociology*. New York, 1895-99.

RUBINOW, I. M., "Dependency Index of New York City," *Am. Econ. Rev.*, December, 1918, pp. 713-740.

WHIPPLE, G. C., *Vital Statistics—An Introduction to the Science of Demography*. New York, Wiley, 1919, first ed.; 1923, second ed.

V. Economic Statistics.

1. *Cycles and forecasting.*

BABSON, ROGER W., *Business Barometers,* Wellesley Hills, Mass. 16th ed., 1923.

DAVIES, G. R., "Social Aspects of the Business Cycle," *The Quarterly Journal,* published by University of North Dakota, January, 1922, 107-121.

DENNISON, H. S., "Management and the Business Cycle," *Jour. Am. Stat. Assn.,* March, 1922, pp. 20-32.

DOUGLAS, P. H., "Personnel Problems and the Business Cycle," *Administration,* September, 1922, pp. 15-27.

HANSEN, A. H., "Cycles of Strikes," *Am. Econ. Rev.,* December, 1921, pp. 616-621.

——— *Cycles of Prosperity and Depression in the United States, Great Britain and Germany,* University of Wisconsin Studies, Madison, 1921.

JORDAN, D. F., *Business Forecasting*. New York, Prentice-Hall, 1921.

MITCHELL, W. C., *Business Cycles*. Berkeley, Cal., University of California Memoirs, Vol. III, 1913.

MOORE, H. L., *Economic Cycles; Their Law and Cause.* Macmillan, 1914.
———— *Forecasting the Yield and the Price of Cotton.* Macmillan, 1917.
———— "Generating Cycles of Products and Prices," *Q. J. Econ.,* 1921, Vol. XXXV, pp. 215-239.
———— "Generating Cycles Reflected in a Century of Prices," *Q. J. Econ.,* Vol. XXXV, pp. 503-523. 1921.
National Bureau of Economic Research, Inc. New York City. Vol. IV. *Business Cycles and Unemployment*—report and recommendations of a committee of the President's Conference on Unemployment, including an investigation made under the auspices of the National Bureau of Economic Research. 1923.
Vol. V. W. I. King, *Employment, Hours and Earnings in Prosperity and Depression—United States, 1920-22.* 1923.
PARKER, FRANK, "The Development of Business Forecasting," *Administration, September,* 1922, pp. 269-275.
PERSONS, W. M., "Indices of Business Conditions," *Rev. of Econ. Statistics, 1919,* pp. 5-107, and "An Index of General Business Conditions," *ibid.,* pp. 111-205. Also published separately.
VANCE, RAY, *Business and Investment Forecasting.* New York. Brookmire Economic Service, Inc., 1922.

2. *Distribution of wealth and income.* (See also "Labor Problems.")
FRIDAY, DAVID, *Profits, Wages and Prices.* Harcourt, Brace & Howe, 1920.
———— "Statistics of Income," *Am. Econ. Rev.,* September, 1919, pp. 502-516.
INGALLS, W. R., *Wealth and Income of the American People,* 2d ed., C. H. Merlin Co., York, Pa.
KING, W. I., *Wealth and Income of the People of the United States.* New York, Macmillan, 1915.
KNIBBS, G. H., *The Private Wealth of Australia and its Growth.* Together with a Report of the War Census of 1915. Melbourne, Commonwealth Bureau of Census and Statistics, 1918.
MOORE, H. L., *Laws of Wages.* Macmillan, 1911.
National Bureau of Economic Research, Inc., New York City. *Income in the United States—Its Amount and Distribution, 1909-19.*
Vol. I. General summary of findings.
Vol. II. Detailed report. Excellent as a study in method as well as for the data presented.
Vol. III. Distribution of Income by States.
STAMP, J. C., *British Incomes and Property—The Application of Official Statistics to Economic Problems.* London, King & Son, 1916.
SYDENSTRICKER, EDGAR, and KING, W. I., "The Measurement of the Relative Economic Status of Families," *Am. Stat. Assn.,* Vol. XVII, pp. 842-857.

YOUNG, A. A., "Do the Statistics of the Concentration of Wealth in the United States Mean What they are Commonly Assumed to Mean?" *Am. Econ. Rev.*, supplement, March, 1917, pp. 144-156.

3. *Labor problems: cost of living; family budgets; wages; unemployment.*

BARNETT, E. G., "A Critique of Cost-of-living Studies." *Am. Stat. Assn.*, Vol. XVII, pp. 904-909.

BERRIDGE, W. A., *Cycles of Unemployment in the United States, 1903-1922.* Houghton Mifflin Co., 1923. Also several articles on similar subjects listed in footnotes to Chap. XII.

BIRD, F. H., "The Cost of Living as a Factor in Wage Adjustments in the Book and Job Branch of the Chicago Printing Industry," *Amer. Econ. Rev.*, December, 1921, pp. 622-642.

BOOTH, CHARLES, *Life and Labor of the People in London.* London, 1889-1892.

BOWLEY, A. L., and BURNETT-HURST, A. R., *Livelihood and Poverty: A Study in the Economic Conditions of Working-class Households in Northampton, Warrington, Stanley and Reading.* London, 1915.

BOWLEY, A. L., *Prices and Wages in the United Kingdom, 1914-1920.* Oxford, 1921 (Carnegie Endowment for International Peace).

Bureau of Municipal Research of Philadelphia, *Workingmen's Standard of Living in Philadelphia.* New York, Macmillan, 1919.

CHAPIN, R. C., *The Standard of Living among Workingmen's Families in New York City.* New York, Charities Publication Committee, 1909 (Bibliography).

DITTMER, C. G., "An Estimate of the Standard of Living in China," *Q. J. Econ.*, November, 1918, pp. 107-128.

DOUGLAS, P. H., and LAMBERSON, FRANCES, "The Movement of Real Wages, 1890-1918," *Amer. Econ. Rev.*, September, 1921, pp. 409-426.

HANSEN, A. H., "The Buying Power of Labor During the War," *Jour. Am. Stat. Assn.*, March, 1922, pp. 56-66.

International Labour Office, *Wage Changes in Various Countries, 1914-1922.* Geneva, 1923 (and similar bulletin for 1914-1921). An analysis of the available statistics on wages, earnings, and cost of living.

KING, W. I., *Employment, Hours, and Earnings in Prosperity and Depression: United States, 1920-1922.* New York, National Bureau of Economic Research. 1923.

MORE, L. B., *Wage Earners' Budgets: A Study of Standards and Cost of Living in New York City.* New York, Holt, 1907.

National Industrial Conference Board. "Family Budgets of American Wage-earners: A Critical Analysis." *Research Report* No. 41, September, 1921, Century Co.

"The Unemployment Problem," *Research Report,* No. 43, Scribners, 1922. (See also their special research reports on wages.)

OGBURN, W. F., "Standard of Living in the District of Columbia," *Am. Stat. Assn.,* Vol. XVI, 1918-19, pp. 374-389.

ROWNTREE, B. S., *Poverty—A Study of Town Life,* London, Macmillan, 1901.

STECKER, MARGARET L., "Family Budgets and Wages," *Am. Econ. Rev.* September, 1921, pp. 447-465.

U. S. Bureau of Labor Statistics, *Mo. Labor Review,* November, 1922, pp. 104-105. List of articles on cost of living.

——— *Methods of Procuring and Computing Statistical Information of the Bureau of Labor Statistics,* Bulletin No. 326, March, 1923.

4. *Index Numbers, the Measurement of Exchange Value, and Price Theory.*

DAVIES, G. R., "The Quantity Theory and Recent Statistical Studies," *Jour. of Pol. Econ.,* 1921, pp. 213-221.

FISHER, IRVING, *The Purchasing Power of Money.* Macmillan, 1911.

——— *The Making of Index Numbers.* Houghton Mifflin Co., 1922.

HANSEN, A. H., "Wholesale Prices for the United States, 1801-1840," *Am. Stat. Assn.,* 1915, pp. 804-812.

MACAULAY, FREDERICK R., "Making and Using of Index Numbers," *American Economic Review,* March, 1916, pp. 203-209. (Review of reference next following.)

MITCHELL, W. C., *Index Numbers of Wholesale Prices in the United States and Foreign Countries,* U. S. Bureau of Labor Statistics, Whole No. 173 (1915); Whole No. 284, revised edition (1921). A standard reference on the construction and use of index numbers.

MOORE, H. L., "Elasticity of Demand and Flexibility of Prices," *Jour. Am. Stat. Assn.,* March, 1922, pp. 8-19 (mathematical).

ROELSE, H. V., "Wholesale Prices in the United States, 1791-1801," *Am. Stat. Assn.,* Vol. XV, pp. 840-846.

WALLACE, H. A., *Agricultural Prices,* Des Moines, Wallace Pub. Co., 1920.

WALSH, C. M., *The Measurement of General-Exchange Value,* Macmillan, 1901.

——— *The Problem of Estimation. A Seventeenth Century Controversy and Its Bearing on Modern Statistical Questions, Especially Index Numbers.* London, P. S. King & Son, 1921.

YOUNG, A. A., "The Measurement of Changes in the General Price Level," *Q. J. Econ.,* 1921, Vol. XXXV, pp. 557-573.

5. *Money and Banking.*

KEMMERER, E. W., *Seasonal Variations in the Relative Demand for*

Money and Capital in the United States, Senate Document 588, 61st Congress, 2d Session, pp. 13-15.

KING, W. I., *Is Our Currency Elastic?* Bankers' Statistics Corporation. New York, September 21, 1920.

MITCHELL, W. C., *History of the Greenbacks.* Chicago, Uni. of Chicago Press, 1903.

NORTON, J. P., *Statistical Studies in the New York Money Market.* Macmillan, 1902.

PERSONS, WM., "An Index Chart Based on Prices and Money Rates," *Rev. Econ. Statistics,* January, 1922, pp. 7-11.

6. *Miscellaneous.*

BOWLEY, A. L., *The Effect of the War on the External Trade of the United Kingdom: An Analysis of the Monthly Statistics, 1906-14.* Cambridge University Press, 1915.

JAMES, A. E., "Measures of Relative Tax Burdens," *Am. Stat. Assn.,* Vol. XV, pp. 80-92.

SMITH, R. MAYO, *Statistics and Economics.* Macmillan, 1896.

VI. Graphic Presentation. (See also references with Chapters IV, V, and VI, which are not repeated at this point.)

EGGLESTON, D. C., and ROBINSON, F. B., *Business Costs.* Appleton, 1921. Chap. XXXVII, "Graphic Charts."

FALKNER, R. P., "Uses and Perils of Business Graphics," *Administration,* January, 1922, pp. 52-56.

GILMAN, STEPHEN, *Graphic Charts for Business Men,* Chicago, LaSalle Extension University, 1918.

Manual of Charting, Business School Series, Prentice-Hall, 1923.

RORTY, M. C., "Making Statistics Talk," three articles in *Industrial Management,* December, 1920, January and February, 1921.

Publications making extensive use of the graphic method.

AYRES, L. P., COLONEL, General Staff, Chief of the Statistics Branch of the General Staff, *The War with Germany—A Statistical Summary.*

Bureau of the Census: *Abstract; Statistical Atlas.*

Monthly Labor Review.

Review of Economic Statistics.

Survey of Current Business.

National Industrial Conference Board, *A Graphic Analysis of the Census of Manufactures of the United States, 1849-1919.* New York, 1923.

VII. History of Statistics. (See general treatises on method.)

KOREN, JOHN, *History of Statistics.* Macmillan, 1918.

MEITZEN, DR. AUGUST, *History, Theory and Technique of Statistics,* translated by R. P. Falkner. Philadelphia, A. A. A., 1891.

VIII. Theory of Probability.

FISHER, ARNE, *The Mathematical Theory of Probabilities.* Macmillan, 1915.

KEYNES, J. M., *A Treatise on Probability*. London, Macmillan, 1921. Bibliography, pp. 433-458.

WELD, L. D., *Theory of Errors and Least Squares,* Macmillan, 1916.

IX. Aids in Computation.

BARLOW, PETER, *Barlow's Tables of Squares, Cubes, Square Roots, Cube Roots, Reciprocals of All Integer Numbers up to 10,000.* New York, Spon & Chamberlain, 1914.

CHAPPELL, E., *Five-Figure Mathematical Tables.* London, W. & R. Chambers, Ltd., or D. VanNostrand, New York, 1915.

CRELLE, A. L., *Calculating Tables*—giving the products of every two numbers from 1 to 1,000 and their application to the multiplication and division of all numbers above 1,000. Revised by C. Bremiker. Berlin, G. Reimer, 1898.

HOLMAN, SILAS W., *Computation Rules and Logarithms.* New York, Macmillan, 1918.

KELLY, T. L., *Tables: To Facilitate the Calculation of Partial Coefficients of Correlation and Regression Equations,* Bulletin of the University of Texas, 1916, No. 27.

MINER, J. R., *Tables of $\sqrt{1-r^2}$ and $1-r^2$ for Use in Partial Correlation and in Trigonometry.* The Johns Hopkins Press, 1922.

PEARSON, KARL, editor, *Tables for Statisticians and Biometricians,* Cambridge University Press (Univ. of Chicago Press, agent).

THORNDIKE, E. L., *Theory of Mental and Social Measurements,* pp. 216-264.

X. Unclassified.

BOWLEY, A. L., *Official Statistics: What They Contain and How to Use Them.* London, Oxford Univ. Press, 1921. Analysis of British statistics.

The Bureau of Vocational Information, *Statistical Work—a Study of Opportunities for Women.* 2 West 43d St., New York City, 1921.

Drapers' Company *Research Memoirs: Biometric Series.* Several articles on statistical method, especially correlation.

APPENDIX B

Data Tables

Containing detail upon which certain derivative tables in the text are based and also statistics used in the exercises in Appendix C.

TABLE 101

1919 RELATIVE WHOLESALE PRICES OF 307 COMMODITIES IN THE UNITED STATES

1913 average price = 100

(United States Bureau of Labor Statistics, Bulletin 269, *Wholesale Prices, 1890 to 1919*)

This list of 307 includes all commodities used in the 1919 compilation of a wholesale price index except those for which 1913 prices are not given.

To save space many of the commodity descriptions are abbreviated. The full list, including the 328 used in the Bureau of Labor's index and 43 for which weights are not given, or 371 in all, are to be found in Appendix A to Bulletin 269.

GROUP I.—FARM PRODUCTS.

File Number	Commodity	Relative Price	File Number	Commodity	Relative Price
	Cotton, middling:			Hides:	
1	New Orleans	250.8	16	Calfskins, No. 1	363.0
2	New York	253.9		Green, salted, packers'	
3	Flaxseed, No. 1	336.0	17	Heavy native steers	213.8
	Grain:		18	Heavy Texas steers	197.5
4	Barley, fair to good, malting	194.6		Hops:	
	Corn, cash—		19	New York State	220.7
5	Contract grades	255.4	20	Pacific Coast	322.7
6	No. 3, mixed	256.7		Live stock (for food):	
7	Oats, cash	186.3		Cattle, steers—	
8	Rye, No. 2, cash	241.1	21	Choice to prime	209.0
	Wheat, cash—		22	Good to choice	205.7
9	Chicago, No. 1 northern spring	280.7	23	Hogs: heavy	218.1
10	Chicago, No. 2 red winter	239.0	24	Hogs: light	216.8
11	Kansas City, No. 2 hard winter	275.8		Sheep—	
			25	Ewes, fed	199.5
12	Minneapolis, No. 1 northern spring	293.8	26	Lambs	206.9
			27	Wethers	205.9
13	Portland, Ore., bluestem	258.1	28	Peanuts, No. 1 grade	207.9
	Hay:			Poultry, live fowls	
			29	Chicago	184.2
14	Alfalfa, No. 1	225.2	30	New York, choice	203.6
15	Timothy, No. 1	200.8	31	Tobacco, burley	245.0

GROUP II.—FOOD, ETC.

File Number	Commodity	Relative Price
32	Beans, medium, choice.......	202.0
	Butter:	
	Boston –	
33	Creamery, extra	188.6
34	Creamery, firsts	194.3
35	Creamery, seconds	199.8
	Chicago	
36	Creamery, extra	188.7
37	Creamery, extra firsts...	189.0
38	Creamery, firsts	200.2
	Cincinnati	
39	Creamery, extra	179.3
40	Creamery, centralized firsts	189.2
41	Creamery, centralized seconds	220.3
	New Orleans	
42	Creamery, fancy	185.3
43	Creamery, choice	190.9
	New York	
44	Creamery, extra	187.7
45	Creamery, firsts	191.5
46	Creamery, seconds	192.6
	Philadelphia	
47	Creamery, extra	189.0
48	Creamery, extra firsts....	190.7
49	Creamery, firsts	188.0
	St. Louis	
50	Creamery, extra	190.7
	San Francisco	
51	Creamery, extra	190.1
52	Creamery, prime firsts...	190.4
	Canned Goods:	
53	Corn, New York standard..	276.0
54	Peas, No. 5 sieve.........	169.2
55	Tomatoes, No. 3..........	157.7
	Cheese:	
56	Chicago	211.9
57	New York	204.4
58	San Francisco	204.2
59	Coffee, Rio, No. 7..........	160.4
	Eggs:	
60	Boston, firsts	210.9
61	Chicago, firsts, fresh......	214.7
62	Cincinnati, firsts, fresh.....	223.5
63	New Orleans, candled.....	169.5
64	New York, firsts, fresh.....	212.3
65	Philadelphia, extra firsts...	209.6
66	San Francisco, fresh......	198.2
	Fish:	
67	Cod	147.4
68	Herring, pickled	146.2
69	Mackerel, salt	193.6
70	Salmon, canned	208.1
	Flour:	
71	Buckwheat	200.5
72	Rye	269.0
	Wheat—	
73	Kansas City, winter patents	292.1

File Number	Commodity	Relative Price
74	Kansas City, winter straights	278.0
75	Minneapolis, standard patents	261.8
76	Minneapolis, second patents	271.0
	Fruits:	
	Apples—	
77	Fresh Baldwin	267.6
78	Bananas	262.6
79	Currants	291.4
80	Lemons	94.6
81	Oranges	108.7
82	Prunes	302.0
83	Raisins	169.7
84	Glucose	257.2
85	Lard	263.6
	Meal. corn:	
86	White, Terre Haute......	216.7
87	White, table, Philadelphia..	259.1
	Meat:	
	Bacon—	
88	Rough sides	215.5
89	Short clear sides.......	228.5
	Beef, fresh	
90	Carcass	180.2
91	Native sides, New York..	171.6
92	Beef, salt	164.2
93	Hams, smoked	206.6
94	Lamb, dressed, round.....	186.3
95	Mutton, dressed	162.7
96	Pork. salt, mess...........	232.3
	Poultry, dressed fowls—	
97	Chicago, iced	205.3
98	New York, dry picked...	195.2
99	Veal, city, dressed........	166.9
	Milk, fresh:	
100	Chicago	194.7
101	New York	214.7
102	San Francisco	190.5
103	Molasses, New Orleans......	183.4
104	Oleomargarine, uncolored ...	210.8
105	Oleo oil, extra...........	265.5
106	Olive oil, Spanish..........	193.0
107	Rice, Honduras, head........	209.1
108	Salt, American, medium.....	201.3
109	Spices: Pepper, black.......	186.5
	Sugar:	
110	96° centrifugal	214.6
111	granulated	209.4
112	Tallow, packer's prime.......	217.1
113	Tea, Formosa, fine..........	142.3
	Vegetables, fresh:	
114	Onions	228.0
115	Potatoes, white	232.3
116	Vinegar, cider	277.1

GROUP III.—CLOTHS AND CLOTHING.

File Number	Commodity	Relative Price	File Number	Commodity	Relative Price
	Boots and shoes:		151	Rough Rider	306.4
117	Children's gun metal, button	255.5	152	Wamsutta	319.5
118	Little boys', gun metal, blucher	235.5	153	Thread	140.6
	Men's		154	Ticking. Amoskeag	260.0
119	Gun metal, Goodyear welt, blucher	300.9		Underwear—	
120	Gun metal, Goodyear welt, button	256.4	155	Men's shirts and drawers	269.7
121	Split seamless Creedmores ½ double sole	176.8	156	Women's union suits	216.3
122	Vici calf, Goodyear welt, blucher	244.3		Yarn—	
				Carded, white, mulespun, northern cones—	
123	Vici kid, Goodyear welt	252.8	157	10/1	241.3
124	Misses', vici, button	265.9	158	22/1	240.8
	Women's—			Leather:	
125	Goodyear welt, gunmetal	270.3	159	Calf	359.6
126	McKay sewed, button	303.2	160	Harness	182.7
127	Patent leather	296.7		Sole—	
128	Youth's gun metal, blucher	206.3	161	Hemlock, middle, No. 1	187.3
	Carpets:		162	Oak, scoured backs, heavy	203.5
129	Axminster	223.3	163	Linen shoe thread	191.1
130	Brussels	263.7		Silk, raw:	
131	Wilton	224.7		Japan—	
	Cotton goods:		164	Kansai, No. 1	244.0
132	Blankets	280.1	165	Special, extra	236.6
133	Denims, Massachusetts	273.8		Woolen goods:	
	Drillings—		166	Blankets	238.1
134	Brown, Pepperel	288.2	167	Flannel	187.1
135	Massachusetts D standard	271.8	168	Overcoating	155.9
	Flannels—			Suiting—	
136	Colored	284.4		Clay worsted, diagonal—	
137	Unbleached	296.5	169	12-ounce	208.3
	Gingham—		170	16-ounce	227.9
138	Amoskeag	290.9	171	Middlesex, wool-dyed, blue	259.5
139	Lancaster	286.1	172	Serge, 11-ounce	264.4
	Hosiery—		173	Trousering, fancy worsted	219.9
140	Men's	261.8		Underwear, merino—	
141	Women's—Full fashioned combed yarn	243.2	174	Men's shirts and drawers, 50 per cent. wool	153.2
142	Seamless combed yarn, double sole	243.6	175	Union suits, 33 per cent. wool	239.6
143	Print cloths	287.0		Women's dress goods—	
	Sheeting—			All wool—	
	Bleached—		176	Broadcloth	262.4
144	Pepperell	242.8	177	French serge	273.3
145	Wamsutta	282.3	178	Storm serge	234.2
	Brown—			Cotton warp—	
146	Indian Head	275.1	179	Cashmere, Hamilton Mills	251.5
147	Pepperell	262.6	180	Poplar cloth, 36-inch	221.9
148	Ware Shoals	273.5	181	Sicilian cloth, 5 inch	215.5
	Shirting, bleached muslin			Wool, Ohio, scoured fleece—	
149	Fruit of the loom	316.6	182	Fine clothing	279.9
150	Lonsdale (new construction)	301.0	183	Medium	248.4
				Yarn—	
			184	2-32s, crossbred stock	209.5
			185	2-40s, half-blood	289.9

Group IV.—Fuel and Lighting.

File Number	Commodity	Relative Price	File Number	Commodity	Relative Price
186	Alcohol, denatured, 180 proof	130.4	194	Coke, Connellsville, furnace..	194.2
	Coal:		195	Gasoline, motor	145.6
	Anthracite—		196	Matches	173.7
187	Broken	174.4		Petroleum:	
188	Chestnut	155.6		Crude—	
189	Egg	156.4	197	California	360.9
190	Stove	161.3	198	Kansas-Oklahoma	243.9
	Bituminous—		199	Pennsylvania	168.8
191	Cincinnati	186.7		Refined—	
	Semi-bituminous—		200	Standard white	209.4
192	Cincinnati, run-of-mine..	188.3	201	Water-white	162.5
193	Norfolk, Pocahontas	163.7			

Group V.—Metal and Metal Products.

File Number	Commodity	Relative Price	File Number	Commodity	Relative Price
	Bar iron:		214	Pipe, cast-iron, 6-inch......	246.0
202	Best refined, Philadelphia..	203.2	215	Silver, bar, fine...........	183.9
203	Common, from mill, Pittsburgh	204.8		Steel:	
			216	Billets, Bessemer	157.2
	Copper:		217	Plates, tank, ¼-inch wide..	183.1
204	Ingot, electrolytic	121.5		Rails, standard—	
205	Wire, bare, No. 8........	132.7	218	Bessemer	168.8
206	Iron ore, Mesabi, Bessemer...	150.9	219	Open-hearth	164.2
	Lead:		220	Structural, Chicago	174.4
207	Pig, desilverized	131.4		Tin:	
208	Pipe	143.0	221	Pig	146.0
	Nails—		222	Plate, coke	198.8
209	Wire	193.4		Wire:	
	Pig iron:		223	Barbed, galvanized	193.4
210	Basic	188.3	224	Plain, annealed	205.9
211	Bessemer	181.7		Zinc:	
	Foundry		225	Sheet	135.8
212	No. 2, northern........	189.4	226	Spelter, pig	126.9
213	No. 2, southern........	215.9			

Group VI.—Building Materials.

File Number	Commodity	Relative Price	File Number	Commodity	Relative Price
	Brick, common:		240	Maple, hard	179.0
227	Chicago, run-of-kiln, salmon	181.2		Oak, white	
228	Cincinnati, red, building...	194.0	241	Plain	168.5
229	New York, red, domestic, building	243.2	242	Quartered	177.6
				Pine—	
230	Cement, Portland, domestic..	164.5	243	White, boards, rough....	173.0
	Glass:		244	White, boards, uppers...	135.8
	Plate, polished, glazing—		245	Yellow, flooring	176.8
231	3 to 5 square feet.......	195.4	246	Yellow, siding	200.5
232	5 to 10 square feet......	183.0	247	Poplar, yellow	178.2
	Window, American single, 25 inch		248	Spruce, eastern	163.7
				Paint materials:	
233	A	288.2	249	Lead, carbonate of, in oil..	194.1
234	B	280.4	250	Linseed oil, raw..........	382.8
235	Lath: Eastern spruce, 1½-inch slab	150.5	251	Turpentine, spirits of......	282.8
			252	Zinc, oxide of............	162.3
236	Lime: Eastern, common.....	233.3	253	Putty	175.8
	Lumber:		254	Rosin	315.6
	Douglas fir—			Shingles	
237	No. 1	276.0	255	Cypress	170.5
238	No. 2 and better........	228.8	256	Red Cedar	228.2
239	Hemlock	164.1			

Group VII.—Chemicals and Drugs.

File Number	Commodity	Relative Price	File Number	Commodity	Relative Price
	Acid:		266	Copper sulphate	156.6
257	Acetic	155.2	267	Glycerin, refined	100.1
258	Muriatic	123.1	268	Opium, natural	187.2
259	Nitric	153.5	269	Quinine	377.4
260	Sulphuric	95.0		Soda:	
	Alcohol:		270	Carbonate of (Salsoda)	239.4
261	Grain	194.3	271	Caustic	211.6
262	Wood	266.2	272	Nitrate of	143.9
263	Alum, lump	234.9	273	Soda ash	344.7
264	Ammonia, anhydrous	121.1	274	Sulphur	127.3
265	Borax	194.7			

Group VIII.—House Furnishing Goods.

File Number	Commodity	Relative Price	File Number	Commodity	Relative Price
	Earthen ware:		280	Tables, kitchen	260.1
275	Plates, 7-inch, white, granite	229.9		Glassware, common:	
276	Teacups and saucers, white, granite	240.1	281	Nappies, 4-inch	250.0
			282	Pitchers, ½-gallon	199.4
	Furniture:		283	Tumblers, table, 1/3-pint	272.9
277	Bedroom sets, 3 pieces	241.0		Table cutlery:	
	Chairs—		284	Carvers, stag handles	165.6
278	Bedroom, rocker, oak	212.3	285	Knives and forks	231.4
279	Kitchen, hardwood	215.1	286	Pails, oak-grained	209.3

Group IX.—Miscellaneous.

File Number	Commodity	Relative Price	File Number	Commodity	Relative Price
287	Bran	211.8	299	Philadelphia	221.9
288	Cottonseed meal	219.0	300	Starch, laundry	199.7
289	Cottonseed oil	331.9		Tobacco:	
290	Jute, raw	168.6	301	Plug, Climax	193.1
291	Lubricating oil, paraffin	214.6	302	Smoking, Bull Durham	162.7
292	Malt: standard keg beer	192.1		Whiskey:	
	Paper:			Bourbon—	
293	News	187.6	303	Barrels	272.7
294	Wrapping	244.9	304	Bottled	251.3
295	Phosphate rock	146.7		Rye—	
296	Rope, pure manila	178.1	305	Barrels	456.8
297	Rubber, Para, island, fine	59.8	306	Bottled	376.7
	Soap, laundry:		307	Wood pulp	158.3
298	Cincinnati	179.5			

TABLE 102

BITUMINOUS COAL PRODUCED IN THE UNITED STATES, BY MONTHS,
1913-1922 [a]

Thousands of net tons

	1913	1914	1915	1916	1917
Total	478,434	422,704	442,626	502,520	551,791
Jan.	42,274	40,191	37,194	46,593	47,969
Feb.	37,057	35,472	29,321	45,187	41,353
Mar.	37,536	45,455	31,801	43,828	47,869
Apr.	34,169	23,609	29,968	33,628	41,854
May	37,205	28,551	30,938	38,804	47,086
June	37,405	31,412	33,957	37,742	46,824
July	38,858	34,305	35,573	38,113	46,292
Aug.	41,590	37,751	38,161	42,696	47,372
Sept.	41,424	39,019	40,964	42,098	45,108
Oct.	46,164	37,685	44,198	44,807	48,337
Nov.	43,233	33,392	44,737	44,927	47,690
Dec.	41,519	35,862	45,814	44,097	44,037

	1918	1919	1920	1921	1922
Total	579,386	465,860	568,667	415,922	407,894
Jan.	42,227	42,193	49,748	41,148	37,489
Feb.	43,777	32,103	41,055	31,524	40,856
Mar.	48,113	34,293	47,850	31,054	49,976
Apr.	46,041	32,712	38,764	28,154	16,000
May	50,443	38,186	39,841	34,057	20,601
June	51,138	37,685	46,095	34,635	22,624
July	54,971	43,425	45,988	31,047	17,147
Aug.	55,114	43,613	49,974	35,291	27,538
Sept.	51,183	48,209	50,241	35,870	39,413
Oct.	52,300	57,200	53,278	44,687	44,907
Nov.	43,895	19,006	52,576	36,805	45,103
Dec.	40,184	37,235	53,257	31,650	46,240

[a] Data for 1913-22 from U. S. Geological Survey, *Mineral Resources of the United States, 1921, part ii,* p. 464; for 1922, from U. S. Geological Survey weekly report on the production of bituminous coal, anthracite, and beehive coke, No. 298.

TABLE 103

CHICAGO BANK CLEARINGS, BY MONTHS, 1890-1914[a]

Millions of dollars

Year	Total	Jan.	Feb.	Mar.	Apr.	May	June	July	Aug.	Sept.	Oct.	Nov.	Dec.
1890	4,093	296	253	305	324	375	359	351	342	360	406	364	359
1891	4,457	346	293	334	348	391	375	363	362	398	422	402	424
1892	5,136	394	369	404	384	423	447	423	429	439	465	465	493
1893	4,677	465	389	443	440	461	378	351	287	335	387	371	371
1894	4,315	367	296	343	338	379	358	323	379	352	402	392	387
1895	4,615	385	311	367	358	430	385	403	366	355	427	408	419
1896	4,413	389	331	362	386	409	395	375	319	318	379	357	394
1897	4,576	318	283	336	347	366	366	364	391	416	451	458	478
1898	5,517	429	411	439	441	502	481	407	416	438	489	469	573
1899	6,612	552	475	586	505	575	550	508	516	549	597	584	615
1900	6,800	589	506	574	548	599	589	561	533	517	608	577	600
1901	7,756	619	513	619	641	706	628	671	618	615	709	699	717
1902	8,395	734	621	734	727	721	660	706	641	672	747	695	738
1903	8,756	760	629	754	725	723	741	733	666	716	825	722	761
1904	8,990	730	670	765	751	708	732	704	718	722	812	818	860
1905	10,142	814	742	866	803	839	830	794	812	834	916	899	995
1906	11,047	987	826	928	871	915	907	902	887	842	1,000	975	1,007
1907	12,088	1,040	928	1,066	1,027	1,121	1,030	1,087	991	993	1,169	822	815
1908	11,854	948	857	1,030	992	964	953	1,002	903	971	1,080	1,020	1,134
1909	13,782	1,123	1,004	1,203	1,117	1,146	1,187	1,176	1,095	1,130	1,214	1,163	1,225
1910	13,940	1,161	1,060	1,341	1,230	1,156	1,182	1,142	1,077	1,081	1,163	1,145	1,201
1911	13,926	1,146	972	1,288	1,122	1,195	1,170	1,165	1,113	1,140	1,203	1,171	1,241
1912	15,381	1,253	1,153	1,302	1,309	1,323	1,199	1,271	1,233	1,207	1,456	1,314	1,360
1913	16,073	1,412	1,240	1,384	1,329	1,334	1,291	1,343	1,245	1,308	1,454	1,295	1,437
1914	15,693	1,436	1,251	1,493	1,389	1,333	1,362	1,377	1,164	1,150	1,261	1,164	1,313

[a] Data for years 1890-1911, compiled from the annual reports of the Board of Trade of the city of Chicago, for years 1895, 1900, 1905, 1911; data for years 1912-14, from weekly issues of the *Commercial and Financial Chronicle*.

TABLE 104

DATA SUITABLE FOR STATIC CORRELATION

The Heights and Weights of Ninety University of Wisconsin Men[a]

Height in inches	Weight in pounds	Height in inches	Weight in pounds	Height in inches	Weight in pounds
68.5	153.0	66.9	113.2	66.1	125.0
69.6	157.0	67.2	125.5	64.1	120.8
68.8	155.5	65.2	112.5	68.8	135.6
73.8	172.0	65.7	126.5	69.0	152.6
68.1	141.5	67.0	119.5	68.1	136.6
66.3	120.8	65.4	136.2	68.3	135.0
68.0	124.5	67.0	130.0	71.0	147.1
65.1	112.5	72.0	174.0	64.5	104.3
64.0	121.5	67.8	140.3	68.0	134.0
71.2	162.0	67.8	129.5	66.1	129.5
71.7	131.2	69.3	128.0	67.3	124.5
70.5	153.5	70.0	136.0	70.3	137.2
67.2	125.2	69.0	123.0	65.7	133.0
64.7	116.2	69.0	122.0	69.2	145.6
73.5	140.5	66.5	128.5	66.1	147.6
65.4	124.0	66.8	138.8	64.3	135.5
67.7	131.5	68.2	147.5	69.7	150.5
69.2	140.5	64.7	125.0	67.9	128.0
73.7	156.5	69.1	138.0	65.6	133.0
65.5	130.0	70.5	142.3	65.0	126.5
68.4	146.0	65.8	132.5	63.4	107.0
71.0	151.0	70.8	146.7	71.0	151.0
64.0	117.0	68.7	171.0	69.5	150.0
73.0	142.5	67.2	129.7	68.8	145.0
66.4	128.4	72.2	161.0	70.3	141.5
70.2	140.2	68.1	146.4	70.8	152.0
66.7	129.0	64.7	117.6	70.0	153.0
70.0	158.5	72.7	153.2	66.8	102.0
69.6	125.5	68.8	136.5	66.4	117.4
66.2	118.5	66.2	134.5	68.5	131.0

[a] From the records of the University of Wisconsin clinic.

TABLE 105

THE BLIND IN THE UNITED STATES

Age When Vision Was Lost [1]	Returning Special Schedule [3]		Blind Population of the United States [2]		
	Number	Per Cent Distribution	Age Group	Number	Per Cent Distribution
Total	29,242	....	Total	57,272	100.0
Age reported..	28,671	100.0	Under 5 years.	551	1.0
Under 20 years	8,819	30.8	Under 1 year	70	0.1
			1 to 4 years..	481	0.8
Under 5 years..	4,697	16.4	5- 9 years....	1,248	2.2
Born blind...	1,900	6.6	10-14 years....	1,997	3.5
Under 1 year	1,422	5.0	15-19 years....	2,200	3.8
1 to 4 years..	1,375	4.8			
5- 9 years..	1,513	5.3	20-24 years....	2,253	3.9
10-14 years..	1,220	4.3	25-29 years....	2,247	3.9
15-19 years..	1,147	4.0	30-34 years....	2,291	4.0
Age not definitely stated..	242	0.8	35-39 years....	2,530	4.4
			40-44 years....	2,797	4.9
			45-49 years....	3,325	5.8
20-64 years....	13,593	47.4	50-54 years....	3,748	6.5
20-24 years....	1,253	4.4	55-59 years....	3,695	6.5
25-34 years....	2,485	8.7	60-64 years....	4,483	7.8
35-44 years....	2,859	10.0	65-69 years....	5,102	8.9
45-54 years....	3,264	11.4	70-74 years....	5,111	8.9
55-59 years....	1,620	5.7	75-79 years....	5,108	8.9
60-64 years....	1,919	6.7			
Age not definitely stated..	193	0.7	80-84 years....	4,129	7.2
65 years or over	6,259	21.8	85 years or over	4,306	7.5
65-69 years....	1,791	6.2	Age not reported	151	0.3
70-74 years....	1,744	6.1			
75-79 years....	1,235	4.3			
80 years or over	1,361	4.7			
Age not definitely stated..	128	0.4			
Age not stated.	571	.....			

[1] Bureau of the Census: *The Blind in the U. S., 1910,* p. 81, part of table 62. [2] *Ibid.,* p. 80, part of table 61.

[3] The age at which vision was lost is known only for those who returned a special schedule to the Bureau of the Census.

TABLE 106

NET PROFITS OF A SELECTED GROUP OF CORPORATIONS[1]
Unit: one million dollars

Industry	Number of Corporations	1919	1920	1921	1922	1923
Total, ten groups.............	203	644	622	252	616	834
Steel and railroad equipment.....	11	111	149	40	50	150
Motor and accessories...........	15	116	78	d42	90	120
Oils	8	14	19	11	15	11
Food and food products.........	16	71	86	d 5	63	86
Clothing, including leather and textiles.......................	10	32	22	16	25	31
Tobacco	6	29	33	39	47	46
Miscellaneous industrials........	31	73	70	30	61	86
Stores	12	59	12	d10	49	64
Telephone	70	77	82	107	126	136
Other public utilities...........	24	62	71	66	90	104

[1] Source: Federal Reserve Bank, New York, *Monthly Review of Credit and Business Conditions,* March 1, 1924, p. 8. The "computations of net profits were made after all charges and tax deductions but before dividends."
d = deficit.

TABLE 107

ESTIMATED DISTRIBUTION OF PERSONAL INCOMES IN THE
UNITED STATES IN 1918[1]

Income class	Number of persons	Amount of income
Total	37,569,060[2]	$57,954,722,341
Under zero[3]..........	200,000	$— 125,000,000
$ 0–$ 500	1,827,554	685,287,806
500– 1,000	12,530,670	9,818,678,617
1,000– 1,500	12,498,120	15,295,790,534
1,500– 2,000	5,222,067	8,917,648,335
2,000– 3,000	3,065,024	7,314,412,994
3,000– 5,000	1,383,167	5,174,090,777
5,000– 10,000	587,824	3,937,183,313
10,000– 25,000	192,062	2,808,290,063
25,000– 50,000	41,119	1,398,785,687
50,000– 100,000	14,011	951,529,576
100,000– 200,000	4,945	671,565,821
200,000– 500,000	1,976	570,019,200
500,000– 1,000,000	369	220,120,399
1,000,000 and over	152	316,319,219

[1] Adapted from National Bureau of Economic Research, *Income in the United States*, Vol. 1, table 27, p. 136.
[2] Excluding 2,500,000 soldiers, sailors and marines.
[3] Deficit.

TABLE 108

EARNINGS OF MALE EMPLOYEES IN THE UNITED STATES: 1919

Earnings per hour	Number receiving the stated earnings					
	Total in 28 industries	Auto-mobiles	Chemi-cals	Bitu-minous coal	Iron and steel	Lum-ber
Total	318,946	17,812	28,478	40,541	31,588	18,022
Under 20 cents.......	1,715	.....	75	36	6	617
20 and under 30 cents..	18,364	17	1,217	464	515	5,118
30 and under 40 cents..	51,557	1,110	7,903	1,803	1,683	6,398
40 and under 50 cents..	80,089	4,943	10,525	4,036	9,509	2,702
50 and under 60 cents..	60,718	5,319	4,470	7,548	5,812	2,619
60 and under 70 cents..	41,551	3,322	2,520	10,790	2,298	370
70 and under 80 cents..	23,689	1,799	1,215	4,378	2,093	64
80 and under 90 cents..	15,152	803	448	3,573	1,828	75
90 cents and under $1..	9,487	369	63	2,791	1,561	18
$1 and under $1.25....	10,646	123	24	3,548	2,914	33
$1.25 and under $1.50..	3,225	6	18	1,033	1,413	8
$1.50 and under $1.75..	1,313	.....	.....	350	767	.....
$1.75 and under $2....	575	1	.....	128	408	.....
$2 and over..........	865	.....	.....	63	781	.....
Average earnings per hour	$0.561	$0.571	$0.456	$0.723	$0.748	$0.358

[1] U. S. Bureau of Labor Statistics, *Monthly Labor Review,* September, 1919, pp. 176-189, based upon an investigation covering 404,758 employees of both sexes, the information being derived from payrolls for periods of one week to one month, mostly in the first four months of 1919.

TABLE 109.—AVERAGE WHOLESALE PRICES AND A COMPOSITE INDEX [1]

Year	Corn [2] Per bushel	Hogs [2] Per 100 lbs.	Steers [2] Per 100 lbs.	Cotton [2] Per lb.	Milk [2] Per quart	Index number, 97 series [2] 1913 = 100
1890...	$0.395	$3.953	$4.870	$0.111	$0.033	76
1891...	.574	4.423	5.885	.086	.033	75
1892...	.450	5.155	5.091	.077	.033	70
1893...	.396	6.549	5.521	.083	.034	72
1894...	.433	4.972	5.159	.070	.033	63
1895...	.396	4.278	5.485	.073	.032	65
1896...	.258	3.358	4.596	.079	.030	62
1897...	.255	3.591	5.226	.072	.030	63
1898...	.314	3.805	5.378	.060	.030	66
1899...	.333	4.039	5.993	.066	.032	72
1900...	.381	5.082	5.783	.096	.034	77
1901...	.497	5.958	6.122	.086	.033	76
1902...	.597	6.970	7.472	.089	.035	81
1903...	.461	6.057	5.568	.112	.035	80
1904...	.505	5.155	5.956	.121	.034	82
1905...	.501	5.291	5.968	.096	.035	82
1906...	.463	6.235	6.130	.110	.037	84
1907..	.528	6.080	6.544	.119	.040	90
1908...	.684	5.799	6.816	.105	.039	87
1909...	.668	7.572	7.339	.121	.040	94
1910...	.581	8.943	7.771	.151	.043	98
1911...	.590	6.747	7.234	.130	.040	89
1912...	.686	7.595	9.359	.115	.044	97
1913...	.625	8.365	8.929	.128	.044	100
1914...	.695	8.361	9.652	.121	.042	100
1915...	.730	7.131	9.312	.102	.042	103
1916...	.825	9.615	10.420	.145	.045	128
1917...	1.637	15.705	13.831	.235	.063	183
1918...	1.605	17.600	17.343	.318	.078	206
1919...	1.597	18.244	18.658	.325	.084	215
1920...	1.414	14.187	15.907	.339	.085	225
1921...	.580	8.473	9.545	.151	.075	132
1922...	.623	9.393	10.317	.212	.073	134

[1] Source: U. S. Bureau of Labor Statistics, *Bulletin 335, Wholesale Prices, 1890-1922,* pp. 25, 34, 38, 48, and 56.
[2] A more complete description of these series is: corn, cash, contract grades; cattle, steers, choice to prime; hogs, heavy; cotton, middling, upland, New York; milk, fresh, New York; index number of 27 raw commodities and 70 manufactured commodities, with base: estimated value in 1913 = 100.

TABLE 110.—INDEXES OF PRODUCTION [1]

1913 monthly average = 100

Year and month	Beef	Cement (shipments)	Cotton (consumption)	Pig iron	Pork	Steel ingots
Weight[2]=	16	2	20	18	14	20
1919	131	96	108	100	120	111
1920	121	108	105	119	111	135
1921	109	107	97	54	116	64
1922	121	131	109	87	129	114
1923	125	153	117	130	159	143
1923						
Jan.	125	76	131	126	188	151
Feb.	107	82	122	117	156	137
Mar.	117	140	134	138	177	160
Apr.	119	175	124	139	153	156
May	129	193	133	151	153	166
June	122	180	116	143	156	149
July	119	186	99	144	146	139
Aug.	133	203	106	134	134	146
Sept.	129	185	104	122	115	131
Oct.	151	193	116	123	148	141
Nov.	135	139	114	113	182	123
Dec.	120	87	99	114	203	113

[1] Source: *Survey of Current Business,* November, 1922, pp. 3, 98: and February, 1924, p. 3.
[2] These weights represent the approximate relative value of the 1919 products of the following industries in the United States: slaughtering and meat packing (represented by beef and pork), cotton manufactures, cement, and iron and steel (represented by pig iron and steel ingots).

TABLE III.—PRODUCTION AND BUSINESS CONDITIONS IN THE
UNITED STATES

Source: Statistical Abstract of the United States

Year	Pig iron produced	Bituminous coal produced	Wheat produced	New York Clearings	Commercial failures, liabilities
	Million long tons	Million long tons	Million bushels	Billion dollars	Million dollars
1900	13.8	189	522	52.0	138
1901	15.9	202	748	77.0	113
1902	17.8	232	670	74.8	117
1903	18.0	252	638	70.8	155
1904	16.5	249	552	59.7	144
1905	23.0	281	693	91.9	103
1906	25.3	306	735	103.8	119
1907	25.8	352	634	95.3	197
1908	15.9	297	665	73.6	222
1909	25.8	339	737	99.3	155
1910	27.3	372	635	102.6	202
1911	23.6	362	621	92.4	191
1912	29.7	402	730	96.7	203
1913	31.0	427	763	98.1	273
1914	23.3	377	891	89.8	358
1915	29.9	395	1,026	90.8	302
1916	39.4	449	636	147.2	196
1917	38.6	493	637	181.5	182
1918	39.1	517	921	174.5	163
1919	31.0	416	968	214.7	113
1920	36.9	503	833	252.3	295
1921	16.7	363	795	204.1	627

TABLE 112.—POPULATION AND DEATH RATES IN THE
UNITED STATES [1]

Year	Estimated population of the U. S. Millions	Death rates in the registration area			
		All causes Per 1,000	Typhoid Per 100,000	Tuberculosis Per 100,000	Malignant tumors [2] Per 100,000
1900	76.0 [3]	17.6	35.9	201.9	63.0
1901	77.7	16.5	32.3	196.9	64.3
1902	79.4	15.9	34.3	184.5	65.1
1903	81.0	16.0	34.1	188.5	68.3
1904	82.6	16.5	31.7	200.7	70.2
1905	84.2	16.0	27.8	192.3	71.4
1906	85.8	15.7	31.3	180.2	69.1
1907	87.5	16.0	29.5	178.5	70.9
1908	89.1	14.8	24.3	167.6	71.5
1909	90.7	14.4	21.1	160.8	73.8
1910	92.3	15.0	23.5	160.3	76.2
1911	93.7	14.2	21.0	159.1	74.4
1912	95.1	13.9	16.5	149.7	77.1
1913	96.5	14.1	17.9	147.9	79.0
1914	97.9	13.6	15.5	147.2	79.6
1915	99.3	13.6	12.4	146.4	81.4
1916	100.8	14.0	13.3	142.1	82.1
1917	102.2	14.3	13.5	147.0	82.0
1918	103.6	18.1	12.6	150.0	80.3
1919	105.0	12.9	9.2	125.7	80.5
1920	106.4	13.1	7.8	114.2	83.4
1921	....	11.6	9.0	99.4	86.0

[1] U. S. Bureau of the Census, *Mortality Statistics:* 1910, p. 83;
1920, pp. 9, 10, 18; 1921 (Bulletin 152, p. 4).
[2] Including cancer.
[3] Census year ending May 31, 1900.

TABLE 113.—PER CENT UNEMPLOYED AMONG ORGANIZED WAGE EARNERS IN MASSACHUSETTS AT THE END OF THE GIVEN MONTH [1]

Year	All causes				Lack of work or material			
	March	June	Sept.	Dec.	March	June	Sept.	Dec.
1908.....	17.9	14.4	10.6	13.9	16.2	12.5	8.7	11.0
1909.....	11.4	6.4	4.8	9.4	9.5	4.6	3.4	4.9
1910.....	7.1	7.0	5.6	10.2	5.3	5.4	4.0	7.3
1911.....	10.4	6.6	5.6	9.7	7.5	4.2	3.7	6.0
1912.....	14.1	5.3	4.7	9.1	5.1	3.4	3.0	6.4
1913.....	11.3	6.4	6.8	10.4	7.3	4.3	4.3	7.3
1914.....	12.9	9.9	11.0	18.3	9.2	6.9	8.5	14.9
1915.....	16.6	10.6	7.0	8.6	12.8	7.6	3.6	4.0
1916.....	8.6	4.2	3.9	6.0	3.9	1.3	1.9	2.7
1917.....	7.3	8.4	5.6	7.4	3.7	3.5	2.7	3.5
1918.....	6.0	3.0	6.0	9.5	3.0	1.0	1.1	5.3
1919.....	13.4	5.1	5.4	6.0	11.2	2.7	2.5	3.8
1920.....	8.7	18.8	19.3	31.8	3.4	14.2	16.1	28.7
1921.....	30.0	25.1	23.4	27.3	21.8	19.9	18.8	23.4
1922.....	27.4	20.2	9.6	14.6	18.8	12.2	3.5	8.7

[1] *Massachusetts Industrial Review*, July, 1923, p. 14.

TABLE 114

DEATHS FROM TYPHOID FEVER IN NEW YORK STATE

Unit: one person. Source of data: U. S. Bureau of the Census,
Mortality Statistics, 1910-1921

Year	Total	Jan.	Feb.	Mar.	Apr.	May	June	July	Aug.	Sept.	Oct.	Nov.	Dec.
1910	1,397	91	92	97	74	66	72	100	142	185	174	168	136
1911	1,320	97	90	94	80	78	75	116	167	154	148	117	104
1912	1,107	109	64	69	71	83	73	77	121	138	143	86	73
1913	999	53	46	52	45	64	48	72	105	126	168	121	99
1914	884	70	56	53	62	63	45	70	74	114	117	94	66
1915	765	51	37	45	36	43	50	52	89	97	101	77	87
1916	611	60	39	33	33	33	39	41	61	72	82	67	51
1917	589	41	47	39	37	40	34	46	65	86	63	55	36
1918	579	28	21	34	29	42	31	53	58	75	140	35	33
1919	374	24	21	22	16	26	14	34	44	58	49	30	36
1920	379	16	12	13	30	17	23	43	49	68	48	27	33
1921	386	28	15	27	17	16	26	34	42	52	60	34	35

TABLE 115

DEATHS FROM PNEUMONIA IN NEW YORK STATE

Unit: one person. Source of data: U. S. Bureau of the Census,
Mortality Statistics, 1910-1921

Year	Total	Jan.	Feb.	Mar.	Apr.	May	June	July	Aug.	Sept.	Oct.	Nov.	Dec.
1910	6,945	830	796	836	741	579	435	379	311	364	407	488	779
1911	9,950	1,403	1,305	1,426	1,334	881	391	359	265	312	524	751	999
1912	9,810	1,266	1,271	1,233	975	881	526	382	331	375	605	775	1,190
1913	9,672	1,254	1,381	1,467	957	902	587	350	312	334	493	695	940
1914	8,930	1,124	1,142	1,433	1,002	847	460	284	259	334	461	657	927
1915	9,999	1,034	911	1,572	1,537	798	536	338	279	309	493	745	1,447
1916	10,365	1,906	1,298	1,235	945	823	516	369	330	339	566	793	1,245
1917	11,994	2,242	1,630	1,387	1,175	1,170	628	325	327	395	679	890	1,146
1918	27,090	1,479	1,324	2,421	1,869	874	444	368	274	644	12,692	2,833	1,868
1919	10,409	2,820	1,872	1,615	1,087	676	290	244	195	205	322	421	662
1920	9,730	1,848	3,276	963	759	626	325	190	173	229	272	406	663
1921	5,945	850	830	845	638	489	301	200	209	203	352	468	560

APPENDIX C

Laboratory Suggestions and Exercises

A thorough grasp of statistical technique is acquired only by practice. The exercises in the following pages are submitted as suggestions to the instructor, to be expanded or modified to conform to the amount and type of practice most suitable for a given group of students. In many cases it may prove feasible to utilize the phraseology or principle of the exercise but to substitute data of local or other special interest.

Ordinarily an exercise is most useful when the student is required to answer interpretative questions designed to illuminate the purpose of the statistical procedure and the significance of the results obtained. While it has been practicable to append only a limited number of such interpretative questions to these exercises, the instructor will ordinarily find it profitable to expand them by the addition of thought-stimulating questions to be answered by the student.

An effort has been made to provide some exercises which call for critical appraisal of statistical work done by others, some which involve primarily the application of the planning faculties, and others which necessitate the precise computation and presentation of finished results.

The student should be required to read the following laboratory suggestions, or a similar set of rules prepared for the particular class, before he begins work on the exercises.

The exercises in Groups A to Q are arranged approximately in the order in which the various processes are discussed in the text. In Group R are suggestions for serial exercises, involving the application of several statistical processes to the same basic data.

ARTICLE I.—PROCEDURE IN PREPARING EXERCISES

Preliminary preparation.—The portions of the text and the articles in these instructions which are applicable to the given exercises should be read before work is commenced.

Methodical work.—Before beginning the actual process, plan exactly what mode of procedure should be followed. In preparing tables or charts, first draw up a rough draft indicating the approximate arrangement and proportions of the contents. Leave no data on loose scraps of paper or without labels sufficient to identify them.

Accuracy.—All figures should be checked over and their accuracy verified before they are used in the next stage in the process or entered in final tables.

Neatness.—In the absence of specific instructions to the contrary, all final work should be done in ink, with table rulings and graphs in India ink. Necessary corrections should be carefully made, and sheets that are badly soiled or crumpled should be copied.

ARTICLE 2.—COMPUTING DEVICES AND METHODS

(See Appendix D)

There are several types of adding machines and helpful mechanical computing devices now on the market. An adding machine, at least, should be available. The writer has found the Monroe Calculating Machine a most valuable aid. For many purposes, however, a slide rule is sufficiently accurate. With the cylindrical Fuller slide rule, for which instructions are given below, results can be read to four places and the fifth estimated.

Multiplication with the adding machine.—Suppose you wish to multiply 637 by 123. Set the "Repeat" key. Put down the keys for 637 and pull the lever three times. Clear without totaling. Put down keys for 6370 and pull lever twice. Clear without totaling. Put down keys for 63700 and pull lever once. Total. The sum is composed thus:

$$
\begin{array}{r}
637 \\
637 \\
637 \\
6,370 \\
6,370 \\
63,700 \\
\hline
\end{array}
$$

Total.................78,351

Computation tables.—The computation tables in Appendix D, and the more elaborate and varied compilations listed in Appendix A, will be found useful in lightening the drudgery and reducing the time required in computation.

Directions for use of the Fuller slide rule.—Identify the following parts of the rule: the cylinder, the fixed point, the upper and lower movable indicators.

DIVISION.

Hold the rule by the handle with the left hand.

(1) Turn the cylinder, upon which appear numbers in consecutive order from 100 to 1000, with the right hand so as to bring the divisor to the fixed pointer;
(2) Set the upper movable indicator to 100 on the cylinder;
(3) Turn the cylinder so as to bring the dividend to the pointer;
(4) Read the quotient off the cylinder at the point of the upper or lower movable indicator.

Whenever you become uncertain as to the procedure test the rules by dividing 200 by 5.

Four digits can be read accurately from the rule and the fifth approximated with the eye. Beyond 650 each of the primary divisions is divided into only five parts, hence the fourth digit is sometimes approximate.

MULTIPLICATION.

(1) Bring the cylinder down and revolve it until it rests against the stop;
(2) Set the lower movable indicator to the multiplier;
(3) Bring the multiplicand to the fixed index;
(4) Read the product at the point of one of the movable indicators.

Method of expressing data.—For each computation a standard of accuracy should be decided upon and consistently maintained. Let us suppose that it has been decided to express all figures to one decimal place. It will aid in the avoidance of small errors if all quotients are computed to two decimal places and then reduced to one. In such reduction drop all fractions less than half, and count all fractions over half as whole units. As to the even halves, one method of treating them is to reduce them always to even numbers. To illustrate, let us reduce the figures in the first column to one decimal place—

Original data	Reduced to one decimal place
11.059	11.1
1.046	1.0
1.05	1.0
1.15	1.2

A final zero in a decimal fraction should be retained when any other digit in the same place would be retained. For example, in a series containing .37, an even half should be expressed as .50.

ARTICLE 3.—DETECTION OF ERRORS IN COMPUTATION

The importance of checking all work done can scarcely be over-emphasized to beginners in statistical practice. Usually the most satisfactory method of detecting errors is to have the same computation made independently by two persons. When this is not practicable, the computations should be made twice by the same person, preferably by different methods, for in the use of the same process errors tend to be repeated automatically. The following suggestions will aid in detecting errors:

(a) *Copied entries.*—Check copied entries by comparison with original from which transcribed. An additional check is obtained by adding the two sets of figures and comparing totals.
(b) *Addition.*—Add twice on adding or computing machine; or, if done mentally, add once from bottom and then reverse, starting at the top of each column.

(c) *Multiplication.*—Multiply once with adding or computing machine and once with slide rule. Or reverse process, dividing product by multiplicand to get multiplier.

(d) *Division.*—Divide twice with slide rule; or reverse the process, multiplying quotient by divisor to get dividend. A percentage distribution can be checked by adding the separate percentages to see if the total is 100, or within the possible range of error due to dropping of fractions.

If a calculating machine is available, division by a constant divisor can be most easily accomplished by multiplying by the reciprocal of the divisor.

ARTICLE 4.—PREPARATION OF TABLES

(See Chapter III)

It may be helpful to distinguish between informal tables, in which the emphasis is upon the contents, and formal tables, in which, in addition, the ruling and contents of the tables are to be carefully spaced, proportioned, and inked.

Eighth-inch cross-section paper is convenient for much tabular work. The publishers of charting papers also sell special data rulings; and paper with columns and horizontal lines to order may be specially printed if desired.

As a rule it is best to make a rough, free-hand sketch of the proposed table form on a sheet of scratch-paper. Then calculate the space the table will occupy on the cross-section paper and, for a formal table, make a carefully ruled pencil draft. When satisfied that the table will be well-centered, correctly proportioned, and otherwise satisfactory, rule it with India ink. Use the ruling pen for all formal table ruling.

Leave adequate space for titles. For formal tables, the titles, stubs, and captions should be in print letters, rather than in ordinary script, with the relative importance of each heading indicated by the relative size of the lettering. Avoid crowding the lettering close to ruled lines.

When practicable both tables and charts should be placed upright on the page.

Order of Procedure in Preparing the Rough Draft of a Table

Facility in preparing just the form of table desired will be increased if the student adopts a regular sequence in his procedure. To that end, the following steps are suggested for a quadruple, cross-classification table. The preliminary steps will be the same for a simpler table.

1. List, on a scratch sheet, the classifications to be inserted or the comparisons to be made, in the order of emphasis.
2. In a bracket opposite each respective class, set the subclasses in the logical sequence in which they should be arranged.

3. Then draw, freehand, on a liberal scale, the essential rulings which appear in even the simplest tables.
   Ordinarily some one of the rulings found in Tables VIII-A to VIII-D will be useful as a starting point.

4. At the top of the space reserved for stubs, insert stubs for the total and for the subclasses of the primary classification.

5. Then immediately above the space which will be occupied by the first columns of figures insert captions for the total and subclasses of the secondary classification.

6. Repeat the stubs for the primary classification as many times (in addition to the set in 4) as there are subclasses in the third classification, leaving space between each set. Then insert the stubs for the subclasses of the third classification above each set of stubs for the primary classifications.

7. Likewise repeat the captions for the secondary classification as often as there are subclasses in the fourth classification, and then above each set place the appropriate captions for the fourth classification.

8. Insert the remaining appropriate rulings and captions, *e.g.*, the caption indicating what is classified in the stubs.

9. Check the ruling to see that double lines are inserted where appropriate.

Article 5.—Charting

(Read Chapters IV and V, particularly the "Working Rules" in Chapter IV)

Charting materials.—A list of specially ruled papers for use in constructing charts is given in W. C. Marshall, *Graphical Methods*, Chapter II, with samples of the rulings. Such papers and other devices for charting purposes are sold by various dealers, including Eugene Dietzen Co., Keuffel & Esser Co., Codex Book Co., Inc., all of New York City, and the Educational Exhibition Co., Providence, Rhode Island.

For finished charting, drawing boards should be available and the equipment of each student should include black India ink, crow-quill or other fine point lettering pens, a ruling pen, a celluloid triangle, art gum for erasing preliminary pencil tracings, an ink eraser, thumb tacks, good pencils, and a ruler with decimal divisions.

In formal charts the title and other lettering should be inserted with the typewriter or by hand lettering. The accompanying "Lettering Guide" gives illustrations of lettering of various types and sizes, as well as the direction of strokes. It will be found helpful to bound with light pencil lines the upper and lower limits of the line of letters to be printed. A lettering angle is convenient in hand lettering. (Such angles are sold by the Braddock Instrument Co., Swissvale, Pa.)

Charts should be done in India ink.

If the chart is to be reproduced, it should be remembered that black and red lines will reproduce clearly, but that blue does not photograph. If the reproduction is to be by blue-printing, tracing paper or other thin paper, or, better yet, tracing cloth, should be used.

LETTERING GUIDE

A B C D E F G H I J K L M
N O P Q R S T U V W X Y Z

A B C D E F G H I J K L M N O P Q
R S T U V W X Y Z 1 2 3 4 5 6 7 8 9 0

a b c d e f g h i j k l m n o p q r s
t u v w x y z 1 2 3 4 5 6 7 8 9 0

COMPRESSED STYLE for use when crowded.

EXTENDED STYLE for main titles chiefly.

Exercises and Study Questions

(Chapter II)

1. Select a sample of 25 from Table 101 [1] by some random method and calculate the mean. (a) Compare the mean of the sample with the mean of the complete list of 307 relative prices in Table 101. (b) Briefly explain why the method used by you may be designated as random.

2. Take a sample of the persons you pass on the street, classified, for example, by color. (a) Compare the distribution in your sample with that revealed for your community by the most recent census. (b) What circumstances tend to make your sample unrepresentative?

3. Take successive samples of twenty-five each of the automobiles which pass you on the street, noting the type of machine or the state in which the license is issued. (a) Is the variance between the samples large enough to indicate that the number in your sample is not adequate to give representative results? (b) How much would the precision of the sample probably be increased by increasing the number in the sample to 100? To 400?

4. Test the validity of the law of permanence of small numbers by examination of the death rates for rare diseases over a period of years. (See U. S. Bureau of the Census, *Mortality Statistics*.)

5. What instances of the use of sampling in commercial practice or scientific study have come to your attention? What elements of bias, if any, were probably present? How could these have been eliminated?

6. From the student directory for your university, find the distribution of the total student body according to some classification, such as the home state of the student, which is given for each name. Then sample for this characteristic by taking each tenth name in the directory. What is the degree of error in the sample? Is there any element of bias in the method?

(Chapter III)

1. *Sales card.*—The instructor will prepare a key for the use of the class in punching sales cards similar to that shown in Plate I,

---

[1] Tables 101-115 are in Appendix B. All other tables are in the main text, except the computation tables in Appendix D. See the index of tables at the beginning of the book.

Chapter III. This key should contain a number for each member of the class, for each county in the state, and for each class and subclass of accounts in a brief classification.

Each member of the class will then make a memorandum of an hypothetical sale to some other specified member of the class, this memorandum to include all the information called for in the several columns of the sales card in Plate I. Next rule a blank tabulating card into fields as in Plate I and with the aid of the key above mentioned mark the numbers on the card to be punched to represent the sale memorandum. Lastly, if a card punch and tabulating machine are available, punch the cards and have them tabulated by county, account, or other classification specified by the instructor.

2. *Labor card.*—Rule a blank tabulation card into fields appropriate for recording the facts necessary to determine the labor cost of several processes in a manufacturing plant.

3. *Accident compensation card.*—Obtain a sample of the schedule used in your state in reporting accidents to workmen and prepare a brief key and card form for coding and recording the data on such schedules and also for recording the subsequent action taken in the way of granting medical care and compensation.

4. *Death report card.*—Obtain a copy of the form used in reporting deaths to the health authorities and prepare a tabulating card form suitable for recording the data included in the report.

5. *Coding schedules.*—(a) Take a set of completed schedules and prepare a suitable code by classifying the data into fields and assigning a number to each subclass in a field; mark the answers on each schedule with the corresponding code number in blue pencil or red ink; prepare a "dummy" card showing where the "fields" lie and the significance of each column and row; then with the "key punch" prepare a punched card for each schedule. (b) Check the punching by reading back from the punched card. (c) With the sorter and tabulating machine compute all desired totals and record in a suitable table.

SERIES C.—THE CONSTRUCTION AND CRITICISM OF TABLES

(See Article 4 and Chapter III)

1. *Tally.*—Prepare a tally table similar to that in Table III-A, except that one line is allowed for each group of five. Then tally the relative prices in Table 101 for Group II, "Food, etc."

2. *Frequency groupings.*—From the tally sheet prepared in the above exercise, draw up frequency distributions with class intervals of ten, fifteen, and twenty-five respectively. Answer the following questions: (a) Which of these distributions gives the best idea of the detail of the sample? (b) Which gives the best picture of the general tendencies of the food group? (c) Is this distribution a fair sample of the entire list of 307 relative prices?

3. Formulate answers to the questions appended to the tables in Appendix A to Chapter III.

4. Find a published table which seems to you to be defective in some respect and draw a sketch of the table giving the title, stubs, captions, and ruling, but not necessarily the numerical data. Then state (a) the respects in which this table corresponds to the criteria of a good table given in Chapter III, and (b) the specific changes you would make to improve it in appearance and particularly to increase the effectiveness of presentation.

5. *Rearrangement.*—Rearrange Table IX, in Appendix A to Chapter III, in the complete classification form, with the order of emphasis as follows: sex, color, union status, year. Insert consistent hypothetical data for the subclasses concerning which information is not given in the above table and show all totals and subtotals.

6. *Rearrangement.*—Rearrange Table XV, Chapter IV, so that the order of emphasis is (1) urban or rural; (2) nativity and parentage; (3) section of the country.

7. *Organization* of a complete cross-classification table. Draw a free-hand draft of a table with title, captions, stubs, and ruling adequate to provide for a complete cross-classification of the population of a city according to sex, color, age, and nativity, with the emphasis in the order stated. Limit the subclasses to two or three for each main classification.

SERIES D.—PREPARATION OF BAR CHARTS

(Article 5 and Chapter IV)

1. Prepare a *horizontal bar chart* showing the comparative increase in the cost of the several budget items as given in Table XLIX, Chapter XI, preparing first a rough free-hand pencil sketch with all elements inserted, and then a finished ink chart. If any of the charting rules given in Chapter IV are not observed, explain reasons for the non-observance.

2. Prepare a bar chart of the appropriate type representing the data in the first two columns of Table XI, Appendix A, Chapter III.

3. *Subdivided bar chart.*—Prepare a horizontal bar chart to represent the data in Table V, Appendix A, Chapter III, with the proportions of males and females distinguished by cross-hatching.

4. *Subdivided bar chart.*—Consult Vol. II of the 1920 Census, p. 973, and from the data there given construct an appropriate bar diagram showing for 1910 and 1920 the total foreign white stock, the number of foreign born whites, and the number of native whites of foreign or mixed parentage, for each of the six leading nationalities.

5. *Frequency bar chart.*—Prepare an unshaded vertical bar chart or rectangular histogram portraying the frequency distribution of amounts of advertising shown in the first column of Table X, Appendix A, Chapter III.

6. *Vertical bar graph for time data.*—(a) Scan the data in Table 106, in Appendix B, and state the types of bar chart suitable, respectively, for (1) comparing the 1923 profits in the several industries; (2) com-

paring profits in one industry over the five-year period; (3) for representing both the profits and the deficits in 1921.

(b) Reduce the data for "Total 10 groups" (or for other group indicated by the instructor) to percentages of the 1919 figure and plot the results as a vertical bar graph with appropriate title. In what year were the profits lowest? Compare with the other groups. Is the high 1923 figure solely the result of cyclical changes or may a trend be present? Give briefly your reasons for the answer made.

7. *Tracing a chart.*—Find in a current issue of one of the government or commercial publications (see list in Chapter XVII) a bar chart (or other type stipulated by the instructor) which is either defective in some significant respect or which affords a good example of some commendable charting practice. Trace this chart on tracing paper or tracing cloth, first in pencil and then in ink. Attach to the chart a memorandum stating (a) the most commendable features of the chart; (b) any defects which cause it to be misleading or ambiguous; and (c) any changes which you would make to increase the clarity and effectiveness of the chart.

8. *Choice of type of chart to be used.*—Indicate the appropriate *form* of bar chart for use in portraying the following data, in each case drawing a rough draft of the chart with all elements included but with no attempt to make a finished chart.

(a) The data in the following text tables: VI, X, VII, one column; VII, one row; XI, first column.
(b) The total sales of several salesmen, by class of article sold.
(c) The percentage distribution of convictions for crime, classified by nationality and sex of the convicted persons and the crimes for which convicted.
(d) A wage frequency distribution.

SERIES E.—FREQUENCY GRAPHS

(Article 5 and Chapter V)

1. *Comparative frequency graphs.*—Prepare frequency polygons representing one of the following sets of data, designated by the instructor, plotting both curves on the same chart. Point out the significant differences between the two distributions.

(a) The age distributions in Table VI.
(b) The percentage distributions in Table X.
(c) The numbers of brides and grooms in Table XXV.
(d) The frequency distributions of the relative prices in Group I (Farm products) and Group II (Food, etc.) of Table 101.

2. *Smoothed frequency graphs.*—Construct a graph showing the age distribution of grooms in Table XXV, and smooth the graph. What appears to be the modal age of grooms?

3. *Smoothing a sample frequency graph.*—(a) By some random method choose a sample of 100 or more from the items in Table 101. Group them into a frequency table with a class interval of twenty.

(b) Plot as a rectangular histogram and smooth. Compare with Chart 21 in the text, Chapter V, and point out significant differences.

4. *Cumulative frequency graph.*—Plot the frequency distribution found in above exercise as a cumulative frequency graph. (See Exercise H-1, in "Averages," for use to be made of this graph.)

SERIES F.—NATURAL SCALE GRAPHS OF CHRONOLOGICAL DATA

(Article 5 and Chapter V)

1. *Data.*—Select one of the chronological series which is to be used in one of the following exercises: M-1, M-2, or O-4.

Procedure: Plot the selected series on a natural scale, in finished form, with appropriate title and the other elements of a good chart.

2. *Year-month chart.*

Data.—One series selected from Table 110.

Procedure.—Construct a chart similar to Chart 16 in the text.

3. *Silhouette graph.*—Plot a silhouette graph of one of the monthly series in Tables 102, 103, 114, or 115, for a period of three years.

SERIES G.—RATIO CHARTING

(Chapter VI and Appendix D)

1. Plot the logs of one of the series in Tables 109, 110, 111, or 112, and draw freehand a curve representing the approximate trend of the series. In your judgment is the series increasing at more or less than a constant percentage rate of increase? Explain.

2. Obtain from the *Survey of Current Business* data for the amount of sales in the most recent twelve months available of the Woolworth ten-cent stores and of one of the mail-order houses. Plot these on ratio paper (or plot the logs of the data on a natural scale). In what month is the percentage increase greatest for each series?

Plot on the same chart another curve representing the hypothetical sales of a local merchant and explain what comparisons could be made from the chart which would be of interest to him.

3. Obtain from Volume II, p. 29, of the *Fourteenth Census of the United States,* the numbers of whites and negroes at each census from 1850 to 1920. Plot these on ratio paper and point out any observed differences in the rates of increase.

4. *Testing seasonal variation by ratio plotting.*—Record the data for the monthly production of bituminous coal, in Table 102, for a period of five years, in terms of millions of tons recorded to the nearest tenth-million. Then find the logarithms of these data, read to the nearest third decimal place. (See Table of Logarithms in Appendix D.)

Plot the logarithms for the months in the first year on millimeter paper, with a horizontal scale of 10 mm. per month and a vertical scale of one mm. = .01 log. For the first year begin the vertical scale at a point slightly below the smallest log in the year. Then, using a marked piece of millimeter paper for a movable scale, plot the next year above the first, moving the scale up sufficiently to separate the curves. Repeat for the other years. Label each curve with the year which it represents. Answer the following questions:

(a) In what months is there a relatively uniform seasonal movement? Cite marked exceptions.

(b) What is gained by plotting the logs rather than the original data?

(c) In what year is the relative change from January to February greatest? How is this determined from the chart?

5. Substitute the data for deaths from typhoid, Table 114, for the production of bituminous coal in above exercise.

SERIES H.—AVERAGES

(Articles 2, 3, and 4, and Chapter VII)

1. *Comparison of types.*

Data.—Earnings of male employees in 28 industries, Table 108.

Procedure.—Assume that the number in each class is evenly distributed within the class and that no workman received over $5 an hour. Compute the following averages and types:

(a) The arithmetic mean, by the short-cut method.
(b) The median, by Formula 9.
(c) The mode, by Formula 7 (in computing the mode, an even distribution within each class is not to be assumed).
(d) The median and lower and upper quartiles, from a smoothed cumulative frequency curve.

Questions.—Which of these types is least affected by the very large or very small earnings? Would the existence of a round number tendency in hourly earnings affect the accuracy of your computations? Which average commends itself to you as most useful? Why?

2. Substitute in Exercise 1 the earnings in one of the industries in Table 108 and proceed as above.

SERIES J.—DISPERSION

(Chapter IX)

1. *Lorenz curve.*

Data.—Distribution of incomes in Table 107.

Procedure.—Prepare a cumulative frequency table similar to Table XXXIV in the text and plot a Lorenz curve therefrom.

Questions.—What per cent of the total income was received by the poorest fifty per cent of the income receivers? By the most prosperous ten per cent? Would you expect a curve of the distribution of wealth to show more or less inequality of distribution? Why?

2. *Numerical measures of dispersion.*

Data.—(a) The samples of relative prices selected and tabulated in Exercises A-1 and E-3, or (b) one of the distributions in Table 108.

Procedure.—Compute the following measures of dispersion: (a) the average deviation from the median (see Exercise H-1 for the median); (b) the standard deviation, by the short-cut method; and (c) the quartile deviation (see H-1, for the quartiles).

Questions.—Which of these three measures gives the most influence to extremes? Which the least? Which is the easiest to compute if the data are in the form of a frequency table? Which, if the data are plotted in a cumulative frequency curve?

3. *Coefficients.*—Find the coefficients of dispersion for the average, standard, and quartile deviations computed in Exercise 2.

SERIES K.—PROBABILITY

(Chapter X)

1. Toss several coins repeatedly, noting each time how many heads are up, and make a frequency table of the actual results and of those which would be indicated by the theory of probability. (Cf. Table XL.) Plot a frequency polygon from this frequency table. What principle is involved in this experiment?

2. *Fitting a normal frequency curve.*

Data.—Frequency distribution of the sample of 100 relative prices in Table XXVI, Chapter V.

Procedure.—Fit a normal frequency curve to the data, as follows:

(a) Find the mean and the standard deviation (see Tables XXIX and XXXVIII).
(b) Find the deviations of the midpoints of the classes from the mean, in multiples of the standard deviation.
(c) Find the ordinates of a normal curve corresponding to the midpoints of the classes (see Table XLII and Formula 27).
(d) Plot, on the same axes and with the same scale, a rectangular histogram of the raw data and of the ordinates of the normal curve connected with a free-hand smoothed curve.

Questions.—Does the normal frequency curve closely resemble the graph of the actual frequency distribution? If not, what reasons can you suggest for the observed differences?

3. Perform the operations indicated in the above exercise, substituting a sample of 100 selected from Table 101 by yourself, or using the frequency distribution of the complete list of 307 relative prices as given in Table XXVI.

SERIES L.—INDEX NUMBERS

(Chapters XI and XII)

1. *Simple relative index numbers.*
   Data.—Wholesale prices, 1890-1922, Table 109.
   Procedure.—Reduce the data to relatives with the 1913 price as a base.

2. *Arithmetic mean of relatives.*—Using the relatives found in Exercise 1, compute the simple arithmetic mean for each year.
   Questions.—What method of weighing would be appropriate for use with these series of relatives? How could the base of the composite relative be shifted from 1913 to 1890?

3. *Index of local food prices.*—Obtain food price quotations from a local newspaper and compute an index of the cost of food, using a simple arithmetic mean of relatives. Illustrate from the data any reasons you may have for believing that a weighted average would be more representative. What additional information would be needed for the computation of a cost-of-living index?

4. *Weighted aggregative index number.*
   Data.—Average wholesale prices in Table 109, for 1890-1922.
   Procedure.—Construct a weighted index of prices, using as weights the following figures, which represent the approximate quantities of the given grade of the respective articles sold in 1919 (see U. S. Bureau of Labor Statistics, Bulletin 335, pp. 195-196), expressed in millions of the units in which the respective prices are quoted. The weights are: corn 164, hogs 33, cattle 45, cotton 3,806, and milk 5,066. Reduce the weighted aggregatives to relatives with 1913 as a base.
   Questions.—If the prices in Table 109 were first reduced to relatives, would the above weights be appropriate? Explain. What are the principal differences between your weighted index and the index for 97 series given in Table 109?

5. *Weighted index of production.*
   Data.—Weights and index numbers of production given in Table 110.
   Procedure.—Multiply each index number by the weight for the respective commodity; summate the products for each year and month; and express the results as a percentage of 1913.
   Questions.—If each of the six series were expressed in terms of the number of units produced in the given year or month, what methods of weighing would be appropriate? Explain.

SERIES M.—TRENDS AND SEASONAL VARIATION

(See Chapter XIII)

1. *Moving average.*
     Data.—Quarterly unemployment data, Table 113.
     Procedure.—Compute a four-quarter moving average and plot it between the second and third dates.
     Questions.—What movement is this procedure designed to eliminate? Have the intended results been accomplished? What would be the additional effect of taking a twenty-quarter moving average?

2. *Least squares trend.* [See "Sums of Squares" in Appendix D.]
     Data.—Select one of the series in Table 103 (first column) or in Tables 109, 110, 111, or 112.
     Procedure.—(a) Compute a straight line trend by the method of least squares. (b) Plot the original data and the trend.
     Questions.—Does the straight line appear to be a good representation of the trend of the data? If not, is the poor fit apparently due to irregular changes in the character of the trend or to the existence of a regular trend other than a straight line trend?

3. *Trend of the logarithms of the data.*
     Data.—Select a series which rises more rapidly than by a constant absolute increase.
     Procedure.—(a) Find the logs of the data. (b) Compute the straight line trend of these logs. (c) Plot the logs and the trend.
     Questions.—If the computed trend is, in your judgment, a good fit to the logs, what type of trend is present in the original data? If the logs near the end of the period rise less rapidly than their straight line trend, is the series then increasing at more or less than a constant percentage rate of increase?

4. *Suggestion to instructor.*—Exercise O-3, in correlation, requires the preliminary determination of trends, which can be made a separate exercise in trend computation and the results subsequently used in the correlation exercise.

5. *Link relative method.*
     Data.—Quarterly statistics of the per cent unemployed in Massachusetts, 1908 to 1922, Table 113, using the data for unemployment due to "lack of work or material."
     Procedure.—Compute an index of unemployment in Massachusetts, corrected for seasonal variation by the link relative method, as follows (for details of method see Appendix to Chapter XIII): (a) compute the quarter-to-quarter link relatives; (b) find the medians of these; (c) weld these medians into a chain and correct for any trend which is evidenced; (d) reduce the adjusted chain to percentages of the mean; (e) compute seasonal base numbers with the average of the 1913 quarterly

figures as a general base; (f) divide the original data by the seasonal base numbers; and (g) plot the results.

Questions.—(a) In your final curve, are the trend, cyclical, and seasonal elements represented? Explain. (b) What additional factors would be introduced if the data for "all causes" were used? (c) Do you judge from the final curve that the method used has satisfactorily eliminated the seasonal movement? Explain.

6. *Simple average method.*

Data.—Same as for Exercise 5.

Procedure.—Average the percentages for each of the four quarters and reduce these averages to percentages of their mean.

Questions.—(a) Is it necessary to correct for a trend in these quarterly index numbers? Why? (b) What differences appear between them and the four adjusted quarterly percentages found by the link relative method? Can you account for these differences?

7. *Link relative method.*

Data.—(a) Deaths from typhoid fever in New York State, or (b) deaths from pneumonia. Table 114 or 115.

Procedure.—Find the twelve monthly indices of seasonal variation by the link relative method (see Appendix to Chapter XIII). Compute seasonal base numbers with 1910 as a base; and then compute and record the index numbers corrected for seasonal variation, for the years 1910-1921.

Questions.—(a) Has the trend been eliminated from the final index number? (b) If not, explain how you would proceed to eliminate both trend and seasonal variation. (c) Is such trend as appears in the raw data due only to a real change in the death rate? Explain.

8. *Monthly average, corrected for trend.*

Data.—The monthly production of coal, Table 102; or the data for Exercise 7 may be used.

Procedure.—Find the typical seasonal variation by the simple average method, corrected by means of a least-squares trend based upon the annual data.

9. *Deviations from a moving average.*—Monthly statistics in Tables 102, 103, 114, or 115.

Procedure.—Select one of the above series and compute a twelve-month moving average centered at the seventh month and the typical seasonal variation based upon the deviations from this moving average, following the steps listed in Chapter XIII, in paragraph concerning "Typical deviation from a trend-cycle curve."

(Chapters XIV and XV)

1. *Comparison of monthly cycles.*—Reduce the data for bank clearings in Table 103, for the years 1911-1914 or for a longer period stipulated by the instructor, to cycles in accordance with the Harvard method outlined in Chapter XIV. Plot your results on a chart with the cycles of pig iron given in Table LXII for the years 1911-1914. Does the correlation between the two series appear to be high or low, positive or negative? Briefly outline the procedure by which you would determine numerically the degree of correlation between these series.

2. Find the current forecasts of future business conditions according to the Brookmire Service, the Harvard Economic Service, the Standard Statistics Co. (or any other three such forecasts), and compare them for points of similarity and of difference. What appears to be the major basis of forecasting in each case?

3. Look up the forecasts made by the above mentioned services a year ago and compare the forecasts with the actual movement of business conditions during the year.

(Chapter XV)

1. *Correlation of non-chronological data.*
   Data.—Heights and weights, Table 104.
   Procedure.—Find the Pearsonian coefficient of correlation for the heights and weights of the first sixteen pairs in Table 104, and compute the probable error.
   Questions.—To what degree would the probable accuracy of the coefficient be increased if the sample used were increased to 64 pairs? Explain the basis for your answer.

2. *Computations from a correlation table.*
   Data.—Heights and weights in Table LXVI, total columns.
   Procedure.—Find the mean height in each weight row, assuming that the midpoint of each class represents the average height of that class; for example, assume that the men in the 64.0-65.9 class have an average height of 65.0 inches. Likewise assume that the average weight in each weight class is represented by the midpoint of the class. Then find the coefficient of correlation of height with weight. In this process it is necessary to make allowance for the number in each class by multiplying the products of the paired deviations from the mean by the respective class frequencies, and a similar allowance must be made in computing the means of the series. Compute the probable error of the coefficient.

Questions.—Would you expect the results obtained in this exercise to agree exactly with the coefficient obtained by a direct computation using each of the original pairs in Table 104? Which method is most practicable for a larger number of items?

3. Using the data in Exercise (1) or (2) compute the coefficient of correlation by the short-cut method (Formula 47).

4. *Correlation of deviations from trends.*

Data.—Annual production of pig iron and the amount of liabilities in commercial failures, Table 111.

Procedure.—Compute the straight line trends for each of these series for the years 1900-1921, by the method of least squares. Find the percentage deviations from the computed trends. Compute the standard deviation of each series of deviations by the short-cut method (see Chapter IX), and divide the percentage deviations by their respective standard deviations. Plot the results in a chart similar to Chart 36, Fig. C. Find the Pearsonian coefficient of correlation for the deviations from trend.

Questions.—(a) What type and degree of correlation is indicated by the charts? Is the evidence of the graph supported by the coefficient of correlation? Do you find any evidence to suggest that the correlation might be greater if one series were lagged one or more years when the correlation was computed?

5. Same as Exercise 4, substituting other series from Tables 111, 112, or 109.

6. *Correlation of concurrent deviations.*

Data.—Average annual wholesale prices in Table 109, for hogs and steers.

Procedure.—Compute the coefficient of concurrent deviations (Formula 37).

Questions.—(a) In what respects does the procedure used in this exercise differ in principle from the computation of the Pearsonian coefficient of correlation for first differences? Do the results of this computation prove a direct causal relation between the prices of hogs and steers?

SERIES P.—PLANNING STATISTICAL INVESTIGATIONS

(Chapter XVI)

1. *Data.*—Select as a subject one of the inquiries listed below or some other subject approved by the instructor.

Procedure.—(a) Explain, with reasons, what method of procedure would be most appropriate and practicable for the proposed investigation. (b) Formulate an appropriate explanatory statement and questionnaire, with questions limited to five unless otherwise stipulated by the instructor. Fill in the questionnaire with hypothetical answers. (c) Draw up a set of instructions for editing the returned schedules. (d) Formulate definitions of the statistical units involved in the investigation.

List of Subjects for Exercise 1

(a) Commerce group.
  (1) The size and distribution of advertising appropriations of manufacturers of toilet articles.
  (2) The costs of labor turnover in shoe factories.
  (3) Rental expenses in the retail drug business in comparison with the volume of business or other significant measures.
  (4) The distribution of effort of salesmen on the various lines each is handling.
  (5) Fluctuations in consumers' demand for luxury goods in a selected state.
  (6) The credit practices of country merchants.
(b) Sociology group.
  (1) The causes of juvenile delinquency in a selected city.
  (2) The effect of prohibition on the amount of crime.
  (3) The relation between housing conditions and infant mortality.
  (4) The change in the size of families in the native-born population as compared with the previous generation.
  (5) The provision for old age being made by self-supporting women of the professional classes.
(c) Economics group.
  (1) The amount and types of traffic on a given highway.
  (2) The amount of time lost by unemployment in one state during a business depression.
  (3) The extent to which unemployment due to the seasonal activities in a selected industry is avoided by the workers engaging in more than one occupation.
  (4) Population tendencies in a selected city as a guide to the extension of the street railway system.
(d) Rural economics and sociology.
  (1) The types, extent, and trends in farm tenancy in one county.
  (2) The migratory history of the inhabitants of a county for a decade.
  (3) A quantitative measure of the extent to which the farmers in a selected locality utilize the several marketing methods.
  (4) The credit needs of an agricultural community with a dominant industry, *e.g.,* dairying.
  (5) The extent to which crop plantings in a selected community vary with price changes.

SERIES Q.—STATISTICAL DATA FROM SECONDARY SOURCES

(Chapter XVII)

1. *Compilation and appraisal.*—Let each member of the class obtain and tabulate in uniform arrangement the annual and monthly data for a single series over a ten-year period. If a single series is not available continuously for the entire period, supplement it for the remainder of the period with a series which appears to be the best substitute. Attach to the data a statement giving full information as to the compiler of the data, the methods of collection, place of publication, and discrepancies; in brief, everything which is necessary as a basis for judgment upon the significance and accuracy of the data. Summarize the most important points to be considered in using the data, and indicate what changes should be made in the methods of collection or publication.

2. Prepare a *critical bibliography* of the statistics on some assigned phase of economics or sociology, including a discussion of the comprehensiveness and continuity of the data, the extent to which they meet the tests for secondary data set forth in Chapter XVI, and the chief respects in which the available data are incomplete or otherwise inadequate.

R.—SERIAL EXERCISES

Particularly when data are available in which the student is especially interested, it is helpful to build a series of exercises upon one set of basic data. This minimizes the necessary preliminary computations and facilitates the comparison of the results of alternative methods of procedure. The two following exercises will suggest some of the possibilities in the way of serial exercises. The first is based upon a sample into which the chronological element does not enter or is subordinated; the second indicates a series of statistical computations which may be based upon a table of monthly data.

1. *Data.*—The list of relative prices in Table 101, or any similar list of individual measurements or observations.

Procedure.—Perform the following indicated operations, recording the data used and the computations made in appropriate tables and appending to each process a discussion of its purpose and a statement of any observed peculiarities of the results:

(a) Select a sample from the list of individual items.
(b) Tally the variate values of the sample and experiment with two or more class-intervals for a frequency distribution. Select the one which appears most appropriate. (Cf. Exercise C-2.)
(c) Construct a frequency histogram, frequency polygon, and a freehand smoothed curve.
(d) Compile a frequency table giving the cumulative frequencies of the data, on the "less than" and "more than" bases respectively.
(e) Plot the cumulated frequencies on the "less than" basis.
(f) Compute the arithmetic mean from the frequency table, by the short-cut method; likewise the mode and median by formula. (Exercise H-1.)
(g) Find the median and quartiles from the cumulative frequency curve.
(h) Find the various measures and coefficients of dispersion. (Cf. Exercises J-2 and J-3.)
(i) Fit a normal frequency curve to the distribution. (Cf. Exercise K-2.)
(j) If the measurements are given in the original data for two characteristics of the data, *e.g.*, heights and weights of men, these may be correlated.

2. *Data.*—Monthly data for a series of years, either selected from the tables in Appendix B or taken from the numerous series published in the *Survey of Current Business,* the *Review of Economics Statistics,* the *Monthly Labor Review,* etc.

Procedure:

(a) Plot the annual totals or averages on both a natural scale and a ratio scale and note the general character of the trend of the data.

(b) Plot the monthly data on a ratio scale, one month above the other, to test the character of the seasonal movement. (Cf. Exercise G-4.)

(c) Compute a simple index number of the annual data, and shift the base thereof.

(d) Compute the straight-line trend of the annual data by the method of least squares, and find the percentage deviations therefrom.

(e) Compute the mean of the deviations from the trend, as a check on the accuracy of the trend computation.

(f) Compute the typical seasonal variation by two or more methods.

(g) Compute the standard deviation of the percentage deviations of the annual items from the computed trend, using the short-cut method with zero as the assumed mean, and divide the percentage deviations by the standard deviation. Plot the results.

(h) Compare the chart of the deviations as prepared in (g) with a similar chart computed for another series by some other member of the class and point out similarities and differences in the cyclical movements. Compute the coefficient of correlation for the two series with the lag which inspection of the charts suggests as likely to give the closest correlation.

(i) Compute the monthly cycles of the deviations from the trend, corrected for seasonal variation, by the Harvard method (see Chapter XIV).

APPENDIX D

AIDS TO COMPUTATION

Squares ....Numbers 100 to 999
Square roots ....Numbers   1 to 999
Logarithms ....Numbers 1.00 to 9.99
Sums of squares ....Numbers   1 to 30

SQUARES

No.	0	1	2	3	4	5	6	7	8	9
10	10000	10201	10404	10609	10816	11025	11236	11449	11664	11881
11	12100	12321	12544	12769	12996	13225	13456	13689	13924	14161
12	14400	14641	14884	15129	15376	15625	15876	16129	16384	16641
13	16900	17161	17424	17689	17956	18225	18496	18769	19044	19321
14	19600	19881	20164	20449	20736	21025	21316	21609	21904	22201
15	22500	22801	23104	23409	23716	24025	24336	24649	24964	25281
16	25600	25921	26244	26569	26896	27225	27556	27889	28224	28561
17	28900	29241	29584	29929	30276	30625	30976	31329	31684	32041
18	32400	32761	33124	33489	33856	34225	34596	34969	35344	35721
19	36100	36481	36864	37249	37636	38025	38416	38809	39204	39601
20	40000	40401	40804	41209	41616	42025	42436	42849	43264	43681
21	44100	44521	44944	45369	45796	46225	46656	47089	47524	47961
22	48400	48841	49284	49729	50176	50625	51076	51529	51984	52441
23	52900	53361	53824	54289	54756	55225	55696	56169	56644	57121
24	57600	58081	58564	59049	59536	60025	60516	61009	61504	62001
25	62500	63001	63504	64009	64516	65025	65536	66049	66564	67081
26	67600	68121	68644	69169	69696	70225	70756	71289	71824	72361
27	72900	73441	73984	74529	75076	75625	76176	76729	77284	77841
28	78400	78961	79524	80089	80656	81225	81796	82369	82944	83521
29	84100	84681	85264	85849	86436	87025	87616	88209	88804	89401
30	90000	90601	91204	91809	92416	93025	93636	94249	94864	95481
31	96100	96721	97344	97969	98596	99225	99856	100489	101124	101761
32	102400	103041	103684	104329	104976	105625	106276	106929	107584	108241
33	108900	109561	110224	110889	111556	112225	112896	113569	114244	114921
34	115600	116281	116964	117649	118336	119025	119716	120409	121104	121801
35	122500	123201	123904	124609	125316	126025	126736	127449	128164	128881
36	129600	130321	131044	131769	132496	133225	133956	134689	135424	136161
37	136900	137641	138384	139129	139876	140625	141376	142129	142884	143641
38	144400	145161	145924	146689	147456	148225	148996	149769	150544	151321
39	152100	152881	153664	154449	155236	156025	156816	157609	158404	159201
40	160000	160801	161604	162409	163216	164025	164836	165649	166464	167281
41	168100	168921	169744	170569	171396	172225	173056	173889	174724	175561
42	176400	177241	178084	178929	179776	180625	181476	182329	183184	184041
43	184900	185761	186624	187489	188356	189225	190096	190969	191844	192721
44	193600	194481	195364	196249	197136	198025	198916	199809	200704	201601
45	202500	203401	204304	205209	206116	207025	207936	208849	209764	210681
46	211600	212521	213444	214369	215296	216225	217156	218089	219024	219961
47	220900	221841	222784	223729	224676	225625	226576	227529	228484	229441
48	230400	231361	232324	233289	234256	235225	236196	237169	238144	239121
49	240100	241081	242064	243049	244036	245025	246016	247009	248004	249001
50	250000	251001	252004	253009	254016	255025	256036	257049	258064	259081
51	260100	261121	262144	263169	264196	265225	266256	267289	268324	269361
52	270400	271441	272484	273529	274576	275625	276676	277729	278784	279841
53	280900	281961	283024	284089	285156	286225	287296	288369	289444	290521
54	291600	292681	293764	294849	295936	297025	298116	299209	300304	301401

SQUARES

No.	0	1	2	3	4	5	6	7	8	9
55	302500	303601	304704	305809	306916	308025	309136	310249	311364	312481
56	313600	314721	315844	316969	318096	319225	320356	321489	322624	323761
57	324900	326041	327184	328329	329476	330625	331776	332929	334084	335241
58	336400	337561	338724	339889	341056	342225	343396	344569	345744	346921
59	348100	349281	350464	351649	352836	354025	355216	356409	357604	358801
60	360000	361201	362404	363609	364816	366025	367236	368449	369664	370881
61	372100	373321	374544	375769	376996	378225	379456	380689	381924	383161
62	384400	385641	386884	388129	389376	390625	391876	393129	394384	395641
63	396900	398161	399424	400689	401956	403225	404496	405769	407044	408321
64	409600	410881	412164	413449	414736	416025	417316	418609	419904	421201
65	422500	423801	425104	426409	427716	429025	430336	431649	432964	434281
66	435600	436921	438244	439569	440896	442225	443556	444889	446224	447561
67	448900	450241	451584	452929	454276	455625	456976	458329	459684	461041
68	462400	463761	465124	466489	467856	469225	470596	471969	473344	474721
69	476100	477481	478864	480249	481636	483025	484416	485809	487204	488601
70	490000	491401	492804	494209	495616	497025	498436	499849	501264	502681
71	504100	505521	506944	508369	509796	511225	512656	514089	515524	516961
72	518400	519841	521284	522729	524176	525625	527076	528529	529984	531441
73	532900	534361	535824	537289	538756	540225	541696	543169	544644	546121
74	547600	549081	550564	552049	553536	555025	556516	558009	559504	561001
75	562500	564001	565504	567009	568516	570025	571536	573049	574564	576081
76	577600	579121	580644	582169	583696	585225	586756	588289	589824	591361
77	592900	594441	595984	597529	599076	600625	602176	603729	605284	606841
78	608400	609961	611524	613089	614656	616225	617796	619369	620944	622521
79	624100	625681	627264	628849	630436	632025	633616	635209	636804	638401
80	640000	641601	643204	644809	646416	648025	649636	651249	652864	654481
81	656100	657721	659344	660969	662596	664225	665856	667489	669124	670761
82	672400	674041	675684	677329	678976	680625	682276	683929	685584	687241
83	688900	690561	692224	693889	695556	697225	698896	700569	702244	703921
84	705600	707281	708964	710649	712336	714025	715716	717409	719104	720801
85	722500	724201	725904	727609	729316	731025	732736	734449	736164	737881
86	739600	741321	743044	744769	746496	748225	749956	751689	753424	755161
87	756900	758641	760384	762129	763876	765625	767376	769129	770884	772641
88	774400	776161	777924	779689	781456	783225	784996	786769	788544	790321
89	792100	793881	795664	797449	799236	801025	802816	804609	806404	808201
90	810000	811801	813604	815409	817216	819025	820836	822649	824464	826281
91	828100	829921	831744	833569	835396	837225	839056	840889	842724	844561
92	846400	848241	850084	851929	853776	855625	857476	859329	861184	863041
93	864900	866761	868624	870489	872356	874225	876096	877969	879844	881721
94	883600	885481	887364	889249	891136	893025	894916	896809	898704	900601
95	902500	904401	906304	908209	910116	912025	913936	915849	917764	919681
96	921600	923521	925444	927369	929296	931225	933156	935089	937024	938961
97	940900	942841	944784	946729	948676	950625	952576	954529	956484	958441
98	960400	962361	964324	966289	968256	970225	972196	974169	976144	978121
99	980100	982081	984064	986049	988036	990025	992016	994009	996004	998001

SQUARE ROOTS

Example: To find the square root of 144, to the right of 14 in the stubs and beneath 4 in the captions find 12.00, the square root of 144.

No.	0	1	2	3	4	5	6	7	8	9
0	...	1.00	1.41	1.73	2.00	2.24	2.45	2.65	2.83	3.00
1	3.16	3.32	3.46	3.61	3.74	3.87	4.00	4.12	4.24	4.36
2	4.47	4.58	4.69	4.80	4.90	5.00	5.10	5.20	5.29	5.39
3	5.48	5.57	5.66	5.74	5.83	5.92	6.00	6.08	6.16	6.24
4	6.32	6.40	6.48	6.56	6.63	6.71	6.78	6.86	6.93	7.00
5	7.07	7.14	7.21	7.28	7.35	7.42	7.48	7.55	7.62	7.69
6	7.75	7.81	7.87	7.94	8.00	8.06	8.12	8.19	8.25	8.31
7	8.37	8.43	8.49	8.54	8.60	8.66	8.72	8.77	8.83	8.89
8	8.94	9.00	9.06	9.11	9.17	9.22	9.27	9.33	9.38	9.43
9	9.49	9.54	9.59	9.64	9.70	9.75	9.80	9.85	9.90	9.95
10	10.00	10.05	10.10	10.15	10.20	10.25	10.30	10.34	10.39	10.44
11	10.49	10.54	10.58	10.63	10.68	10.72	10.77	10.82	10.86	10.91
12	10.95	11.00	11.05	11.09	11.14	11.18	11.22	11.27	11.31	11.36
13	11.40	11.45	11.49	11.53	11.58	11.62	11.66	11.70	11.75	11.79
14	11.83	11.87	11.92	11.96	12.00	12.04	12.08	12.12	12.17	12.21
15	12.25	12.29	12.33	12.37	12.41	12.45	12.49	12.53	12.57	12.61
16	12.65	12.69	12.73	12.77	12.81	12.85	12.88	12.92	12.96	13.00
17	13.04	13.08	13.11	13.15	13.19	13.23	13.27	13.30	13.34	13.38
18	13.42	13.45	13.49	13.53	13.56	13.60	13.64	13.67	13.71	13.75
19	13.78	13.82	13.86	13.89	13.93	13.96	14.00	14.04	14.07	14.11
20	14.14	14.18	14.21	14.25	14.28	14.32	14.35	14.39	14.42	14.46
21	14.49	14.53	14.56	14.59	14.63	14.66	14.70	14.73	14.76	14.80
22	14.83	14.87	14.90	14.93	14.97	15.00	15.03	15.07	15.10	15.13
23	15.17	15.20	15.23	15.26	15.30	15.33	15.36	15.39	15.43	15.46
24	15.49	15.52	15.56	15.59	15.62	15.65	15.68	15.72	15.75	15.78
25	15.81	15.84	15.87	15.91	15.94	15.97	16.00	16.03	16.06	16.09
26	16.12	16.16	16.19	16.22	16.25	16.28	16.31	16.34	16.37	16.40
27	16.43	16.46	16.49	16.52	16.55	16.58	16.61	16.64	16.67	16.70
28	16.73	16.76	16.79	16.82	16.85	16.88	16.91	16.94	16.97	17.00
29	17.03	17.06	17.09	17.12	17.15	17.18	17.20	17.23	17.26	17.29
30	17.32	17.35	17.38	17.41	17.44	17.46	17.49	17.52	17.55	17.58
31	17.61	17.64	17.66	17.69	17.72	17.75	17.78	17.80	17.83	17.86
32	17.89	17.92	17.94	17.97	18.00	18.03	18.06	18.08	18.11	18.14
33	18.17	18.19	18.22	18.25	18.28	18.30	18.33	18.36	18.38	18.41
34	18.44	18.47	18.49	18.52	18.55	18.57	18.60	18.63	18.65	18.68
35	18.71	18.73	18.76	18.79	18.81	18.84	18.87	18.89	18.92	18.95
36	18.97	19.00	19.03	19.05	19.08	19.10	19.13	19.16	19.18	19.21
37	19.24	19.26	19.29	19.31	19.34	19.36	19.39	19.42	19.44	19.47
38	19.49	19.52	19.54	19.57	19.60	19.62	19.65	19.67	19.70	19.72
39	19.75	19.77	19.80	19.82	19.85	19.87	19.90	19.92	19.95	19.97
40	20.00	20.02	20.05	20.07	20.10	20.12	20.15	20.17	20.20	20.22
41	20.25	20.27	20.30	20.32	20.35	20.37	20.40	20.42	20.45	20.47
42	20.49	20.52	20.54	20.57	20.59	20.62	20.64	20.66	20.69	20.71
43	20.74	20.76	20.78	20.81	20.83	20.86	20.88	20.90	20.93	20.95
44	20.98	21.00	21.02	21.05	21.07	21.10	21.12	21.14	21.17	21.19
45	21.21	21.24	21.26	21.28	21.31	21.33	21.35	21.38	21.40	21.42
46	21.45	21.47	21.49	21.52	21.54	21.56	21.59	21.61	21.63	21.66
47	21.68	21.70	21.73	21.75	21.77	21.79	21.82	21.84	21.86	21.89
48	21.91	21.93	21.95	21.98	22.00	22.02	22.05	22.07	22.09	22.11
49	22.14	22.16	22.18	22.20	22.23	22.25	22.27	22.29	22.32	22.34

SQUARE ROOTS

No.	0	1	2	3	4	5	6	7	8	9
50	22.36	22.38	22.41	22.43	22.45	22.47	22.49	22.52	22.54	22.56
51	22.58	22.61	22.63	22.65	22.67	22.69	22.72	22.74	22.76	22.78
52	22.80	22.83	22.85	22.87	22.89	22.91	22.93	22.96	22.98	23.00
53	23.02	23.04	23.07	23.09	23.11	23.13	23.15	23.17	23.19	23.22
54	23.24	23.26	23.28	23.30	23.32	23.35	23.37	23.39	23.41	23.43
55	23.45	23.47	23.49	23.52	23.54	23.56	23.58	23.60	23.62	23.64
56	23.66	23.69	23.71	23.73	23.75	23.77	23.79	23.81	23.83	23.85
57	23.87	23.90	23.92	23.94	23.96	23.98	24.00	24.02	24.04	24.06
58	24.08	24.10	24.12	24.15	24.17	24.19	24.21	24.23	24.25	24.27
59	24.29	24.31	24.33	24.35	24.37	24.39	24.41	24.43	24.45	24.47
60	24.49	24.52	24.54	24.56	24.58	24.60	24.62	24.64	24.66	24.68
61	24.70	24.72	24.74	24.76	24.78	24.80	24.82	24.84	24.86	24.88
62	24.90	24.92	24.94	24.96	24.98	25.00	25.02	25.04	25.06	25.08
63	25.10	25.12	25.14	25.16	25.18	25.20	25.22	25.24	25.26	25.28
64	25.30	25.32	25.34	25.36	25.38	25.40	25.42	25.44	25.46	25.48
65	25.50	25.51	25.53	25.55	25.57	25.59	25.61	25.63	25.65	25.67
66	25.69	25.71	25.73	25.75	25.77	25.79	25.81	25.83	25.85	25.87
67	25.88	25.90	25.92	25.94	25.96	25.98	26.00	26.02	26.04	26.06
68	26.08	26.10	26.12	26.13	26.15	26.17	26.19	26.21	26.23	26.25
69	26.27	26.29	26.31	26.32	26.34	26.36	26.38	26.40	26.42	26.44
70	26.46	26.48	26.50	26.51	26.53	26.55	26.57	26.59	26.61	26.63
71	26.65	26.66	26.68	26.70	26.72	26.74	26.76	26.78	26.80	26.81
72	26.83	26.85	26.87	26.89	26.91	26.93	26.94	26.96	26.98	27.00
73	27.02	27.04	27.06	27.07	27.09	27.11	27.13	27.15	27.17	27.18
74	27.20	27.22	27.24	27.26	27.28	27.29	27.31	27.33	27.35	27.37
75	27.39	27.40	27.42	27.44	27.46	27.48	27.50	27.51	27.53	27.55
76	27.57	27.59	27.60	27.62	27.64	27.66	27.68	27.69	27.71	27.73
77	27.75	27.77	27.78	27.80	27.82	27.84	27.86	27.87	27.89	27.91
78	27.93	27.95	27.96	27.98	28.00	28.02	28.04	28.05	28.07	28.09
79	28.11	28.12	28.14	28.16	28.18	28.20	28.21	28.23	28.25	28.27
80	28.28	28.30	28.32	28.34	28.35	28.37	28.39	28.41	28.43	28.44
81	28.46	28.48	28.50	28.51	28.53	28.55	28.57	28.58	28.60	28.62
82	28.64	28.65	28.67	28.69	28.71	28.72	28.74	28.76	28.77	28.79
83	28.81	28.83	28.84	28.86	28.88	28.90	28.91	28.93	28.95	28.97
84	28.98	29.00	29.02	29.03	29.05	29.07	29.09	29.10	29.12	29.14
85	29.15	29.17	29.19	29.21	29.22	29.24	29.26	29.27	29.29	29.31
86	29.33	29.34	29.36	29.38	29.39	29.41	29.43	29.44	29.46	29.48
87	29.50	29.51	29.53	29.55	29.56	29.58	29.60	29.61	29.63	29.65
88	29.66	29.68	29.70	29.72	29.73	29.75	29.77	29.78	29.80	29.82
89	29.83	29.85	29.87	29.88	29.90	29.92	29.93	29.95	29.97	29.98
90	30.00	30.02	30.03	30.05	30.07	30.08	30.10	30.12	30.13	30.15
91	30.17	30.18	30.20	30.22	30.23	30.25	30.27	30.28	30.30	30.32
92	30.33	30.35	30.36	30.38	30.40	30.41	30.43	30.45	30.46	30.48
93	30.50	30.51	30.53	30.55	30.56	30.58	30.59	30.61	30.63	30.64
94	30.66	30.68	30.69	30.71	30.72	30.74	30.76	30.77	30.79	30.81
95	30.82	30.84	30.85	30.87	30.89	30.90	30.92	30.94	30.95	30.97
96	30.98	31.00	31.02	31.03	31.05	31.06	31.08	31.10	31.11	31.13
97	31.14	31.16	31.18	31.19	31.21	31.22	31.24	31.26	31.27	31.29
98	31.30	31.32	31.34	31.35	31.37	31.38	31.40	31.42	31.43	31.45
99	31.46	31.48	31.50	31.51	31.53	31.54	31.56	31.58	31.59	31.61

LOGARITHMS

Examples: (1) To find the logarithm of 153. On the line 1.5 and in the column headed 3 will be found .1847, which is the log of 1.53. Therefore the log of 153 is 2.1847.

(2) *Interpolation.* To find the log of 153.5. To log of 153 add 0.5 of the difference (28) between the log of 153 and the log of 154. See the fifth line under 28 in the INTERPOLATION DIFFERENCES.

INTERPOLATION DIFFERENCES

38	36	34	32
4	4	3	3
8	7	7	6
11	11	10	10
15	14	14	13
19	18	17	16
23	22	20	19
27	25	24	22
30	29	27	26
34	32	31	29

No.	0	1	2	3	4	5	6	7	8	9				
1.0	.0000	.0043	.0086	.0128	.0170	.0212	.0253	.0294	.0334	.0374	30	28	26	24
.1	0414	0453	0492	0531	0569	0607	0645	0682	0719	0755	3	3	3	2
.2	0792	0828	0864	0899	0934	0969	1004	1038	1072	1106	6	6	5	5
.3	1139	1173	1206	1239	1271	1303	1335	1367	1399	1430	9	8	8	7
.4	1461	1492	1523	1553	1584	1614	1644	1673	1703	1732	12	11	10	10
1.5	.1761	.1790	.1818	.1847	.1875	.1903	.1931	.1959	.1987	.2014	15	14	13	12
.6	2041	2068	2095	2122	2148	2175	2201	2227	2253	2279	18	17	16	14
.7	2304	2330	2355	2380	2405	2430	2455	2480	2504	2529	21	20	18	17
.8	2553	2577	2601	2625	2648	2672	2695	2718	2742	2765	24	22	21	19
.9	2788	2810	2833	2856	2878	2900	2923	2945	2967	2989	27	25	23	22
2.0	.3010	.3032	.3054	.3075	.3096	.3118	.3139	.3160	.3181	.3201	22	20	18	16
.1	3222	3243	3263	3284	3304	3324	3345	3365	3385	3404	2	2	2	2
.2	3424	3444	3464	3483	3502	3522	3541	3560	3579	3598	4	4	4	3
.3	3617	3636	3655	3674	3692	3711	3729	3747	3766	3784	7	6	5	5
.4	3802	3820	3838	3856	3874	3892	3909	3927	3945	3962	9	8	7	6
2.5	.3979	.3997	.4014	.4031	.4048	.4065	.4082	.4099	.4116	.4133	11	10	9	8
.6	4150	4166	4183	4200	4216	4232	4249	4265	4281	4298	13	12	11	11
.7	4314	4330	4346	4362	4378	4393	4409	4425	4440	4456	15	14	13	11
.8	4472	4487	4502	4518	4533	4548	4564	4579	4594	4609	18	16	14	13
.9	4624	4639	4654	4669	4683	4698	4713	4728	4742	4757	20	18	16	14
3.0	.4771	.4786	.4800	.4814	.4829	.4843	.4857	.4871	.4886	.4900	15	14	13	12
.1	4914	4928	4942	4955	4969	4983	4997	5011	5024	5038	2	1	1	1
.2	5051	5065	5079	5092	5105	5119	5132	5145	5159	5172	3	3	3	2
.3	5185	5198	5211	5224	5237	5250	5263	5276	5289	5302	5	4	4	4
.4	5315	5328	5340	5353	5366	5378	5391	5403	5416	5428	6	6	5	5
3.5	.5441	.5453	.5465	.5478	.5490	.5502	.5514	.5527	.5539	.5551	8	7	7	6
.6	5563	5575	5587	5599	5611	5623	5635	5647	5658	5670	9	8	8	7
.7	5682	5694	5705	5717	5729	5740	5752	5763	5775	5786	11	10	9	8
.8	5798	5809	5821	5832	5843	5855	5866	5877	5888	5899	12	11	10	10
.9	5911	5922	5933	5944	5955	5966	5977	5988	5999	6010	14	13	12	11
4.0	.6021	.6031	.6042	.6053	.6064	.6075	.6085	.6096	.6107	.6117	11	10	9	8
.1	6128	6138	6149	6160	6170	6180	6191	6201	6212	6222	1	1	1	1
.2	6232	6243	6253	6263	6274	6284	6294	6304	6314	6325	2	2	2	2
.3	6335	6345	6355	6365	6375	6385	6395	6405	6415	6425	3	3	3	2
.4	6435	6444	6454	6464	6474	6484	6493	6503	6513	6522	4	4	4	3
4.5	.6532	.6542	.6551	.6561	.6571	.6580	.6590	.6599	.6609	.6618	6	5	5	4
.6	6628	6637	6646	6656	6665	6675	6684	6693	6702	6712	7	6	5	5
.7	6721	6730	6739	6749	6758	6767	6776	6785	6794	6803	8	7	6	6
.8	6812	6821	6830	6839	6848	6857	6866	6875	6884	6893	9	8	7	6
.9	6902	6911	6920	6928	6937	6946	6955	6964	6972	6981	10	9	8	7

LOGARITHMS

No.	0	1	2	3	4	5	6	7	8	9	INTERPOLATION DIFFERENCES		
5.0	.6990	.6998	.7007	.7016	.7024	.7033	.7042	.7050	.7059	.7067	9	8	7
.1	7076	7084	7093	7101	7110	7118	7126	7135	7143	7152	1	1	1
.2	7160	7168	7177	7185	7193	7202	7210	7218	7226	7235	2	2	1
.3	7243	7251	7259	7267	7275	7284	7292	7300	7308	7316	3	2	2
.4	7324	7332	7340	7348	7356	7364	7372	7380	7388	7396	4	3	3
5.5	.7404	.7412	.7419	.7427	.7435	.7443	.7451	.7459	.7466	.7474	5	4	4
.6	7482	7490	7497	7505	7513	7520	7528	7536	7543	7551	5	5	4
.7	7559	7566	7574	7582	7589	7597	7604	7612	7619	7627	6	6	5
.8	7634	7642	7649	7657	7664	7672	7679	7686	7694	7701	7	6	6
.9	7709	7716	7723	7731	7738	7745	7752	7760	7767	7774	8	7	6
6.0	.7782	.7789	.7796	.7803	.7810	.7818	.7825	.7832	.7839	.7846	7	6	
.1	7853	7860	7868	7875	7882	7889	7896	7903	7910	7917	1	1	
.2	7924	7931	7938	7945	7952	7959	7966	7973	7980	7987	1	1	
.3	7993	8000	8007	8014	8021	8028	8035	8041	8048	8055	2	2	
.4	8062	8069	8075	8082	8089	8096	8102	8109	8116	8122	3	2	
6.5	.8129	.8136	.8142	.8149	.8156	.8162	.8169	.8176	.8182	.8189	4	3	
.6	8195	8202	8209	8215	8222	8228	8235	8241	8248	8254	4	4	
.7	8261	8267	8274	8280	8287	8293	8299	8306	8312	8319	5	4	
.8	8325	8331	8338	8344	8351	8357	8363	8370	8376	8382	6	5	
.9	8388	8395	8401	8407	8414	8420	8426	8432	8439	8445	6	5	
7.0	.8451	.8457	.8463	.8470	.8476	.8482	.8488	.8494	.8500	.8506	6	5	
.1	8513	8519	8525	8531	8537	8543	8549	8555	8561	8567	1	1	
.2	8573	8579	8585	8591	8597	8603	8609	8615	8621	8627	1	1	
.3	8633	8639	8645	8651	8657	8663	8669	8675	8681	8686	2	2	
.4	8692	8698	8704	8710	8716	8722	8727	8733	8739	8745	2	2	
7.5	.8751	.8756	.8762	.8768	.8774	.8779	.8785	.8791	.8797	.8802	3	3	
.6	8808	8814	8820	8825	8831	8837	8842	8848	8854	8859	4	3	
.7	8865	8871	8876	8882	8887	8893	8899	8904	8910	8915	4	4	
.8	8921	8927	8932	8938	8943	8949	8954	8960	8965	8971	5	4	
.9	8976	8982	8987	8993	8998	9004	9009	9015	9020	9025	5	5	
8.0	.9031	.9036	.9042	.9047	.9053	.9058	.9063	.9069	.9074	.9079	6	5	
.1	9085	9090	9096	9101	9106	9112	9117	9122	9128	9133	1	1	
.2	9138	9143	9149	9154	9159	9165	9170	9175	9180	9186	1	1	
.3	9191	9196	9201	9206	9212	9217	9222	9227	9232	9238	2	2	
.4	9243	9248	9253	9258	9263	9269	9274	9279	9284	9289	2	2	
8.5	.9294	.9299	.9304	.9309	.9315	.9320	.9325	.9330	.9335	.9340	3	3	
.6	9345	9350	9355	9360	9365	9370	9375	9380	9385	9390	4	3	
.7	9395	9400	9405	9410	9415	9420	9425	9430	9435	9440	4	4	
.8	9445	9450	9455	9460	9465	9469	9474	9479	9484	9489	5	4	
.9	9494	9499	9504	9509	9513	9518	9523	9528	9533	9538	5	5	
9.0	.9542	.9547	.9552	.9557	.9562	.9566	.9571	.9576	.9581	.9586	5	4	
.1	9590	9595	9600	9605	9609	9614	9619	9624	9628	9633	1	0	
.2	9638	9643	9647	9652	9657	9661	9666	9671	9675	9680	1	1	
.3	9685	9689	9694	9699	9703	9708	9713	9717	9722	9727	2	1	
.4	9731	9736	9741	9745	9750	9754	9759	9763	9768	9773	2	2	
9.5	.9777	.9782	.9786	.9791	.9795	.9800	.9805	.9809	.9814	.9818	3	2	
.6	9823	9827	9832	9836	9841	9845	9850	9854	9859	9863	3	2	
.7	9868	9872	9877	9881	9886	9890	9894	9899	9903	9908	4	3	
.8	9912	9917	9921	9926	9930	9934	9939	9943	9948	9952	4	3	
.9	9956	9961	9965	9969	9974	9978	9983	9987	9991	9996	5	4	

SUMS OF SQUARES

Number	Sum of squares of all integers to and including given number	Number	Sum of squares of all integers to and including given number
1	1	16	1,496
2	5	17	1,785
3	14	18	2,109
4	30	19	2,470
5	55	20	2,870
6	91	21	3,311
7	140	22	3,795
8	204	23	4,324
9	285	24	4,900
10	385	25	5,525
11	506	26	6,201
12	650	27	6,930
13	819	28	7,714
14	1,015	29	8,555
15	1,240	30	9,455

The above table is for use in finding the value of Σx^2 in the formula for a straight line trend by the method of least squares.

LIST OF SYMBOLS

Index to the Principal Symbols and Abbreviations Used in the Formulas
in This Book, with Leading Page References
(n = footnote; t = table, on given page)

A, arithmetic mean, 112, 157

A.D., average deviation, 155

b, ordinate of the line of least squares at the mid-point of the period,
230-231

C, class or group interval, 119, 124, 177-179t

c, number of concurrent deviations, 269

D, decile, 122t, 127

d, deviation, 157, 287

d_E, deviation from an assumed mean, 157

$d_{\bar{x}}$, deviation of assumed mean from the true mean of the x-series, 287

$d_{\bar{y}}$, deviation of assumed mean from the true mean of the y-series, 287

E, arbitrary or assumed mean, 112, 157, 288

E_x, assumed mean for the x-series, 288t

E_y, assumed mean for the y-series, 288t

e, 2.71828, the base of the *Natural* or *Naperian* system of logarithms, 177

f, the frequency, or the number of items, in a class or group, 112, 124

f_1, frequency of the adjacent class below the modal class, 119

f_2, frequency of the adjacent class above the modal class, 119

G, geometric mean, 130

H, harmonic average, 132; head of a coin, 166

i, rank within a class, *e.g.*, rank of the median in the median class, 124

L, lower limit of a given class, 119, 124

L.Q., magnitude of the lower or first quartile, 122t, 127, 154

m, a varying magnitude, 112; the slope of a straight line, 230-231, 278

Mi, abscissal value of the median, 124

Mo, abscissal value of the mode, 119

N, total number, 112n; particularly the total number in a universe or
population, 175

n, total number, particularly the number of items in a sample, 112, 175,
269, 270, 281

P_1, price index in a given year, 199

P.E., probable error, 154, 174-175, 283

p, the chance of success, 166n; the proportion of items having a given
characteristic, 175

p', proportion shown in a sample, 175

LIST OF FORMULAS

(Includes only the formulas numbered in sequence)

INDEX

(The citations are to pages. The subject-matter of the appendixes and footnotes has been indexed only in selected instances. n = footnote; t = table, on given page.)

Abbreviations (*see* list of symbols preceding this index)

THE END